Natural Environment Research

INSTITUTE OF TERRESTRIAL E⌣⌣⌣⌣⌣

Agriculture and the environment

Proceedings of ITE symposium no. 13
held at Monks Wood Experimental Station
on 28–29 February and 1 March 1984

Edited by
DAVID JENKINS
Banchory Research Station
Hill of Brathens, Glassel
BANCHORY
Kincardineshire

Printed in Great Britain by
The Lavenham Press Ltd, Lavenham, Suffolk

Published in 1984 by
Institute of Terrestrial Ecology
68 Hills Road
Cambridge
CB2 1LA

ISBN 0 904282 78 3
ISSN 0263-8614

COVER ILLUSTRATION
A mosaic of agriculture, forestry and semi-natural habitats at the edge of
the hills. Feughside, Finzean, Kincardineshire, September 1984
(Photograph N Picozzi)

Acknowledgements
Most papers were typed by Mrs E Allan and Mrs L Burnett at
ITE Brathens. Abstracts for circulation before the symposium,
lists of references and the texts of some of the papers were
typed at ITE Monks Wood by Mrs B J Stocker. Mrs J Welch and
Dr D Osborn helped with the organization of the symposium.
Mrs J King checked all the references and Mrs P A Ward helped
with the final editing and proof reading.

The *Institute of Terrestrial Ecology (ITE)* was established in 1973, from
the former Nature Conservancy's research stations and staff, joined
later by the Institute of Tree Biology and the Culture Centre of Algae and
Protozoa. ITE contributes to, and draws upon, the collective knowledge
of the 14 sister institutes which make up the *Natural Environment
Research Council*, spanning all the environmental sciences.

The Institute studies the factors determining the structure, composition
and processes of land and freshwater systems, and of individual plant
and animal species. It is developing a sounder scientific basis for
predicting and modelling environmental trends arising from natural or
man-made change. The results of this research are available to those
responsible for the protection, management and wise use of our natural
resources.

One quarter of ITE's work is research commissioned by customers,
such as the Department of Environment, the European Economic
Community, the Nature Conservancy Council and the Overseas
Development Administration. The remainder is fundamental research
supported by NERC.

ITE's expertise is widely used by international organizations in overseas
projects and programmes of research.

Dr D Jenkins
Banchory Research Station
Hill of Brathens, Glassel
BANCHORY
Kincardineshire
AB3 4BY
033 02 (Banchory) 3434

Preface

Since the beginning of the Second World War, there have been major changes in British agriculture. The most noteworthy of these changes have been the switch from livestock to cereals and the steady decline in landscape features such as hedges, walls, ponds, trees and small woods which are regarded as redundant for the new farming. In the uplands, extensive reclamation of semi-natural vegetation has also occurred. Throughout, there has been an increased use of inorganic fertilizers and of pesticides and herbicides.

The gross effects of many of these changes on the landscape have been well documented in recent years, but there seem to be few quantitative studies of the effects on landscape and wildlife. There also seems to be little work on the functioning of ecosystems within the agricultural unit. The Institute of Terrestrial Ecology, as the institute concerned with carrying out research on ecological processes on the land surface of Britain, believed that there would be considerable merit in organizing a symposium at which the results of recent work could be presented and discussed. It was hoped that any gaps in research programmes would be identified in the discussion, and hence that priorities for future research could be assigned. Herein lies a danger; strategic research must not be planned to solve present problems, but to solve those of the future. The conference therefore had to consider in some detail the likely future trends in British agriculture policy. Would the present broad policy of maximizing outputs continue? If not, what policies might take its place, and what consequences might there be for research?

The main results of the symposium were to bring together agricultural and ecological scientists, farmers and some politicians for the exchange of ideas. Full discussion was held on the reasons for the existence of gaps and why problems recognized years ago had not been properly tackled. Gaps at interfaces between research organizations and in funding were exposed. The need for further regular collaboration was emphasized. Two particular gaps in knowledge were highlighted. The first was that too little is known about changes in the flora and fauna of farmed land and their response to different agricultural practices. Second, concern was expressed about our lack of knowledge on the viability of animals and plant populations living on small 'islands' of semi-natural habitats within the 'sea' of agricultural land. It is to be hoped that the symposium will result in renewed collaboration between scientists in the Research Councils and in other government-funded as well as private research organizations.

David Jenkins
Brathens
June 1984

Contents

Preface   3

Trends in agricultural land use: the lowlands   7
(W F Raymond, Christmas Common, Watlington

Trends in agricultural land use: the hills and uplands   13
(J Eadie, Hill Farming Research Organisation, Edinburgh)

How is the EEC likely to influence changes in agricultural impacts in Britain? 20
(B Huber, Commission of the European Communities, Brussels)

Pesticide usage: is the Pesticide Safety Precautions Scheme satisfactory?   24
(N W Moore, The Farm House, Swavesey, Cambridge)

Recent economic trends in British agriculture   28
(J S Marsh, University of Reading)

What are the main recent impacts of agriculture on wildlife? Could they   33
    have been predicted, and what can be predicted for the future?
(M D Hooper, Institute of Terrestrial Ecology, Monks Wood)

Models for predicting changes in rural land use in Great Britain   37
(R G H Bunce, Institute of Terrestrial Ecology, Merlewood; R B Tranter &
    A M M Thompson, University of Reading; C P Mitchell, University of
    Aberdeen; C J Barr, Institute of Terrestrial Ecology, Merlewood)

Trends in mechanization in the lowlands   44
(D B Davies, ADAS, Ministry of Agriculture, Fisheries and Food, Cambridge)

Drainage for agriculture   48
(J Morris, P B Leeds-Harrison, A M Ryan & T M Hess, Silsoe College,
    Silsoe, Bedford)

Changes in agricultural practice and their impact on soil organisms   56
(C A Edwards, Rothamsted Experimental Station, Harpenden)

The environmental implications of current pesticide usage on cereals   66
(P I Stanley* & A R Hardy†, Ministry of Agriculture, Fisheries and Food,
    *Slough; †Tolworth)

The impact of the commercial agricultural use of organophosphorus and   72
    carbamate pesticides on British wildlife
(A R Hardy* & P I Stanley†, Ministry of Agriculture, Fisheries and Food,
    *Tolworth; †Slough)

Uses and effects on bird populations of organochlorine pesticides   80
(I Newton, Institute of Terrestrial Ecology, Monks Wood)

The effects of agricultural practices on weeds in arable land   89
(R J Chancellor, J D Fryer & G W Cussans, Weed Research Organization,
    Yarnton)

Impacts of agriculture on southern grasslands   95
(M G Morris, Institute of Terrestrial Ecology, Furzebrook)

Effects of drainage on natural vegetation   98
(J O Mountford & J Sheail, Institute of Terrestrial Ecology, Monks Wood)

The effects of eutrophication on aquatic wildlife   101
(P S Maitland, Institute of Terrestrial Ecology, Edinburgh)

The effects of flood alleviation and land drainage on birds of wet grasslands   108
(C J Cadbury, Royal Society for the Protection of Birds, Sandy)

The importance of hedges to songbirds   117
(R J O'Connor, British Trust for Ornithology, Tring)

The use of birds as indicators of change in agriculture   123
(Anne Brenchley, Maidstone)

Monitoring changes in the cereal ecosystem   128
(G R Potts, The Game Conservancy, Fordingbridge)

Ecological principles in upland management   135
(W E S Mutch, University of Edinburgh)

Some ecological principles underlying hill sheep management   139
(C Milner, Institute of Terrestrial Ecology, Bangor)

Some effects of sheep management on heather moorlands in northern   143
   England
(P J Hudson, The Game Conservancy, Leyburn)

The impact of upland pasture improvement on solute outputs in surface   150
   waters
(M Hornung, Institute of Terrestrial Ecology, Bangor)

Studies by ITE on the impact of agriculture on wildlife and semi-natural   155
   habitats in the uplands
(D F Ball, Institute of Terrestrial Ecology, Bangor)

The use of remote sensing for monitoring change in agriculture in the   162
   uplands and lowlands
(B K Wyatt, Institute of Terrestrial Ecology, Bangor)

Wildlife as disease carriers   168
(H V Thompson, Cantab Group Ltd, Lower Farm Road, Effingham, Leatherhead)

A questionnaire survey of farmers' opinions and actions towards wildlife   171
   on farmlands
(D W Macdonald, Animal Behaviour Research Group, Zoology Department,
   Oxford)

Ministry of Agriculture, Fisheries and Food (MAFF) interests in the results   177
   of ecological research on wildlife and the countryside
(J M Way, MAFF, London)

Discussions
   i. Report on the syndicate on *Lowlands*   183
       (D F Ball, Reporter)
   ii. Report on the syndicate on *Uplands*   185
       (O W Heal, Reporter)
   iii. Report on the syndicate on the *Use of agrochemicals*   188
       (I Newton, Reporter)

Conclusions   190
(J N R Jeffers, Director, Institute of Terrestrial Ecology)

Acknowledgements   191

Appendix I: List of contributors and participants   191

Appendix II: List of plant and animal species referred to in the text   192

Trends in agricultural land use: the lowlands

W F RAYMOND
Christmas Common, Watlington, Oxon

1 The post-war change

Agriculture in the United Kingdom has undergone considerable change since the War, a change initiated by the 1947 Agriculture Act, which aimed to ensure both a secure and reasonably priced food supply for consumers, and an adequate income for those working in farming. Food production was supported by guaranteed prices and markets for most farm output, and by grants for capital investment and farm improvement, and these incentives encouraged the wide adoption of the new production techniques being developed by the research and advisory services and by leading farmers. Farm output increased rapidly, so that national food self-sufficiency has increased from half the requirement for temperate-type foodstuffs in the late 1940s to about three-quarters today, and that for a larger population.

While some 50 000 ha of agricultural land have been lost each year to urban development, roads and forestry, the total tillage area in the UK has remained almost unchanged, because economics and technology have combined to make it both practical and profitable to bring lower grade land into cultivation. Technology has also removed many of the previous restraints on the management of arable land; agrochemicals allow greatly simplified cropping rotations, so that continuous cereal growing is now possible on many soils, and there has been a marked decline in mixed arable/livestock farming. These trends have led to a concentration of arable farming in the south and east of the UK, and of livestock farming in the wetter and hillier areas of the north and west. Many livestock, of course, remain in arable areas, but increasingly these are kept under intensive, housed, conditions often not directly linked to adjacent farmland and so presenting problems of manure disposal. The separation of crop and livestock farming has had other consequences. Less straw is now used for animal feeding and bedding, so that more straw is burnt, to wide public concern; new crops, in particular oilseed rape, have been introduced; the seasonal nature of arable farming, compared with livestock, has encouraged mechanization, so that less labour is employed; to allow efficient use of machines, hedges, no longer needed to restrain livestock, have been removed to make fields larger; and with less straw used for bedding, much livestock manure is handled as slurry, posing problems of efficient and acceptable disposal.

These changed patterns of production have led to greatly increased levels of output; wheat yields have more than doubled and milk output per cow has increased by 80% since 1950. Farm structure and employment have also changed; the number of holdings has halved, to under 250 000, and the number of agricultural workers has fallen by two-thirds, to less than 175 000. Two-thirds of farmers are now owner-occupiers, in contrast to the earlier predominance of tenant farmers, and average farm size has risen from 40 to over 70 ha since 1970.

2 The effects of entry to the European Economic Community (EEC)

These trends were accelerated when the UK began operating the EEC Common Agricultural Policy (CAP) in the mid-1970s. Increasingly, the UK support system had included measures, such as 'standard quantities', aimed at limiting the cost of farm support. In contrast, with a few exceptions such as sugar beet and hops, the CAP offered effectively open-ended support, and at higher price levels, for farm output. As expected, farmers responded to this improved opportunity by speeding up their adoption of new technology. Cereal yields, which had seemed to be levelling out, began to rise again and cereal output rose from 13M tonnes in 1970 to 22M tonnes in 1982, a level not conceived of in the Government White Paper *Food from our own resources* (HMSO 1975), only 7 years before. Milk yield per cow, which had risen by 2% each year up to 1974, has since increased by 4% a year.

Further pressure to intensify also came from the sharp increase in land value which followed EEC entry. The price of land, which had doubled in the 35 years up to 1972, more than doubled again in the next 8 years, the greatest gains being for the poorer land (Body 1982). In fact, the amount of land that has changed hands has been trivial, at about 60 000 ha per year, less than 0.3% of the farmed area. Much of the rise in land price has been speculative, reflecting scarcity value, and often with little relation to potential earning capacity. It has, however, had the effect of forcing owners, who have borrowed against the high notional value of their land, and tenants, through the 'knock-on' effect on rentals, to farm their land more intensively.

The increased intensity and output of UK agriculture have thus resulted from a series of economic inducements and pressures which have made profitable the adoption of new technical and management practices, and the cultivation of inherently less productive land.

3 The economic effects of more intensive agriculture

For 35 years, the principles of the 1947 Agriculture Act *did* achieve both stability and prosperity in agriculture and a secure and increasingly varied food supply to consumers. Agricultural support came mainly from taxation, with its redistributive element, and was based on subsidizing producer incomes to bring food prices down towards world levels. Various measures were introduced to limit the Exchequer liability and, although not uniformly effective, the 'subsidy' component of farmers' incomes declined from 70% in the mid-1950s to about 20% by 1970 (Body 1982), arguably indicating a real increase in farming 'efficiency'.

Accession to the EEC involved a radical change in the form of support, to a system based on high internal food prices, maintained by levies on food imports, and with effectively no limit on the level of output that would be supported. This high price, open-ended market inevitably led to a further increase in UK agricultural production. More importantly, production also increased in the other Member States, and the output of a number of commodities, including milk and dairy products, cereals, sugar and beef, rapidly began to exceed consumer demand. This demand, particularly with dairy products, was significantly reduced by high prices and by concern over health aspects of consuming animal fats. Excess production is purchased for intervention storage, and must then be subsidized before it can compete on the world export market, at high cost to Community taxpayers, and with increasing complaint from other exporting countries. This is not a new problem; there was surplus EEC production in the 1960s. But the size of the present surpluses now threatens the EEC budget, and the Commission has proposed measures aimed at restraining production, in particular of cereals and milk (though such measures seem to offer little immediate benefit to consumers) (EEC 1983).

Agricultural support has been strongly challenged by Body (1982), who has proposed that the protective CAP should be replaced by a system of 'free trade', so as to make food available at 'world prices', to the benefit of both consumers and farmers. These proposals have been questioned by the Centre for Agricultural Strategy (CAS 1983); but the underlying problem remains, that current EEC support policy has led to the production, at high cost, of quantities of food well in excess of Community needs. There is thus urgent need to bring Community food production more into line with effective demand, and at lower cost, yet without unduly damaging farm incomes or rural stability, a formidable task which becomes progressively more difficult as a solution is delayed.

4 The environmental effects of intensive agriculture
In 1947, there was severe food shortage in Europe, and food rationing in the UK was to continue for a further 7 years. A primary objective of the 1947 Act was to increase food production. This priority was continued when food shortage was replaced by balance of payments problems, so that the White Paper (HMSO 1975) concluded that 'a continuing expansion of food production in Britain will be in the national interest'. By 1975, public concern about the possible environmental effects of intensive agriculture

was such that the White Paper also needed to note that 'the projected increases in output . . . should not result in any undesirable changes in the environment'.

Within 3 years, the Advisory Council for Agriculture and Horticulture (1978) was advising that 'MAFF must in future take a wider view of countryside affairs, extending well beyond the obligation "to have regard to" natural beauty and amenity. The Ministry should take a more active and positive role'. The White Paper in the following year (HMSO 1979) accepted the need 'to find new measures and improve existing techniques to reconcile the needs of agricultural development and the environment'. Limited steps to this end were included in the Wildlife and Countryside Act (HMSO 1981), with increased protection afforded to Sites of Special Scientific Interest (SSSI); then, in December 1983, MAFF announced reduced grant support to lowland farms for land reclamation and grassland improvement, and increased grants for hedges, stone walls and shelter belts in the uplands.

While there is now wider recognition that changes in agricultural practice since the War *have* caused environmental damage, the quantitative evidence for this recognition is limited. The Nature Conservancy Council (NCC 1977), while noting that 'in all published studies since the War . . . wildlife habitats have declined', recorded that 'no comprehensive survey of changes in area of wildlife habitats in Britain has been made'. This lack of information remains: the NCC report was quoted as 'an authoritative study' by Bowers and Cheshire (1983), and much public debate still depends on polemic rather than quantified argument. Yet, although not quantified, intensive agriculture has clearly changed the landscape of much of lowland Britain, and there is concern that irreversible damage could occur unless the *rate of change* is reduced. Numerous 'before' and 'after' pictures show the effect on rural landscapes of the removal of trees and hedges, drainage of wetlands, and erecting of farm buildings, as well as the ravages of Dutch elm disease; the Ramblers' Association (1982) has recorded the loss of footpaths and access; and NCC (1981) has estimated that at least 13% of SSSIs have been damaged by agricultural activity. Further, although the Royal Commission on Environmental Pollution (1979) found little evidence that agrochemicals had caused serious environmental damage, and noted that Government had been quick to respond to threats such as that from the chlorinated hydrocarbons, the Commission advised an increased research effort to forestall future risks.

It is important to recognize that the main public concerns are with the loss of land to urban use and the risks from agrochemicals (MORI 1983), and with the appearance and accessibility of the countryside, rather than with the more scientific aspects, such as loss of species diversity (except for birds), which are the primary concern of ecologists. However, as O'Riordan

(1983) notes, 'these two strands of sustainability' are related; preventing significant loss of traditional countryside is a most effective way of maintaining biological diversity. This is in line with the concept that the maintenance of habitats, rather than the preservation of nominated species, should be the primary objective of conservation policy.

5 The future impact of agriculture on the environment
These separate problems, the 'over-production' of food, the cost of the production, and the resulting risk of environmental damage, have now merged into a wider debate on the advisability of yet further intensification of agriculture. This concern can be posed in the question 'how best can the interests of farmers, farm workers and consumers be combined with effective protection of the amenity, scientific and historical values of the countryside, and at acceptable cost?'

It is not possible here to review the many strategies being proposed for UK agriculture; it is more useful to examine briefly the range of options that have been proposed, and their likely environmental consequences. In doing so, it is essential to recognize the extreme hazard of prediction. As an example, the 1966 National Plan (HMSO 1966) forecast that agriculture would need to release substantial manpower resources so as to close the manpower gap in the rest of the economy, an objective which soon became irrelevant.

6 The 'free trade' strategy
As already noted, the failings of the present (CAP) system of agricultural support, and the case for a return to the 'free trade' which followed the 1846 repeal of the Corn Laws, have been forcefully presented by Body (1982), and in the Omega Report on agriculture (1983). In summary, these argue that UK consumers should be permitted to buy their food from the cheapest producers; that this situation would stimulate competition between overseas producers; and that such competition would ensure that plenty of food was available, though there would be losers: landowners and farmers with inflated assets, institutional investors, and agricultural supply companies.

The CAS (1983) has questioned the economic advantages that have been claimed for the adoption of 'free trade'; but it is the agricultural and environmental consequences that concern us here, in particular the conclusion that, if EEC and national aids were withdrawn, grassland farming would replace intensive crop production on all but the best land, and that 'livestock farmers would gain immeasurably' (Body 1982). This prediction must be doubted. The UK is already self-sufficient in beef, and 80% so for milk, the main products of grassland farming. Yet, as Body (1982, p90) notes, 'New Zealand can produce cheese cheaper than any other country; there is no country . . . better suited to ranching beef than Argentina; Austra-

lia used to send considerable quantities of butter'. It seems unlikely that, under conditions of free trade, even the present level of beef and milk production could compete with imports, let alone that from an increased grassland area, if support were limited to 'grants to owners and occupiers of the countryside for the purpose of maintaining the beauty of the landscape' (Body 1982, p98). More likely would be a return to the derelict land and run-down villages, typical of the Warwickshire lias clays and Cotswold brash on which Stapledon set up the Grassland Improvement Station in 1939.

While it can be argued that support for agriculture has been excessive, and has caused damage to the countryside, removal of that support, certainly on the scale proposed in the Omega Report, and by The Economist (1983), would almost inevitably lead to subsistence farming in many parts of the UK. This change might increase the areas of wilderness for ecological research, but hedges growing to the middle of fields (as at Dodwell-Drayton in 1939) can be as effective as barbed wire in restricting access to the countryside. A less drastic run-down of agricultural support is indicated, certainly as long as the UK, and its farmers, must compete with the farmers and the national subsidies of the other Member States of the EEC.

7 The planning approach
The free trade solution aims primarily to correct the economic failings of present agricultural support policy; conservation is a secondary issue. In contrast to this 'laissez faire' policy is the comprehensive application of planning control to agriculture advocated by Shoard (1980). This author accepts that environmental damage would be reduced if less financial support were given to agriculture, but considers that damage is already so extensive that future protection of the countryside cannot be based on selective financial support coupled with the good intentions of farmers; statutory control of farming operations is essential, covering a wide range of activities, including removing hedges and walls, ploughing 'old' pastures, cutting down trees and woods, constructing farm roads, and erecting farm buildings. Each local planning authority would thus need precise information on 'the location of all those landscape features ... that would be covered by the new controls' (Shoard 1980, p209). 'That this would be a big task' is possibly an under-statement; certainly the proposal that much of the mapping, and, by implication 'the detection of breaches of the law', should be carried out by volunteers would seem to invite conflict.

As discussed in the following section, there does appear to be a good case for more effective control over agricultural activity on SSSIs than that included in the 1981 Wildlife and Agriculture Act, and in National Parks and Areas of Outstanding Natural Beauty (AONB), and for provision of adequate funds for this purpose. To extend planning control to all agricultural land would, however, risk 'having one costly bureaucracy . . . viz MAFF . . . paying farmers to do one thing, and another . . . the planning system, telling them not to' (Bowers & Cheshire 1983). These authors conclude (unfortunately in a prose which risks alienating those they seek to influence) that, while strict planning control is needed in the most sensitive conservation areas, the environment of the remainder, mainly farmland, will best be protected by greatly reducing the end-prices and grants which encourage intensive production.

8 An intermediate strategy

A system is thus indicated allowing greater control than at present of potentially damaging activity in important conservation areas, but with minimal formal control over a productive, but less highly supported, agriculture in the remainder of the country. This is the basis of the system of Countryside Categories, proposed by O'Riordan (1983) in the UK input to the World Conservation Strategy. It would classify land into (a) Agriculture and Forestry Landscapes, (b) Conservation Zones, and (c) Heritage Sites, with the degree of control increasing from (a) to (c). Swingland *et al.* (1983) consider 'that this monumental undertaking is . . . inoperable'; but any system other than that of complete 'laissez faire' will require some form of land classification, and O'Riordan's proposals offer a useful basis.

Agriculture and Forestry Landscapes (a) would probably include more than 90% of lowland UK; on this land, productive agriculture would continue at an intensity determined by current EEC price levels, but with both EEC and national grants progressively reduced, most immediately for activities such as drainage and reclamation intended to bring marginal land into cultivation. Agricultural support is examined in greater detail by Potter (1983), who proposes an Alternative Package of Agricultural Support (APAS), which would transfer grants from production-orientated activities on the better land (on which agriculture would be expected to be viable with reduced support) towards mainly livestock farming on more marginal areas (these latter areas would include part of O'Riordan's categories (b) and (c), on which grants would also encourage conservation activities and maintenance of rural employment). Advice would form an integral part of all schemes approved by the Agricultural and Development Advisory Service (ADAS) and the Scottish Colleges, supported by the Countryside Commission, Farming and Wildlife Advisory Groups, and other bodies, and aided by specific grants and tax concessions. Potter proposes that areas with high agricultural potential, but also of high conservation value, should be nominated as Special Assistance Areas (SAA), for which both EEC and national funds should be available to compensate farmers for loss of income; O'Riordan has also proposed that Local Authorities should have power to

protect limited Areas of Local Conservation Importance (ALCI), compensation in this case being paid by the Local Authority.

Heritage Sites (c) would be areas with 'special and irreplaceable nature conservation qualities . . . which should be given the strongest possible safeguards' (O'Riordan 1983), including most of the present SSSIs, the heritage coasts, and parts of the National Parks and AONBs. The presumption would be that, with food now in more than adequate supply, conservation and amenity in these areas would take priority over food production; there would be provision for compensation for loss of farm income, but this compensation would be based on income foregone from an 'ecologically sustainable management', and not from the maximum output technically achievable, an important proviso, which would exclude claims for loss of income from proposed intensive management of marginal land. This category would include many areas of high landscape value, but public access to some areas might need to be restricted to avoid damage to scientific features.

Intermediate in both conservation value and in the extent of protection proposed, Conservation Zones (b) would include major scenic areas, in which preservation of landscape and amenity would take precedence over changes in farming practice designed to improve profitability; these areas would be controlled more strictly than under the Wildlife and Countryside Act, but with adequate funds to compensate for loss of 'reasonable' farming improvement (see also Bowers & Cheshire 1983, p144). Grants would support conservation activities (such as those for walls and shelter belts recently introduced by MAFF), and 'community enterprises' to assist economic viability in areas which in future might receive less direct income from agriculture. The difficult task would remain of combining public access with viable farming.

Much of the land in categories (b) and (c) would be in the upland areas, discussed by Eadie (1984). Comment is included here because it is necessary to identify areas in which a greater degree of control of agricultural activity may be needed, in order to define the much wider area, including much of lowland UK, on which there would be only limited control.

9 Lowland agriculture

The proposition then is that most of the present lowlands would continue to support productive agriculture, with minimum control, except on those areas classified under categories (b) or (c), or nominated as Areas of Local Conservation Importance or Special Assistance Areas. Agriculture would operate at a level of intensity determined mainly by market forces, and with less support from structural and capital subsidies, although selective support for conservation activities, as proposed by Potter (1983), might be available.

Several consequences can be foreseen.

i. As CAP prices are brought closer to world prices (a stated Community objective, EEC 1983), and with reduced support for land drainage and reclamation, arable production on poorer land would become less profitable, but so also would milk, beef and sheep production, the main alternative enterprises on such land (grade 4 and much of grade 3). For these areas, an APAS would thus be needed to support livestock production, for example by revised Livestock Compensatory Allowances so as to benefit smaller farms (Potter 1983, p37). Cereal growing in marginal areas, which makes sense neither to conservationists nor to rational economists, would be discouraged.

ii. Much grade 3 land would continue in mixed crop/livestock farming, but aiming for greater on-farm self-sufficiency to reduce purchases of fertilizers and feed stuffs; some APAS support would almost certainly be needed.

iii. On grades 1 and 2 land, the high cost of setting up new livestock units would tend to discourage a return to mixed farming; intensive cropping would continue, but possibly with more sowing of alternative crops to cereals, such as oilseed rape, field peas and field vegetables.

The initial response to a cost/price squeeze on lowland agriculture would almost certainly be an increase in intensity and output, as farmers sought to maintain their incomes. Although, in the longer term, agriculture would become less intensive (Bowers & Cheshire 1983), there would be real risk in this initial stage of environmental damage as farmers 'cut corners'. However, an important new factor could emerge: the EEC Commission has concluded that end-price restraint alone is unlikely to prevent excess food production, and that there must also be some limitation on the amount of production that is guaranteed price support, payment above this amount being so low as to make additional production unprofitable. *Effectively, this limitation would mean the introduction of production quotas.* Superimposed on lower end-prices and reduced subsidies, a restriction on output would pose considerable problems for the viability of agriculture. *Together, they present a strong argument against imposing additional environmental constraints on lowland farming.*

In fact, restriction of agricultural output could well reduce the potential for environmental damage. The unlimited market for farm output has provided the main stimulus for land reclamation, removal of hedges, and use of agrochemicals, which have formed the principal threats to the environment. Once output is limited, a new production strategy may be needed *to produce the permitted amount (the quota) with the lowest possible inputs.* Unfortunately, because most

research and development have been planned within the framework of a high input/high output agriculture, we lack critical information on the likely consequences of adopting lower input systems on either production/economics or the 'environment'. There is some evidence, however, that, while a reduction in inputs may lead to some decrease in output, it does not necessarily reduce profitability. Examples are the Wheat '83 results reported by ADAS (1983) and the joint GRI/ADAS experiments, in which grass/clover swards have given up to 80% of the yield of grass swards receiving 400 kg N/ha (Morrison *et al.* 1983). Certainly, to produce a given quantity of milk as cheaply as possible may need a different strategy from that now used to get more milk per cow, and a milk quota would underline the urgent need for better management and forage conservation techniques on permanent grassland farms, though this strategy might not be welcomed by conservationists.

Lowland agriculture could thus face considerable economic problems, to solve which will need more research and development on lower input systems, research, incidentally, unlikely to be given high priority by the agricultural supply industry. Such research could include work on:

i. integrated pest management, combining 'resistant' crop varieties with agronomic management, pest forecasting, economic studies to define pest thresholds (RCEP 1979), and research on microbiological control;

ii. improving the timeliness and range of applicability of reduced cultivation techniques (Matthews 1979), methods of straw disposal other than burning, and new uses for straw (ADAS 1983);

iii. reducing fuel consumption by better tractor operation, improved design of crop driers Blackman 1982), more efficient glasshouse operation, and use of 'waste' heat from industry;

iv. more efficient storage and application of the mineral nutrients in animal wastes and new uses for animal wastes;

v. application regimes to increase efficiency of N use by grassland, including slow-release N fertilizers and better use of storage legumes (Morrison *et al.* 1983);

vi. breeding more efficient animals; after only 3 generations, workers at the Poultry Research Centre have produced broilers with 20% less fat, and with improved feed conversion efficiency (ARC 1983).

10 The environmental impact
This paper brings together the proposal by O'Riordan (1983) that lowland UK, with the important exceptions noted, should be used for productive agriculture and

with minimal environmental constraint, and those of Potter (1983) for a progressive transfer of agricultural grant support from farms on productive land to farms on less productive land.

By themselves, these measures could well lead to further increase in the intensity of production, and the risk of accelerated environmental damage, on large areas of the lowlands, were it not for the coincidence of the EEC proposal to restrict the amount of agricultural production that will be supported.

Yet it remains difficult to foresee the overall outcome. An APAS which sought to limit cereal production on marginal land might, within a national cereal quota, lead to even more intensive cereal cultivation on the better land. On the other hand, a decrease in (real) cereal prices might encourage lower input production systems, with a decrease in intensity. A price squeeze might, instead, lead to removal of hedges and erection of sub-standard buildings, as farmers sought alternative ways of cutting costs; and it is not certain that the smaller farms, which would be encouraged by the APAS proposed by Potter (1983), would be more favourable to the environment than larger farms. It is this uncertainty about the likely environmental consequences of the expected pressures on lowland farming that makes the provision for designating ALCIs and SAAs, and the increased protection sought for SSSIs, so essential.

11 The implications for ecological research

It is in the broad consequences of farming activity, rather than in the ecological detail, that the general public, who must fund the whole exercise, are mainly interested. While research should clearly continue on SSSIs and other areas of the proposed Heritage Sites, greater priority now needs to be given to research on the ecology of the much more extensive areas that will continue to be farmed intensively and which will mainly fashion the lowland landscape. The urgent need then is for ecological research effort to be more closely integrated with that from a range of other disciplines in detailed studies on farmed land, such as the collaboration of the Universities of Cambridge and Southampton in the major Boxworth project (Stanley & Hardy 1984) and the extension of the Game Conservancy studies reported by Potts (1984).

Farming will continue to be the predominant activity in the countryside, and research on the impact of different levels of farming intensity on production and on the total environment is of the highest priority. Yet the paradox is that, while both economic and environmental factors at present point the need for some reduction in the intensity of 'developed' country agriculture, much of the world's population remains under-fed, and that population continues to increase more rapidly than food production. We must believe, though, that, at some future time, ways will be found to distribute 'surplus' food without destroying legitimate food trade. While the closer collaboration between ecologists and agriculturalists which is urged here may be within a context that accepts some immediate reduction in output of food from lowland agriculture, the longer term objective must surely be to develop the high output, but environmentally more acceptable, production methods needed to contribute to future world feeding.

12 Summary

UK agriculture has had considerable financial support since the War, initially from Government, and more recently also from the European Economic Community. This support has encouraged the wide adoption of more intensive systems of farming. While these systems have greatly increased food output, they have also led to changes in the countryside which, if continued, could lead to unacceptable environmental damage, with particular public concern about likely effects on amenity and rural landscape.

The production in the EEC of several commodities, notably cereals and milk, is now well above effective demand, and the Commission has proposed measures to restrain future production. At the same time, there are proposals that the level of 'support' for agriculture should be greatly reduced (eg Body 1982) and that agriculture should be subject to greater planning control so as to protect the environment (eg Shoard 1980). Together, these measures would pose considerable problems in the continuing viability of lowland agriculture.

The paper examines different ways in which increased protection might be given to the rural environment, while sustaining a viable farming industry, and concludes that the strategies proposed by O'Riordan (1983) and by Potter (1983) may, together, offer a practical basis. In the immediate future, this would require the development and adoption of farming systems which place more emphasis on reducing inputs than on increasing output, and it is considered that this should be a priority subject for joint research between ecologists and agriculturalists. It is suggested that, in the longer term, UK agriculture must be able to contribute fully to the solution of the world feeding problem; the present period of 'surplus' food production should be used to develop the high output, but ecologically sustainable, production systems that will be needed in the future.

13 References

Advisory Council for Agriculture and Horticulture. 1978. *Agriculture and the countryside.* London: Ministry of Agriculture, Fisheries and Food.

Agricultural Development and Advisory Service. 1983. *Papers, Conf. Straw Utilization, 6th, Oxford, 1982.* London: HMSO.

Agricultural Development and Advisory Service. 1983. *Report on demonstrations at 'Wheat '83'.* London: Ministry of Agriculture, Fisheries and Food.

Agricultural Research Council. 1983. Breakthrough in breeding leaner broiler chickens. *ARC News*, Autumn, 18.

Blakeman, R. 1982. Fuel saving in grain drying. *Agric. Eng.*, **37**, 60-67.

Body, R. 1982. *Agriculture: the triumph and the shame.* London: Temple Smith.

Bowers, J.K. & Cheshire, P. 1983. *Agriculture, the countryside and land use: an economic critique.* London: Methuen.

Centre for Agricultural Strategy. 1983. *Agriculture: the triumph and the shame – an independent assessment.* Joint report. Reading: Centre for Agricultural Strategy, University of Reading; Ashford: Centre for European Agricultural Studies, Wye College, University of London.

Eadie, J. 1984. Trends in agricultural land use: the hills and uplands. In: *Agriculture and the environment*, edited by D. Jenkins, 13–20. (ITE symposium no. 13). Cambridge: Institute of Terrestrial Ecology.

Economist, The. 1983. Reducing agricultural subsidies. *Economist*, 26 November, 30-31.

European Economic Community. 1983. *Communication from the Commission of the European Communities to the Council.* (Doc 1-645/83, Com (83), 500 final).

Her Majesty's Stationery Office. 1966. *The national plan. Chapter 13: Agriculture.* London: HMSO.

Her Majesty's Stationery Office. 1975. *Food from our own resources.* (Cmnd 6020). London: HMSO.

Her Majesty's Stationery Office. 1979. *Farming and the nation.* (Cmnd 7458). London: HMSO.

Her Majesty's Stationery Office. 1981. *Wildlife and Countryside Act.* London: HMSO.

Matthews, J. 1979. The power requirement for tillage in the next decade. *Agric. Eng.*, **34**, 99-104.

Market and Opinion Research International. 1983. *Public attitudes towards farmers.* Research study conducted for the National Farmers' Union by MORI.

Morrison, J., Denehy, H. & Chapman, P.F. 1983. Possibilities for the strategic use of fertilizer N on white clover/grass swards. *Proc. Gen. Meet. Eur. Grassl. Fed., 9th*, 227-231.

Nature Conservancy Council. 1977. *Nature conservation and agriculture.* Banbury: NCC.

Nature Conservancy Council. 1981. *Annual Report, 7th, 1980–81.* Banbury: NCC.

Omega Report. 1983. *Agricultural policy.* London: Adam Smith Institute.

O'Riordan, T. 1983. Putting trust in the countryside. In: *Earth's survival: a conservation and development programme for the UK*, 171-261. London: Kogan-Page.

Potter, C. 1983. *Investing in rural harmony.* Godalming: World Wildlife Fund.

Potts, G. R. 1984. Monitoring changes in the cereal ecosystem. In: *Agriculture and the environment*, edited by D. Jenkins, 128–134. (ITE symposium no. 13). Cambridge: Institute of Terrestrial Ecology.

Ramblers' Association. 1982. *Open country; public asset or private domain?* London: Ramblers' Association.

Royal Commission on Environmental Pollution. 1979. *Agriculture and pollution.* (Cmnd 7644). London: HMSO.

Shoard, M. 1980. *The theft of the countryside.* London: Temple Smith.

Stanley, P.I. & Hardy, A.R. 1984. The environmental implications of current pesticide usage on cereals. In: *Agriculture and the environment*, edited by D. Jenkins, 66–72. (ITE symposium no. 13). Cambridge: Institute of Terrestrial Ecology.

Swingland, I.R., Carter, E.S., Quicke, J.G., Dick, W., Leslie, R. & Rands, M. 1983. Responsible management of land and the environment. *Inaugural Conf. Society for Responsible Use of Resources in Agriculture and on the Land, 1983*, 57-84.

Trends in agricultural land use: the hills and uplands

J EADIE
Hill Farming Research Organisation, Edinburgh

1 Introduction

For the purposes of this paper, both hill and upland farming will be considered. For convenience, it will be assumed that hill and upland farms are those classified by the Ministry of Agriculture, Fisheries and Food (MAFF) and the Department of Agriculture and Fisheries for Scotland (DAFS) as follows:

Region	Hill farms	Upland farms
England & Wales	Livestock rearing and fattening (mostly sheep)	Livestock rearing and fattening (cattle and sheep)
Scotland	Hill farms	Upland farms

The agriculture of the hills and uplands has been determined by the interplay of soils, climate, topography, remoteness, and economic and social history. The climate and soils determine that plant growth is depressed as a consequence of short, cold, growing seasons. Crop harvesting, including grass conservation, is difficult and uncertain. Topography constrains agricultural possibilities by limiting access, and

the operation of cultivation and harvesting equipment. These factors act together to determine that hill and upland farming is primarily devoted to livestock production, mainly breeding sheep and cattle, whose progeny, except for replacements, is traditionally disposed of before winter begins.

1.1 Hill sheep farms

The land resources of hill sheep farms are primarily the indigenous plant communities described in the agricultural statistics as rough grazings. Hill sheep are traditionally pure-breds, set stocked in a free range grazing system in which they obtain the large part of their nutrient intake from grazed pasture the whole year round. Beef cow numbers on these farms are traditionally limited by the small area of sown and cultivated grassland from which their winter food may be made.

1.2 Upland farms

The land resources of upland farms include a much larger proportion of enclosed sown grassland. The extent and the role of indigenous pasture in farming systems in the uplands vary greatly. Levels of sown pasture production are poorer than in the lowlands. Apart from the effect of higher altitudes and shorter and colder growing seasons, much upland pasture is renewed less frequently. Drainage is often poor. Management is more difficult, partly because topography constrains the integration of fodder conservation and grazing much more than in the lowlands. The sheep in the uplands are often cross-breds derived from one or other of the hill breeds. Beef suckler cow production is generally more important in upland farming than in hill farming.

Hill sheep farming and upland farming present different kinds of problems in agricultural development. It is, however, important to recognize that the land resources of hill and upland farming form a spectrum of continuous variation in respect of the ratio of indigenous to enclosed sown grassland.

Hill and upland farms are less profitable than lowland farms. Despite their often fairly large physical size, these farms are comparatively small farm businesses, and lack of profitability is in part a function of this fact.

2 Land resources
The land resources employed in hill and upland farming in Great Britain are shown in Table 1. The proportion of the total land area which exists as rough grazings can be calculated from Table 2; proportions are shown by regions as they relate to hill and upland farming. These data confirm the general subjective impression of the regional differences in the land resources and the farming practices of the 3 regions. Perhaps the most important point to note in the context of the present discussion is the substantial proportion of the total rough grazings area to be found on upland farms.

3 Output
The gross output of hill and upland farming amounts to some 7.5% of the total gross output of agriculture in Great Britain. That of hill and upland farming amounts currently to some £830M per annum. However, the significance of hill and upland farming to the rural areas in which it is the dominant land use is more clearly indicated by Jones (1978), who calculated that it contributes around 26-30% of the gross output of agriculture in Scotland and Wales respectively. The

Table 2. Rough grazings as percentage total area of land in hill and upland farming

	Scotland	North of England	Wales
Hill farms	97	84	74
Upland farms	78	55	30

same author computed the relative contribution of hill farming to be around 13%, 19% and 7% of the total hill and upland sector in the north of England, Wales and Scotland respectively.

Hill and upland farms contribute nearly one half of the sheep and wool production and one quarter of the total value of the cattle produced in Great Britain. There are some 21 000 full-time hill and upland farms in Great Britain. Approximately one in 6 of these holdings is a hill farm. Table 3, based on MAFF and DAFS statistics, allocates the total number of full-time farms between hill and upland farms and among the 3 main hill farming regions.

Table 3. Distribution of hill and upland holdings (1974-75)

	Hill sheep	Upland
Scotland	1043	9352
North of England	619	3144
Wales	1720	5187

4 Trends
Much the most important single trend in hill and upland land use to be observed since 1945 is the substantial transfer of land out of hill farming into forestry.

Of the 1.3M ha of high conifer forest in Great Britain, some 70% has been established since 1950, mostly in the hill areas. Rates of planting (State and private afforestation aggregated) proceeded at around 33 000-34 000 ha per annum in the 1950s and 1960s. Planting rates increased markedly in the early 1970s to reach a peak of over 50 000 ha per annum, but declined to around 25 000 ha by the end of that decade. Re-stocking accounted for about 15-20% of the total area planted each year in the 1970s. Recent rates of planting have declined significantly below that

Table 1. Areas of hill land in Great Britain (Million ha)
(Source: Economic Development Committee for Agriculture 1973)

	Scotland		North of England		Wales		Total GB
	Hill sheep	Upland	LMS*	LCS†	LMS	LCS	
Total area	1.53	1.89	0.20	0.68	0.34	0.47	5.43
Rough grazings	1.48	1.47	0.16	0.38	0.25	0.14	3.95
Grass	0.04	0.32	0.04	0.25	0.08	0.28	1.07
Tillage		0.09		0.05	0.01	0.05	0.30

*Livestock, mainly sheep
†Livestock, cattle and sheep

level, but are picking up again towards the officially intended rate of around 30 000 ha per annum. These rates of land transfer set into context a national figure of somewhere in the region of 4500 ha per annum taken out of semi-natural vegetation and re-seeded for farming purposes.

The regional distribution of afforestation in the 1950s and 1960s remained fairly stable. Approximately 30% took place in England, mainly in northern England, some 15% in Wales, and rather more than half in Scotland. In the 1970s, however, 75% of the new planting took place in Scotland. In earlier years, much was made of the difficulty of demonstrating any significant decline in output from the hills of Scotland consequent upon afforestation. The presumption, probably correct, was that losses of stock from planted areas were made good by intensification elsewhere. However, Cunningham *et al.* (1978) produced evidence to suggest that hill ewe numbers in Scotland were beginning to decline, and that this loss was accounted for largely in those parts of the country in which land transfers to forestry had been greatest.

The comparative stability of the hill sheep population at around 5.5M ewes probably reflects a decline in sheep numbers in the most extensively grazed farms, in north and north-west Scotland for example, and an increase on the better grazings in association with land improvement, eg in Wales. The beef cow population on hill and upland farms increased rapidly from around 340 000 in 1962 to a peak of some 826 000 in 1976. Since then, however, the discouraging economics of suckler cow production have led to a reduction in numbers in recent times. Most of these cows are on upland farms. There has been a marked increase in sheep numbers on upland farms, further encouraged recently by the establishment of the EEC Sheepmeat Regime which has brought both better prices and a more guaranteed future.

Hill and upland farms are, typically, small farm businesses, and, over the years, the minimum business size compatible with viability has steadily increased. Major changes have taken place since 1945 in the number of people deriving a living from hill and upland farming in response to economic pressures. In lowland agriculture, pricing policies and the developing technology available to arable farmers and intensive livestock producers have led to substantial increases in output per ha. By contrast, output in the hills has remained much more static.

The response to the need to maintain *per capita* incomes at levels which bear some reasonable relationship to those enjoyed by the remainder of the community has, in many hill areas, been to spread a not greatly increased total output over fewer and fewer people. In the uplands, the possibilities for intensifying output have been greater and, particularly

in recent years, have been increasingly taken up. In contrast, the structural problem has been more severe in many upland areas.

Thus, hired labour has been disposed of, and family employment has declined. Where resources have been available and where opportunities have existed, farms have amalgamated in an attempt to spread the increasing burden of fixed costs over a greater volume of output. The Uplands Landscape Study (Allaby 1983) indicates that, in the study area, farm size increased by 20% and the number of farms declined by some 40% over the period 1950-76. The age structure of the farming population gives cause for concern.

Farm capital grant schemes have led to an improvement in the quality of the buildings and fixed equipment on hill and upland farms, especially in the last 15 years. New buildings can sometimes appear intrusive, and some of the many disused buildings can be unsightly, but very often good siting and appropriate styling, though adding somewhat to costs, have reconciled changing farming needs and sensitivity to the landscape satisfactorily.

Technical changes in the hill sector include a large increase in the supplementary feeding of hill sheep in late pregnancy. The practice has given rise to some local problems, particularly on heather moorland. Lean ewes are now identified and given special treatment on many hill sheep farms. More attention is paid to achieving good body condition at mating, and many more hill ewes are mated and lambed under controlled conditions. Whilst hill land improvement has proceeded in some areas, it has done so at a modest pace overall. Some hill grazings are fenced internally, but the reasons often have more to do with ease of management in the face of labour shortages than with more positive approaches to vegetation management.

Perhaps the most obvious trend in the management of indigenous hill vegetation, as a direct consequence of the great reduction in available labour, is the decline in good burning management. To some extent, this decline has been exacerbated by a long run of moderate to poor burning years so far as weather is concerned, and, to some extent, by the reduction in cattle numbers on hill farms. This deficiency is probably of greatest importance on heather moorland, but it is also significant on many other vegetation types.

The quality of grassland resources and the production of grasslands on upland farms have improved greatly, particularly in recent years. This improvement has been accompanied by greater intensities of stocking, particularly by sheep. The sheep have been changed in many areas to more productive cross-breds. Winter housing of sheep is more widely practised. The traditional beef cow has largely given way to the dairy-cross animal, and the continental sire is now widely used on the better upland farms. Winter housing of beef cows is widespread, and the advantages of silage making over hay making in the more adverse upland climate are increasingly being reflected in farm practice. The general levels of awareness of, and interest in, the technologies of sheep and beef production are both increasing.

The developments in hill and upland farming, and the present state of the industry have, of course, depended heavily on the support system. The occasional use of a hill sheep subsidy to sustain the hill sector following periods of exceptionally adverse weather conditions gave way in the mid-1960s to an annual payment. The payments were later extended to the upland sector at a lower level, and incorporated into the application of the Less Favoured Areas Directive to the United Kingdom. More recently, the EEC Sheepmeat Regime has had a considerable effect on sheepmeat prices, reflected to a much greater extent in the incomes of upland farmers and hill farmers on the better hills. In the poorer hill farming environments, modest levels of lambing performance and lamb growth and the lack of any real possibility of finishing lambs on any scale continue to constrain the better opportunities which now exist in the more favoured environments.

These general comments should not disguise the fact that many regional and local factors have had a significant influence on trends which create wide divergencies from place to place. Generalization can indeed be dangerous. One very obvious regional example concerns the conversion of indigenous vegetation to sown pasture in Wales. Here, the economic pressures generated by the very small size of the average hill farm business have forced the pace and encouraged a tradition of hill land improvement which is not paralleled in most parts of the north of England or Scotland. Stocking practices on common grazings have sometimes led to intensities of stocking which would be regarded as irresponsible by the majority of farmers utilizing similar vegetation on their own holdings. Much attention has, rightly, been focused on the north Yorkshire moors, but the rates of moorland conversion and the set of problems encountered there are no more typical of the general situation than is the erosion consequent upon the peculiar interaction of sheep grazing and visitor trampling one sees in parts of the Peak District National Park.

5 The future

Any view of the future in an uncertain world must be speculative in the extreme, especially in the present circumstances. Any view of the future of hill and upland farming must be conditioned by a view of the outcome of the conflicting arguments which currently surround agriculture in general, and hill and upland farming in particular. The general disenchantment with the Common Agricultural Policy and prevailing political attitudes have created a climate in which the 'free trade' arguments of Body (1982), the Omega Report on agriculture (1983), and The Economist (1983) may take root and flourish. At the other extreme, it is also clear that many believe, with Shoard (1980) and others, that nothing short of a complete rural planning system will secure what are believed to be appropriate balances between the community interest, on the one hand, and the private interests of landowners, farmers, foresters and rural developers, on the other.

The implications of the 'free trade' argument are unlikely to be thought to be as potentially beneficial to the lowlands as Body (1982) states. The outcome for the hills would almost certainly be a combination of extensive ranching and conifer forest and the decimation of the rural population in the hills and uplands. On the other hand, there is no good reason to think that planning controls will necessarily resolve the problems of the future of the hills and uplands. These opinions have less to do with political ideology and more to do with the nature of the problem than either of the contending parties will easily concede.

Stated public policy wishes to see landowners and farmers weigh landscape and amenity values and what is referred to as good conservation practice more heavily in their decision-making. The central issue has to do with attitudes, habits of mind, and motivation. The agricultural, social and environmental issues are so inseparable, and the role of those who carry on the agriculture so vital, that nothing less than their willing and active co-operation will bring about the desired result. However that may be, in making judgements about the future, it would seem to be more in tune with the mood of the times to assume that neither the 'free trade' nor the 'planning control' lobbies will prevail in the medium-term future at least.

This background provides a perspective on competing objectives in the management of a very large proportion of this country's land surface. The process, given the many competing calls on the public purse, should be as cost-effective as possible. If cost-effectiveness is to be achieved, the land resources should continue to yield useful products for the community such as sheepmeat, wool, beef, grouse, and deer. In the process, their attractiveness to the people who live there, and to the tourist, should be maintained, and enhanced if possible, and those parts which are of high scientific value should not be destroyed.

The arguable policy options, then, become those which range between the 'status quo', and the complete reformation of the support system, together with incentives for 'better' resource management.

In considering these alternatives, it is important to identify the nature of the balance which is central to the objectives as stated above. That balance is essentially between the future economic development of hill and upland agriculture to achieve social and agricultural objectives on the one hand, and the retention of as large a proportion as possible of the existing semi-natural vegetation in its present state of low fertility, and providing the fairly stable mosaics which characterize open hill country, on the other. The fear is that a production-oriented agriculture will progressively destroy the character of the hills and upland countryside. In examining that fear, it is useful to consider hill and upland farming in 3 parts.

i. In the higher and more remote hills, agricultural production as a major objective will doubtless continue to decline. Its role in sustaining a population to manage the countryside for conservation and landscape objectives will become more explicitly important than it is now. A continued agricultural production orientation may, however, remain the best way of ensuring that the countryside management element of its objectives is secured at least cost to the community. This can be done without danger of significant conversion of rough grazings to sown pasture, but, if these farms are to retain enough people for the management purposes suggested, the headage payment system will require to be adjustable to take account of the new objective.

ii. There would appear to be no good basis on which to challenge the agricultural objectives of the upland farms, and particularly those which have higher than average ratios of enclosed sown pasture to indigenous hill vegetation. Many of them are small farm businesses. They do not contribute to products which are in surplus. Their contribution to the rural economy and the population of the rural areas is considerable. They are good subjects for the developing technologies in pasture production and utilization, and sheep and beef production.

Amalgamation will most likely continue, but these farms are also capable of a significant degree of intensification. Intensification should be encouraged to minimize unit costs of production and thereby lessen dependence on outside support, while maintaining their current contribution to the rural population. A failure to sustain these farms as economic units would lead to a very rapid and obvious dereliction which would be unacceptable in terms of landscape and amenity values, and from which there is nothing to be gained in conservation terms.

iii. The future role of the better hill farms in the less remote places is perhaps more controversial. The key issue is the extent to which a production oriented, population sustaining agriculture would conflict with landscape and conservation objectives.

Unless costs are to escalate, or population objectives are to fall by the wayside, production agriculture will have to be allowed to develop its practices in the light of modern knowledge, and in response to cost and price pressures. A central requirement is the continued conversion of some indigenous pasture land to sown grassland. The justification for the assertion that land improvement is a key requirement in the development of hill sheep farming systems is elaborated elsewhere (Eadie 1978), and a detailed account of the management practices involved in a development study, and its results, is given by Armstrong et al. (1978). Similar work being carried out on Experimental Husbandry Farms in England and Wales and by the Scottish Colleges of Agriculture is confirming the validity of the approach.

Two aspects of this argument, in particular, require further discussion. First, in their survey of vegetation changes at a range of locations in England and Wales, Ball et al. (1982) found that the majority of the changes observed took place on only 11% of the total area. They indicated that the whole land resource could be subdivided into 3 components: (i) cultivated pasture land, (ii) a moorland core which had always been under extensive management, and (iii) the fringe area which over 200 years has changed between moorland and farmland and forest. It is suggested that much of the required re-seeded pasture would come from the fringe area, and that the extent of any further incursion into the moorland core would be comparatively small in many hill areas.

Ball and his colleagues indicate that, although debate and discussion frequently highlight the absolute loss of vegetation, the changes within the remaining moorland are of equal consequence, at least visually. The semi-natural vegetation types included in these studies ranged from bent/fescue grassland to grass heaths and shrub heaths. The authors point out that vegetational change is normal in semi-natural vegetation, and that, although the vegetation at one site may change, compensating changes are likely to take place at another site. Diversity is likely to be maintained, although the location of the components may change. However, they do express concern at the sensitivity of some communities (eg *Calluna* shrub heath) to increases in grazing pressure, and to uncontrolled burning. Within the suggested framework of a system in which improved pasture is integrated in its use with a large component of semi-natural vegetation, there is neither any need for, nor any useful agricultural purpose to be served by, managing the semi-natural vegetation in other than an ecologically sound fashion. There is, in fact, the safeguard of an added degree of flexibility with which to respond to any concern for the indigenous vegetation by changing grazing pressure in space and time to an extent which would not be possible in systems which do not have an improved pasture component.

Second, it is important to recognize that these farms are also attractive for forestry purposes. Much of this land is of interest to foresters, and under current rules attracts Forest Authority grant-aids. The only bulwark against an even more rapid advance of forestry is a continuing profitability in livestock farming. Forestry is important, and governments are likely to continue to encourage the transfer of hill land out of agriculture and into forestry. However, in the light of changing perspectives on hill land use, a more deliberate encouragement of the possibilities afforded by agriculture/forestry integration should be more actively explored. Those possibilities include the generation of significantly greater volumes of economic activity in well planned, integrated developments. This activity would create a much needed examination of that aspect of hill land use in which change is both most rapid and most widely criticized. It would also capitalize on the enhanced opportunities presented by change to foster wider discussions of resource management in all its aspects, and to consider the potential role and nature of resource management incentives of the kind proposed by MacEwen and Sinclair (1983). It does, however, seem realistic to accept that rates of planting will continue to be determined by the balance between the fiscal incentives offered to forestry and the profitability of hill sheep farming. That, in turn, argues for a reasonably profitable hill farming with all its implications for further development, if the large proportion of the land resources of the better hill farms are to remain as open country.

A specific example might serve to underline the general argument. Generally speaking, land improvement has been discouraged on heather moorland. The changing economics of hill sheep farming on heather moorland have therefore had to be accommodated by farm amalgamations, which, in company with the increase in keepers' wages, have led to many fewer people being available for muirburn. The result has been inadequate burning and large, poorly controlled fires, and a downwards spiral of events which has been good for neither grouse, sheep, the rural population, nor the environment.

In seeking solutions, there have been many misunderstandings. Heather moor which includes a good proportion of bent/fescue grassland, especially where that grassland is well distributed throughout the moor, can carry a lot of sheep at good levels of performance.

The danger is that too high a grazing pressure on the heather will weaken and eliminate it, but, on many heather moors, the limitations of heather as the major constituent of the sheep's diet are reflected in both stock performance and a stocking rate which severely under-utilizes heather: hence the importance of burning as a management tool, and hence the enthusiasm to feed sheep in winter.

The limitations of heather as a food for sheep require it to be supported by, and integrated with, better pasture. Where such pasture exists naturally in insufficient amount, it must be provided artificially not only to upgrade sheep performance, but also to ensure the flexibility required for good resource management. Local circumstances, farm structure, and so on will determine the extent to which this pasture can be provided by existing inbye land. It may also require to come, in part, from newly re-seeded land. Many moorland fringes from which the heather has retreated would be much better re-seeded and enclosed. Sheep also require to be fed in winter. There is no doubt that winter feeding practices which have encouraged high concentrations of sheep year after year in the same place have damaged and even eliminated heather in some places. The answer is to move the feeding sites regularly, to keep them away from old heather, and to use good young heather which recovers so very much more rapidly.

In some situations and, thankfully, they are in the minority, the heather problem has reached the proportions of a production, sporting and environmental disaster. The clear need is for an integrated solution in which all interests may have to make some sacrifices. In the last analysis, only agriculture will be able to afford the resources to deal with the association problems of bracken and ticks. It is difficult to see that a complex of planning controls would either help to prevent or resolve a problem of this nature. The real need is for understanding and awareness.

It is, therefore, argued that there is no viable alternative to continuing to secure the balances to be held among the various interests in the hills and uplands within a broadly agricultural framework. The extent to which agricultural activity is aimed at securing production and social objectives will depend upon the nature of the land resources under consideration. In the uplands, there seems to be a good possibility of obtaining worthwhile agricultural production at reasonable levels of cost relative to animal production in the lowlands, and, concurrently, achieving worthwhile social objectives. In the poorer, higher and more remote hills, agriculture would simply be a vehicle for sustaining the best possible population of resource managers whose main objective would be the maintenance of grazed open hill country. On the better hills, it is also important to maintain as high a population of people on the land as possible, but this population will not be achieved at reasonable cost unless agricultural development possibilities are accepted and, indeed, encouraged.

Within this framework, there is an obvious need to consider increasing the Hill Livestock Compensatory Allowances on the higher hills. On the better hills, relationships between forestry and agriculture on the potentially plantable land could be reconsidered with advantage, including an exploration of the question of resource management incentives, which would also take account of landscape and conservation aspects. It seems likely that any broadly voluntary set of arrangements will not be acceptable without fall-back controls to prevent abuses. Within this general framework, the provisions of the Wildlife and Countryside Act will continue to apply, but it seems likely that its limitations will become increasingly obvious with the passage of time.

6 Implications for ecological research

It is, of course, axiomatic that more research is needed. It sometimes appears that the major revelation of research is the extent and depth of the lack of knowledge. The ecology of soil/plant/animal relationships in extensively grazed environments is very complex. A qualitative understanding of the components of the whole is difficult to obtain; the quantitative understanding of the whole to the extent necessary for responses to management change to be predicted with the precision required by resource managers remains a distant objective.

However, priorities have to be determined, and 3 areas of ignorance are selected as being worth special mention.

i. There is clear need to monitor *vegetational change*, and particularly vegetational change in semi-natural vegetation in the hills and uplands. It will no doubt be a matter of argument as to whether such monitoring is best done within the framework of a natural 'all purpose' vegetational monitoring system. Others more experienced in these matters than the writer will no doubt contribute a view as to the best method. What is required is the ability to know with some precision what is happening at the level of the individual plant community in different parts of the country.

ii. If conservation objectives become more important relative to production objectives in the hills and uplands, and, as a consequence, become less of a by-product, so it will become more necessary for the *costs of competing proposals to the community* to receive more consideration. As Cobham (1983) has pointed out, the resources used in managing semi-natural vegetation in these circumstances compete with alternative claims on those same resources. It

may be difficult to evaluate a comparison of the benefit gained by the community from a particular piece of wildlife conservation or a certain amount of aid to the aged. It would, however, be helpful at least to know something about the costs involved. The state of the art undoubtedly leaves a great deal to be desired. It is unlikely to be a perfectable art, but there seems to be little doubt that it could be greatly improved. It would be too easy to dismiss this plea as yet another manifestation of the modern fashion to quantify everything in monetary terms. Nonetheless, sooner rather than later, it will be necessary to sort out the competing claims on financial resources of alternative objectives in conservation; costing what it is appropriate to cost will help.

iii. Current knowledge on which to base *predictions about the consequences to vegetational change of management manipulation*, and particularly *grazing animal manipulation*, depends on an understanding of descriptive ecology and a certain amount of grazed plot study. Quantitative knowledge about some kinds of vegetation is reasonably adequate, for example bent/fescue grasslands and heather-dominant moorland. Work is proceeding in the Hill Farming Research Organisation and in the Institute of Terrestrial Ecology on others, eg moor-grass and mat-grass grasslands, but much remains to be done and must be done if prediction is to be tolerably accurate.

The field problem has a dimension which scientists have barely begun to tackle. Many hill pastures are vegetationally heterogeneous, and often the only practical means of controlling livestock grazing is by altering animal numbers. Changing grazing pressure on a sensitive pasture type by altering overall stocking rate on an area of hill grazing requires assumptions to be made about the implications of that change on the grazing pressure applied to the sensitive pasture type. Some important information has been obtained from grazing behaviour studies (Hunter 1962), which is helpful in a broad and general way. More detailed basic studies are required of the factors which influence choice among plant communities by grazing sheep and beef cattle, if it is eventually to become possible to make realistic predictions.

7 Summary

Hill and upland agriculture has changed considerably since the War. This sector of the industry now employs many fewer people on a substantially reduced number of farm holdings. A considerable area of semi-natural vegetation has been afforested, and some land has been taken out of indigenous pasture for agricultural improvement.

The grassland resources of upland farms have been greatly improved, and are now generally much more intensively stocked and farmed. Practices have changed, too, on hill sheep farms. Many hill sheep are now fed in late winter as a matter of routine, and traditional practices of a variety of kinds have been changed to give greater control at key times.

There has been a rapidly developing interest in landscape value, amenity, recreation, tourism and conservation in the hills in the last few years, which has led to a questioning of the extent to which the effects of existing agricultural policy in the hills and uplands may be in conflict with these other objectives.

These issues are briefly explored, with particular reference to the impact of agriculture on semi-natural vegetation. It is contended that agricultural, social and environmental issues are inseparable in the hills and uplands, and that agriculture will continue to play a leading role. The way forward is to influence attitudes with the role of controls limited to last resort measures to prevent abuses. Important areas where more research is required include the monitoring of vegetational change, estimation of the costs of competing proposals, and the preparation of base-lines for predictions about the consequences to vegetational change of management manipulation, particularly the manipulation of grazing animals.

8 References

Allaby, M. 1983. *The changing uplands: based on the report of the Upland Landscapes Study by Geoffrey Sinclair, Susan Bell* et al. (CCP 153). Cheltenham: Countryside Commission.

Armstrong, R.H., Eadie, J. & Maxwell, T.J. 1978. The development and assessment of a modified hill sheep production system at Sourhope, in the Cheviot hills. *Rep. Hill Fmg Res. Org. 1974–77*, 69–101.

Ball, D.F., Dale, J., Sheail, J. & Heal, O.W. 1982. *Vegetation change in upland landscapes*. Cambridge: Institute of Terrestrial Ecology.

Body, R. 1982. *Agriculture: the triumph and the shame*. London: Temple Smith.

Cobham, R.O. 1983. The economics of vegetation management. In: *Management of vegetation*, edited by J.M. Way, 35-66. (Monograph no. 26). Croydon: British Crop Protection Council.

Cunningham, J.M.M., Eadie, J., Maxewell, T.J. & Sibbald, A.R. 1978. Inter-relations between agriculture and forestry: an agricultural view. *Scott. For.*, **32**, 182–193.

Eadie, J. 1978. Increasing output in sheep farming. *Jl R. agric. Soc.*, **139**, 103–114.

Economic Development Committee for Agriculture. 1973. *UK farming and the Common Market: hills and uplands*. London: National Economic Development Office.

Economist, The. 1983. Reducing agricultural subsidies. *Economist*, 26 November, 30–31.

Hunter, R.F. 1962. Hill sheep and their pasture: a study of sheep-grazing in south-east Scotland. *J. Ecol.*, **50**, 651–680.

Jones, W.D. 1978. A review of some economic aspects of hill and upland farming. In: *The future of upland Britain*, edited by R.B. Tranter, 50-74. (CAS paper no. 2). Reading: Centre for Agricultural Strategy, University of Reading.

MacEwen, M. & Sinclair, G. 1983. *New life for the hills*. London: Council for National Parks.

Omega Report. 1983. *Agricultural policy*. London: Adam Smith Institute.

Shoard, M. 1980. *The theft of the countryside*. London: Temple Smith.

How is the EEC likely to influence changes in agricultural impacts in Britain?

B HUBER
Division VI-F-2, Commission of the European Communities, Brussels

1 Introduction

First, I would like to make a number of points concerning the inter-relationship between agriculture and the natural environment. Over thousands of years, farming has changed the landscape quite remarkably to adapt it more to the main objective of food production. To realize this aim, forests have been cut down to a large extent, terraces have been built on steep farm slopes, stones and rocks have been removed, stone walls built up, wet lands drained, hedges planted, and in some cases eliminated, and the land has been levelled according to the system of land use and the techniques available. Farmers have a special value in the rural scene as they have used farm building methods and local materials adapted to the local landscape. Because farmhouses are situated in the rural landscape, sometimes at very visible points, this aspect has a high importance.

On the typical family farms which predominate in Europe, one of the greatest gains has been the maintenance and improvement of soil structure and fertility over the centuries. This effect can be explained by the existing family farm structure, which aims to hand down the inheritance from one generation to the next in the same family. The farmer is thus motivated not to over-exploit his valuable plot of land which will be handed over to his children. Actual cases of famine caused by heavy soil destruction and loss of fertility prove that this aspect was not given proper attention in some parts of the world. Even in some parts of southern Europe, there are examples where over-exploitation of the soil resources can be seen, resulting in soil erosion and total infertility in some mountainous regions, with secondary negative effects of water control and flooding problems in the lowlands, and water pollution and negative effects on the micro-climate. European agriculture has been largely successful in the past in maintaining the landscape, soil fertility, and the rural scene in general, but this task is becoming more difficult because of the high pollution from urban and industrial areas. Acid rainfall, heavy metals, and water pollution due to inadequate waste disposal systems from urban areas and from industry cause widespread negative effects on soil quality, reducing the soil pH and destroying the micro-aggregates which make up the soil structure and maintain its water and plant nutrient retention capacity as main factors of soil fertility. Only by the maintenance of a correct balance of water, air, nutrients, and soil fauna and flora can the natural conversion of organic matter to mineralized nutrients and to further vegetation be continued in the nutrient cycle. The negative effects which are now dramatically present in some forest regions, and in orchards and vineyards, are probably only the first warning signs of a general deterioration of the environment, which could have disastrous long-term results in the irreversible loss of soil fertility.

The common agricultural structures policy developed mainly from the Mansholt Plan of 1968. From this base, the Council of Agricultural Ministers adopted 3 basic directives in 1972, which represent a logical unit. In the farm modernization directive (Directive 72/159/EEC), investment aids are given to full-time farmers who can ensure a long-term viability without further structural aid after carrying out a development plan. Other farmers unable to achieve this objective, corresponding to the comparable income earned outside farming, could benefit from a pre-retirement scheme (Directive 72/160/EEC) by handing over their land to more effective farmers, or, in the case of younger farmers, receive training for another profession outside agriculture. The third directive (Directive 72/161/EEC) provides aid, on the one hand, for the introduction of a socio-economic extension service to persuade farmers either to develop their farm or to choose another employment to give them a sufficient income, and, on the other hand, a special training scheme for young farmers. These 3 directives were completed in 1975 by the directive on mountain and hill farming and farming in less favoured areas (Directive 75/268/EEC), which provides for higher investment aids and the payment of compensatory allowances for permanent natural handicaps.

These 4 directives, through the principle of priority for Community schemes, at the same time orientate all national schemes of investment aid. It has long been recognized that the greatest pollution danger related to agriculture comes from the intensive livestock sector. For this reason, and also because of the larger import content of intensive livestock production, due to the tax free import of GATT (General Agreement on Tariffs and Trade) consolidated imports corresponding actually to around 34M tonnes of cereals units, investment aid to these sectors has been severely restricted. Investment aid for poultry and egg production has been banned right from the start of the common structural policy for agriculture. Similarly, aid for the purchase of pigs, poultry or veal calves is banned. In the pig sector, aid may only be given up to a physical limit of size of herd (550 pig places), and on the strict conditions that there is sufficient land to produce 35% of the feed requirement on the land available, and hence sufficient land available for slurry spreading. Aid for dairying is similarly restricted to a herd size of 40 cows per man work unit, with a maximum of 1.5 man work units per farm (cf Table 1). All these physical limits, as well as the overall limit of aid per man work unit and per farm, tend to favour smaller family farms which can provide a certain assurance as to their long-term viability. The physical bans and limitations on aid apply both to Community-funded and national investment aids.

Table 1. Structure of the dairy herd in the 10 Member States

Member states		Number of dairy farms ('000) 1981	Number of dairy cows (M) 1981	Average number of dairy cows per farm		
				1973	1979	1981
Germany		431	5·5	9	12	13
France		458	7·1	11	14	15
Italy		468	3·0	5	6	6
Netherlands		67	2·4	23	32	36
Belgium		53	1·0	12	17	18
Luxembourg		3	0·07	14	21	24
United Kingdom		59	3·3	38	53	56
Ireland		92	1·5	10	14	16
Denmark		39	1·0	15	23	26
Greece		94	0·2	—	—	3
	EC	1 764	24·8	11[1]	14[1]	14

[1] Without Greece

All the Community aids are conditional on a proper respect of the need for environmental protection. This protection requires adequate slurry storage capacities attached to farm buildings (so that slurry need not be spread on land outside the growing season) and proper collection and storage of silage effluents, etc.

The higher aids provided for farms situated in the less favoured areas were established to cater for farms in areas with greater physical handicaps and to compensate for the higher building costs and the longer winter feeding period in such areas. The compensatory allowances paid to farmers in the less favoured areas, which are based on the number of livestock units within a limit of one livestock unit per hectare, are set according to the severity of the permanent natural handicap. Such payment helps with the preservation of small farms and all their related structures of fields, hedgerows, walls and housing, which go to form important elements in our European landscapes. To some extent, these payments represent an income transfer which avoids forcing the farmer to over-intensify his production in order to meet his income requirements. The fact that the payments are based on grassland enterprises is useful in the preservation of soils and the prevention of erosion. In the temperate zones, the presence of grazing animals is necessary to preserve grazed moorland landscapes. In alpine regions, the effect of grazing animals is even more dramatic, with the discontinuation of grazing leading to degradation of the landscape, landslides and avalanches.

The economic importance in the UK of the compensatory allowances can be shown by the following figures from 1982: 44 000 farms received direct payments on the scheme, with an average of £1,930 per farm. The total was £85M, of which 25% was paid by the European Agricultural Guidance and Guarantee Fund (EAGGF).

At the end of the 1970s, the Commission presented to the Council a special structural package to encourage agricultural development in some particularly handicapped areas, special attention being paid to smaller farms which could not benefit from the horizontal schemes.

Included in this package, which was agreed in 1981, was a measure for Northern Ireland (Council Regulation (EEC) 1942/81). Where land improvement and drainage measures are involved in these specific measures, special studies are necessary to avoid negative effects on the environment, especially near sites of environmental interest. A similar 'environmental clause' was foreseen in the special drainage measure in Ireland (Council Regulation (EEC) 2195/81) and was applied in the cross-border arterial drainage measure between Ireland and Northern Ireland (Council Directive 79/197/EEC).

2 New proposal in 1983

Bearing in mind the remarkable change in general economic circumstances, and especially the growth of unemployment, the agricultural structures policy must be adapted to take account of the changed situation. In addition, the surplus situation in some sectors of agriculture needs appropriate restrictions on the structural policy side to ensure proper co-ordination between the micro- and macro-economy.

For these reasons, in the new package of structural proposals (COM 83 (559)), presented by the Commission to the Council of Agricultural Ministers to replace the existing horizontal directives, in the normal areas of the Community no extension of production capacity would be subsidized in the surplus sectors. This proposal follows the same line as for the market side, especially for the production of extra milk. Certain exceptions would be allowed for some well defined, less favoured areas which are covered by special livestock programmes. The other physical limits on intensive livestock production are maintained in the new proposal, as well as the total ban on investment aid for egg and poultry production.

In future, aid under farm improvement plans would be restricted to:

  i. the qualitative improvement and conversion of production in the light of market requirements;

  ii. the adaptation of the holding to
      – reduce production costs
      – improve working conditions
      – save energy;

  iii. measures for the protection and improvement of the environment.

The measures introduce a combination of investment aid for productive ends and for reducing the farmer's costs and thereby increasing his income. New aspects can be seen in the aids for energy saving, which could be used for energy recovery from milk cooling, or possibly the development of energy sources from animal or crop wastes. The aid for the protection and improvement of the environment will have obvious beneficial effects on pollution from buildings, and represents a quite remarkable re-orientation of the structural policy. In the past, in order to meet the requirement to reach the level of comparable income at the end of the development period, smaller farmers were encouraged to intensify beyond the level that they would otherwise have done, as the factor of land mobility had a negligible impact.

By contrast, the new concept stresses mainly the reduction of production costs and the improvement of the farmer's living and working conditions. Another positive aspect for the environment is the introduction of aid for woodland investment on farms.

As for the special aids for less favoured areas, the most important changes are as follows.

i. The compensatory allowance can be paid in the first 15 years of establishment for farmland planted with trees for wood production. It is hoped that small areas of farmland will be afforested with an appropriate mixture of varieties to give a number of different positive effects on the landscape and wildlife habitats.

ii. A larger amount of aid for farm tourism and craft industries on the farm would improve the possibility of income combination. The proposal foresees an increase of 50% of aid in the case of farm tourism or craft industries, where the investment is combined with an extensification of farming.

iii. To cover more effectively small areas with a special environmental interest, the proportion allowed of small areas with specific handicaps under Article 3 (5) of Council Directive 75/268/EEC would be increased from 2.5% to 4% of the total area of the Member State.

iv. A special allowance for national aid paid to farms specifically to improve or maintain the natural landscape has been provided for in Article 13 (3) of the proposed regulation.

Without this provision, such types of aid would not conform with the Treaty of Rome which insists on the avoidance of aids that might give rise to unfair competition.

The aim of the new proposal is to widen the possibilities for investment aid in favour of the smaller farmer. The number of possible beneficiaries will be increased. From the environmental viewpoint, this proposal has been received negatively by some people. However, such an attitude is not justified because of the various restrictions and the ban on aid for intensification in the surplus sectors. This widened system will help reduce production costs, especially in smaller farm units which profit less from the guarantee side of the different market regulations.

To a large degree, this approach is the logical answer to the very restricted price policy which was announced by the Commission in 1983, and which forms part of the present price package proposed for the 1984–85 season.

It should be stressed that the common structures policy for agriculture is based on the agricultural socio-economic objectives laid down in Article 39 of the Treaty of Rome. In no way does the Commission pretend that the agricultural structures policy is an environmental policy. Nevertheless, the structures policy must take proper account of environmental

Table 2. Farm size classes in the European Community in 1970 and 1981

Member State	Year	Percentage of size classes[1]					
		1–5 ha	5–10 ha	10–20 ha	20–50 ha	More than 50 ha	Average size (ha)[1]
Federal Republic of	1970	37·5	21·5	24·7	14·5	1·8	11·7
Germany	1981	32·2	18·5	22·6	22·6	4·2	15·3
France	1970	22·9	17·6	25·0	26·0	8·5	21·0
	1981	20·5	14·4	21·1	30·4	13·6	25·4
Italy	1970	68·4	17·8	8·4	3·7	1·7	7·7
	1981	68·5	17·2	8·4	4·2	1·7	7·4
Netherlands	1970	25·9	23·9	31·7	17·0	1·5	13·0
	1981	23·7	20·0	28·7	24·5	3·2	15·6
Belgium	1970	33·9	25·3	25·7	13·1	2·0	11·6
	1981	28·3	19·6	26·5	21·3	4·4	15·4
Luxembourg	1970	21·3	14·3	22·3	37·8	4·3	19·4
	1981	17·3	11·1	14·4	38·0	19·2	27·6
United Kingdom	1970	18·9	14·6	18·9	24·3	23·3	57·4
	1981	11·4	12·3	16·1	27·3	32·6	68·7
Ireland	1970	17·9	20·1	30·2	24·3	7·5	17·7
	1981	14·9	16·7	30·0	29·8	8·7	22·5
Denmark	1970	9·4	21·3	31·4	31·7	6·2	20·7
	1981	10·8	17·3	25·8	35·1	10·8	24·9
Greece	1970	—	—	—	—	—	—
	1981	70·9	20·6	6·5	1·7	0·2	4·3
European Community	1970[2]	42·6	18·8	18·9	14·7	5·0	15·6
	1981	46·7	17·1	14·9	15·0	6·2	15·7

[1] In hectares of utilized agricultural area
[2] Without Greece

concerns, and, in its 3rd Action Programme on the Environment, the Council of Ministers of the European Communities has asked that environmental concerns be integrated into other common policies such as the agricultural policy. I hope that I have shown you that some of these concerns have been given concrete recognition in the existing policy for agriculture, and that this orientation is intensified in the new proposals for both the Guidance and Guarantee side of the EAGGF.

As a final point, I should underline that common policies can provide an overall framework of measures to be applied throughout the regions of the Community. The common policy must therefore be sufficiently flexible to deal with a wide variety of agricultural and environmental conditions and must allow Member Governments sufficient liberty to deal with special circumstances. In this context, it is interesting to note the differences that have arisen from historical and social-economic causes between the United Kingdom, especially England and Scotland, and other areas of the Community. While the average farm size in the Community in 1981 was only 15.7 ha (Table 2), the average British farm was some 69 ha (the Greek average was only 4.3 ha and Italy 7.4 ha). Because only 2.8% of civilian employment is employed in British agriculture, and because of the large urban concentrations, Britain has been considered a non-agricultural country, but it should be recognized that British agriculture contains some of the most technically advanced and productive farmers of Europe. For the most part, the structure of British agriculture can only be envied by other European nations. Obviously, the priority areas for further reforms of agricultural structures largely lie outside Britain, but, at the same time, structural policy must allow individual farmers in Britain to attain or maintain a reasonable level of income. In so doing, the common structures policy provides sufficient flexibility to the Member State to take account of specific local economic and environmental elements. This provision ensures a policy which is at the same time both Community-wide and well adapted to local economic and environmental interests.

3 References

European Economic Community legislative acts

Common Organization of the Market (COM) 83 (559). Proposal for a Council Regulation on improving the efficiency of agricultural structures.

Council Directive 72/159 on the modernization of farms.

Council Directive 72/160 concerning measures to encourage the cessation of farming and the real location of utilized agricultural area for the purposes of structural improvement.

Council Directive 72/161 concerning the provision of socio-economic guidance for and the acquisition of occupational skills by persons engaged in agriculture.

Council Directive 75/268 on mountain and hill farming and farming in certain less-favoured areas.

Council Directive 79/197 on a programme to promote drainage in catchment areas including land on both sides of the border between Ireland and Northern Ireland.

Council Regulation 1942/81 for the stimulation of agricultural development in the less-favoured areas of Northern Ireland.

Council Regulation 2195/81 on a special programme concerning drainage operations in the less-favoured areas of the west of Ireland.

Pesticide usage: is the Pesticide Safety Precautions Scheme satisfactory?

N W MOORE
The Farm House, Swavesey, Cambridge

1 Introduction

Pesticides are chemicals for the control of organisms inimical to man. They include herbicides, fungicides, insecticides and rodenticides. Most are novel synthetic organic substances used to kill weeds and pests, but the term is usually extended to cover naturally occurring substances, such as derris, and growth regulators, such as maleic hydrazide. Thus defined, pesticides have been used for centuries, but they only became an integral part of agriculture in the post-War period.

In the 1950s and 1960s, the most widely used pesticides were the phenoxyacetic acid herbicides such as MCPA, organomercury fungicides, and organochlorine and organophosphorus insecticides. When the harmful environmental effects of persistent organochlorine insecticides were discovered in the 1960s, these chemicals were replaced by a wide range of organophosphorus and carbamate insecticides. Later, in the 1970s and 1980s, some uses of the older insecticides were replaced by synthetic pyrethroids. A new generation of herbicides was produced to deal with the weeds, notably monocotyledonous ones such as wild oats, which had increased as the result of the successful control of broad-leaved species. The translocated herbicide glyphosate has partially replaced the contact herbicide paraquat as a total weedkiller in recent years.

An increase in pesticide use to control aquatic weeds has run parallel with the increase of pesticide use in agriculture and horticulture. For conservation reasons, the use of herbicides on road verges is on a smaller scale than in many other countries. The use of pesticides in forests is also smaller because the incidence of pest outbreaks has been less in Britain.

Pesticide use varies from year to year according to weather, economic conditions and the pesticides available. However, in general, the total amount of pesticides applied is increasing and so are the types of pesticide. Pesticides have brought great benefits to mankind in preventative medicine, agriculture, forestry, and in preserving stored food and timber. Yet, because they are used to kill living organisms, they are potentially hazardous to non-target species, including man himself. The damage they can do depends on their toxicity, their persistence, on the ways they are applied, and on their scale of use. As no pesticide is specific to the pest it is used to control, no pesticide is entirely safe. Therefore, the aim of every regulatory scheme should be to ensure that pesticides give maximal benefit with minimal risk.

I was associated with the United Kingdom Pesticide Safety Precautions Scheme for over 20 years, and I shall discuss the extent to which we achieved that aim by using a system largely based on voluntary co-operation between Government and industry. I say largely because some aspects, for example the wearing of protective clothing, are controlled by law (Health and Safety (Agriculture) (Poisonous Substances) Regulations), and because the 'threat' of legislation almost certainly has an important role in ensuring the effective co-operation of industry.

2 The Pesticide Safety Precautions Scheme
The Pesticide Safety Precautions Scheme (PSPS) works in this way: the chemical firm is responsible for providing to the Scientific Sub-Committee, and later to the Advisory Committee on Pesticides, data on the pesticide it seeks to sell. The Committees, backed where necessary by specialist panels (eg on Carcinogenicity and on the Environment), study the data on the chemistry of the substance, its residues, its toxicology and its effects in the field. The Committees have outlined the basic requirements through working documents, but, if extra tests are required, the Scientific Sub-Committee can, and does, ask for them. The chemical goes through a series of clearances in order that the firm and the Committees can learn from experience in the field. Initially, the chemical is given trials clearance, then clearance limited to use on a defined hectarage, or provisional clearance dependent on receiving further data, and finally full commercial clearance. Thereafter, the compound is kept under continuous review, and, if unforeseen hazards become apparent, the use of the pesticide is modified or it is withdrawn altogether.

The Advisory Committee is made up of independent members and representatives of the relevant Government departments, although there is a move afoot to restrict it to independent members. The members of the Scientific Sub-Committee and its Panels are appointed on an *ad hominem* basis. In practice, most are employed by Government. There are no members from industry on the Committees, although industrial representatives are sometimes asked to attend parts of meetings for specific purposes.

Safety is achieved by farmers carrying out the recommendations of the Committee concerning such matters as interval time between spraying and harvesting and dilution rates. These recommendations have been worked out on the basis of the residue studies, toxicological studies and field experience reported by industry. Safety is not achieved by prosecuting farmers whenever residue levels in crops exceed stated limits. Thus, the system is not constrained by exact legal requirements, but it is wholly dependent upon the good faith of industry in producing honest data, and on industry agreeing to abide by decisions over which it has no control. It also depends on the user applying the pesticide in the manner described on the label, whose wording has been cleared by the Committees.

3 The effectiveness of the Scheme
The PSPS has been in operation for 30 years, and some general conclusions can be drawn about its effectiveness. It is designed to protect operators, consumers, domestic animals and the environment. To what extent has it succeeded? As regards acute effects on human beings, the PSPS has been outstandingly successful. No deaths in the UK have ever resulted from the proper use of any of the pesticides cleared by the Scheme. Even deaths due to gross mis-use (mainly suicides) are extremely rare. When compared with fatal casualties due each year to tractor accidents, to falling off ladders, or to bulls and boars, those caused by pesticides are negligible.

It is sometimes argued that some pesticides may have insidious sublethal effects which increase the likelihood of death by some other cause. Considering the quantities used, it is probable that pesticides do sometimes have undesirable subacute effects on man, but there is no evidence whatever that such effects are widespread or significant. Only very extensive epidemiological studies could determine the contribution (if any) which is made by pesticides to the human death rate. Similarly, extremely few casualties of domestic stock have been recorded, and, where they have occurred, they have nearly always been caused by accident or gross mis-use.

It is impossible to protect wildlife entirely from the effects of pesticide use. Animals in a sprayed area are bound to come in contact with the pesticide: beneficial insects, such as bees, parasitic hymenoptera and carabid beetles, will often be killed along with the pest species. Herbicides and insecticides, by removing important sources of food, may have serious indirect ecological effects, even if they have no direct toxicological ones. It has to be accepted that pesticides are bound to kill many individuals of non-pest species. The important point is whether they have serious effects on total populations. Pesticides do not operate in a vacuum, so it is extremely difficult to determine the relative importance of different environmental factors in causing the observed decline of a given species. For example, the use of pesticides in many parts of England has coincided with the removal of more than half the hedges present in 1945, and with the greatly increased use of artificial fertilizers. Yet it can be stated that very few, if any, species in the UK have become extinct as a result of pesticide use. On the other hand, the relative abundance of many species has been altered profoundly by pesticides; more seem to have declined than to have increased, and some are now so rare that their eventual extinction is probable. A number of species would almost certainly have become extinct as a result of the use of persistent organochlorine insecticides, if restrictions had not been put on these substances.

To conclude, the PSPS has been extremely effective in protecting man and domestic animals from pesticide hazards, and no environmental disasters due to pesticides have yet occurred. The record in the UK with the voluntary PSPS is a great deal better than in many countries where schemes are based primarily on legal constraints. What is the reason for this success?

4 The advantages of the voluntary Scheme
There are 2 major advantages in the voluntary Scheme. The first is its flexibility. On one side, the Committees are not forced to ask for irrelevant information because it is required by a law, which perforce has to deal with average situations; on the other, the Committees can ask for special tests to be done to deal with special circumstances.

The other advantage, and it is a very important one, is psychological. If there is no law, there is no law to break. Industry is encouraged to take a pragmatic rather than legalistic view of its safety responsibilities. At best, this pragmatism leads to a genuine and constructive partnership between industry and Government departments and agencies over safety matters, which, in turn, favours the development of a truly scientific approach to the subject so that all concerned can react quickly to new ideas and new research.

5 The disadvantages of the voluntary Scheme
At best, the voluntary Scheme works extremely well, but its operation does depend on everyone concerned obeying written (and unwritten) codes of practice. For example, it depends on industry not putting pressure on members of the Committees and the Secretariat behind the scenes. It depends on honest reporting of experimental studies by industry. And, above all, it depends on operators applying pesticides sensibly. Of course, in the real world, accidents do occur, and some operators do behave irresponsibly. The Com-

mittees are fully aware of this fact and so apply very large safety margins. Safe use of pesticides also depends on agricultural advisers, both Governmental and commercial, giving sound and responsible advice. A great deal depends on individual people behaving responsibly, but, if they do not, there are few legal sanctions which can be applied against them.

6 Particular cases
The extent to which the Scheme works effectively can best be judged by looking at particular issues. One of the situations most likely to show its strength or weakness is when new information is discovered showing that a pesticide, already cleared under the Scheme, is more hazardous than at first believed. The first 2 cases mentioned are of this kind.

6.1 Carbophenothion
This organophosphorus insecticide is used as a seed dressing to control wheat bulb fly. Toxicological studies submitted under the PSPS suggested that its use would not cause serious damage to birds; and, in general, experience has confirmed that assessment. However, field observations in the early 1970s showed that geese of the genus Anser were unusually sensitive to the compound. Several hundred greylag and pink-footed geese were killed as a result of eating corn dressed with it. As it happens, these geese are largely confined to Scotland. Informal arrangements were made between Government officials and the manufacturers of carbophenothion to restrict its use to England and Wales and, as a consequence, the kills of grey geese have now largely ceased. This case showed how the PSPS could react quickly and effectively to a new problem, without resorting to time-taking legal procedures.

6.2 Persistent organochlorine insecticides
Possible hazards due to the unselectiveness of these compounds were recognized nearly 40 years ago, but not until the early 1960s was it realized that their long persistence in the environment could cause serious problems. The PSPS then faced a very difficult problem: these insecticides were extremely effective, and, at least in the case of DDT, safe to use. However, extensive research showed that many birds and mammals were killed through acute poisoning by aldrin and dieldrin, and many others were affected sublethally by DDE, a metabolite of DDT. Several species of raptor were endangered by the compounds, and there was an obvious potential risk to freshwater and marine fisheries. In some cases, residues in human foods (notably mutton fat) were considered excessive. As a result of this knowledge, the persistent organochlorine insecticides were largely phased out in the period 1961-75. There followed a dramatic increase in the populations of the peregrine and other species which had proved useful biological indicators of this serious environmental problem. Nevertheless, new studies on the use (and mis-use) of chemicals and on monitoring residues in birds suggest that DDT is

still used on a large enough scale to be having some environmental effects, so the organochlorine problem has not been entirely solved. With this qualification, one can say that the PSPS arrangement was successful in solving a difficult problem without resort to time-wasting legislation.

6.3 Mis-use of mevinphos, α-chloralose and strychnine

The PSPS has cleared these chemicals for certain specific uses, and field experience has not revealed hazards. However, there is growing evidence to show that a rather large number of gamekeepers mis-use these compounds by inserting them into eggs and carcases of rabbits and other carrion, in order to use them as poisoned baits. This irresponsible action provides a serious risk to children, has caused several casualties among domestic animals, and has killed hundreds of protected birds. Despite considerable publicity, the malpractice continues, and the PSPS is powerless to prevent it under its present remit.

6.4 Excessive use of pesticides

Excessive use of pesticides causes unnecessary environmental damage, and favours the rapid build-up of resistant strains of pest, and, by indirect means, produces new pests. The PSPS examines new pesticides and new uses of pesticides one by one. It has no means of controlling what the farmer does once a chemical has been cleared, and so has no control over the sum total of pesticide use, which indeed appears to be excessive and hence uneconomical.

7 Agricultural Chemicals Approval Scheme (ACAS) and efficacy

When pesticides have been cleared under the PSPS, their efficacy is assessed by the Agricultural Chemicals Approval Scheme, and the cumulative results of its work are published annually in the booklet entitled *Approved products for farmers and growers*. Some account of efficacy is taken when new pesticides are considered by the Advisory Committee on Pesticides and the Scientific Sub-Committee. The Committees would usually be unwilling to clear a very toxic new compound if much safer compounds were already giving effective control of a pest. The ACAS helps to ensure that appropriate chemicals are used, but, as with the PSPS, it does not deal with such problems as excessive use or the build-up of pest resistance.

8 Conclusions on the control of pesticides

I hope I have said enough to show that the problem of pesticide control in its widest sense is complex, and that neither a purely voluntary nor an entirely mandatory system would be desirable. I think it is important to recognize that there are 3 main elements of the situation and that they each require different measures.

First, for the clearance of individual pesticides, the present voluntary system, with its merits of flexibility and practical co-operation between Government and industry, would seem to be preferable to any mandatory system, unless the latter could be made equally flexible and co-operative, which seems extremely unlikely.

Second, the PSPS does not control mis-use; it was not designed to do so. Yet undiluted paraquat does still get into the hands (and mouths) of children and others, and, as we have seen, several other chemicals are used for illegal purposes. Some farmers do use pesticides for purposes which have not been cleared by the PSPS, and some use them too near to harvest. Mis-use can never be wholly prevented by law, but, as with motor cars, law can greatly reduce hazards. I believe that there is a need to consider new measures to reduce hazards due to mis-use.

Third, the PSPS was not designed to deal with major 'across the board' problems such as those caused by the mis-use of pesticides and the trend of increasing use. These complicated problems can only be solved by carrying out extensive field-based research, and eventually by altering the nature of advice given by Governmental and commercial advisers. The PSPS, which has no funds, has no adequate mechanism for getting the necessary work done. Here again is an important gap that needs to be filled.

In the last resort, the decision on which elements of control should rest on voluntary action and which should depend on law depends on the political and sociological characteristics of the nation concerned. In the United Kingdom, I believe we have demonstrated the value of a voluntary system for dealing with some aspects of pesticide control under our circumstances, but we should be very careful about recommending our system to countries where industry is less responsible. Indeed, we should not be complacent about the situation in the UK. Our system is already a mix of mandatory and voluntary elements, but have we got the mix right? The PSPS Committees always review new evidence about the safety of pesticides already cleared, making changes when necessary. This objective and scientific approach should also be applied to improving practice in the field, so that effectiveness is enhanced and safety improved.

9 Research required

I hope that I have shown by this review of the PSPS that there is a considerable need to carry out research on the environmental effects of pesticides. The moment is particularly opportune, because, according to the Department of the Environment, there is wide support for the idea that 'the Advisory Committee on Pesticides should be empowered to consider and advise upon research needs: (and) should engage actively in wider issues arising from pesticide usage, including any ecological impact' (the Government's response to the Seventh Report of the Royal Commission on Environmental Pollution).

May I conclude by listing research topic headings, which the deficiencies of the present arrangements suggest should be undertaken.

i. *Monitoring.* Apart from a few groups like birds and butterflies, we simply do not know what is happening to the flora and fauna of agricultural land. Therefore, monitoring of selected species is required along the lines adopted by the Game Conservancy at North Farm, Washington, West Sussex.

ii. *Large field experiments.* We do not know what are the effects of different pesticide regimes on the crops, flora and fauna on different farm types. Large-scale, long-term, multidisciplinary replicated experiments should be undertaken to determine the more important effects.

iii. *Sociological studies.* The extent and causes of the mis-use and abuse of pesticides are not known accurately. Sociological studies on the scale of mis-use and abuse, and on the attitudes of land managers and operators, which underlie both proper and incorrect uses of pesticides, should be made.

The need for studies of the kinds outlined above has long been recognized. Very similar recommendations were made here at Monks Wood in the 1960s. That studies have not been undertaken on an adequate scale has been due to a lack of manpower and land resources. However, the gains accruing from the effective use of natural predators, the reduction of pesticide use, and the slowing down of pesticide resistance are likely greatly to exceed the admittedly high costs of the proposed research.

10 Summary
Pesticide use is an integral part of agriculture, horticulture, water management and forestry in Britain. Considerable changes have occurred in the types of pesticides during the last 40 years. The total amount used continues to increase.

The purpose of the Pesticide Safety Precautions Scheme is to provide as much protection as practicable for the consumer, operator, domestic animals and the environment. The Scheme is based on a voluntary agreement between Government and the agrochemical industry. Its voluntary nature provides for flexibility, which is of great value in getting relevant tests done by industry and in revising clearance of pesticides in the light of new knowledge. On the other hand, the PSPS provides no method of dealing with mis-use of pesticides, and has no control over the amount of pesticides used. Therefore, it cannot control deleterious ecological effects due to the combined use of all pesticides. In particular, it has no means of preventing their excessive use or the build-up of resistance in pests, and no funds to support research into these interdisciplinary problems. The effects of pesticides on the environment should be monitored. Large-scale experiments should be undertaken to determine the effects of different spraying regimes on crops and wildlife, so that pesticides can be used more effectively and hazards to the environment reduced.

Footnote – This paper is based on one given by the author at the conference on *The principles of pollution control: the British experience*, organized by the Royal Society of Arts on 18 November 1980.

Recent economic trends in British agriculture

J S MARSH
Department of Agricultural Economics & Management, University of Reading

1 Introduction
Every activity exists within economic constraints. Whatever we do requires resources which have alternative uses, so, if we are to continue any one task, its outcome must be valued more than the alternatives. Such values may be purely personal, eg for resources such as our own leisure time. Many derive from the market and reflect values which people in general attach to alternative bundles of goods and services. Some are given effect through political decisions, especially those where the costs and benefits of actions to society as a whole are not reflected adequately in private systems of value, eg where smoke from one factory makes dirty the buildings belonging to other firms. However derived, such valuations of resources form a necessary condition of any continuing stream of outputs from business.

Agriculture is no exception. We value its outputs partly through conventional markets, and partly through policy decisions. We buy food, and we may or may not enjoy the scenery which farming produces. Both sets of values change through time. As the title of this conference suggests, attitudes to the value of the resources used and the outputs produced by agriculture have changed. One reason for this change is straightforwardly economic. Particular types of resource become more scarce (eg wetlands) or some outputs become more abundant, so a shift in relative values of extra outputs of different sorts is inevitable. To such changes the farm business has to respond. For those who manage farms, this pressure for change is likely to be difficult and may be resented. This paper examines some of the economic trends in agriculture, changes to which farmers and others have had to respond. It develops an argument which contains 5 main steps.

i. Since the Second World War, agriculture has been transformed by the application of a range of powerful technologies which have greatly increased its output.

ii. This technology has operated within a policy framework which has stressed goals, including increased output, high farm incomes, stable prices and increased productivity.

iii. The combined effect of policy and new technology has resulted in some of these goals being met more adequately than others. In the process, some unintended, and sometimes unwelcome, changes have taken place, for example in areas such as rural community life and the loss of, or damage to, important environmental characteristics.

iv. Today, the financial implications of advancing technology make it impossible to sustain existing policy unchanged. However, simply reducing agricultural support would not, by itself, ameliorate the consequential problems of new agricultural technology, restore the damaged environment, or sustain rural communities.

v. The new methods of farming will not go away; indeed, further development along the same lines is inevitable and should be welcomed. It can, however, only be welcome if it is managed. This management requires an adjustment in policy which channels the new technology in ways which take account of the shifting value of the differing bundles of output made possible. We need a positive policy for development, not an attempt "to 'uninvent' the wheel".

The rest of this paper elaborates this argument in the context of the economic issues facing British farmers.

2 The impact of new technology

The most striking evidence of change in agriculture is in crop yields. Table 1 shows that, since 1973, UK farmers have increased the yield of all major crops and done so at a faster rate than their competitors in the European Community. Similar measures of yield are not generally available for livestock. Table 1 shows that milk output per cow rose at an annual rate of 2%, and we know from UK statistics that the number of eggs laid per laying fowl rose from 227.5 in 1971-73 to 250.5 by 1982. Meat production figures such as those shown in Table 2 reflect market pressures and cannot give clear guidance about technology. However, it is interesting to note the very sharp contrast between poultry and other meats. This is an area of relatively rapid technical change for which falling real prices have been sustainable. Another important contrast within Table 2 is the much smaller growth (or actual decline) in UK livestock production, compared with that of the EC as a whole. This contrast probably stems from the change in the support system and the greater protection given to crop products under the Common Agricultural Policy than had been the case before the UK joined the EC.

Table 2. Average annual percentage change in net production, 1974–80
(Source: Commission of European Communities 1982)

	UK	EC9
Beef and veal	0·1	1·6
Pigmeat	−0·8	2·9
Poultrymeat	1·7	3·2
Eggs	−0·7	0·9

One important feature of the new technology has been to increase the optimum scale of farm enterprise. Table 3 shows some of the changes which have taken place in UK farming since 1972. The significance of this development is both economic and ecological. In economic terms, it tends to concentrate the farm's capital and the farmer's skills on a decreasing range of enterprises. Success hinges upon excellent performance on the farm and a secure market. The policy environment, which prevents prices collapsing when over-supply occurs, is crucial. Without it (and to some degree even with it), small and medium-sized farm businesses would face greatly increased uncertainty. The implication is that, in the absence of support, farm

Table 3. Average size of farm enterprise in the UK, 1973–82
(Source: HMSO 1975, 1984)

	1973	1982
Cereals (ha)	29·9	40·4
Potatoes (ha)	3·5	4·5
Sugar beet (ha)	10·5	16·6
Dairy cows (number)	36	55
Beef cows (number)	16	18
Breeding sheep (number)	153	188
Breeding pigs (number)	20	39
Laying fowls (number)	521	824
Broilers (number)	16 905	27 375

Table 1. Average annual percentage increase in yields, 1973–80
(Source: Commission of European Communities 1982)

	UK	EC9
Wheat	4·3	2·3
Barley	1·6	1·3
Sugar	7·8	4·8
Rapeseed	5·5	4·2
Hops	1·4	0·6
Potatoes	2·0	0·9
Milk per cow	2·2	2·0

structures would need to adapt to allow for more diversity, but to achieve this diversity and sustain low unit costs would require further increases in farm size.

For those whose interest is more broadly in the countryside, this process of increased specialization presents obvious anxieties. The diminution of cattle in arable areas, the problem of effluent from large pig or poultry units, and the seasonal crisis of straw burning provide ample illustration. More subtle changes in wildlife are also implied. It becomes sensible to 'improve' land, to enlarge fields, and so to eliminate some traditional sources of refuge and food for wildlife. Even where farmers themselves are anxious to avoid damage, the economic pressures unleashed by changed technology force them to adopt practices which reduce the former diversity of the countryside.

The new technology has necessitated a change in the mix of inputs used by the industry. Labour, both that of the farmer and his family and of hired workers, has declined. New capital equipment in the form of machines, buildings, and such installations as power and irrigation equipment has grown in importance. By the careful use of chemicals, whether fertilizers, herbicides, pesticides or medicines, the performance of crops and animals has been improved. Purchased feeds, containing a balanced, least cost diet, make their contribution to the efficiency of the business. Thus, today, the mix of farm costs (Table 4) includes

many items bought from other sectors. Such products have to be bought at prices which will compete with the value of the resources in other uses. Thus, modern farming cannot escape the impact of cost changes which originate elsewhere in the economy.

Across the EC as a whole, including the UK, this situation has exposed farmers to an important deterioration in terms of trade (the implicit value per unit of farm production divided by the implicit prices of inputs) (Table 5).

Table 5. The development of the 'terms of trade' for agriculture, in the EC9 and the UK, 1973–81
(Source: Commission of European Communities 1982)

| | 1975 = 100 | |
	UK	EC9
1973	101·4	107·8
1974	91·0	95·3
1975	100	100
1976	106·3	103·2
1977	95·6	100·5
1978	93·6	101·6
1979	93·4	99·2
1980	87·1	93·4
1981	87·7	90·9

The implications are that the new technology, whilst it has increased output, has not enabled the industry as a whole to avoid a narrowing of margins. As a result, if

Table 4. Resources used in UK farming in 1982
(Source: HMSO 1984)

		£M	% final output
1. Value of final output		10 382	100
2. Purchased inputs			
(a) Feeding stuffs		1 476	(24)
(b) Seeds and livestock		467	(4)
(c) Fertilizer and lime		808	(8)
(d) Machinery (fuel, repairs, other)		838	(8)
(e) Farm maintenance		201	(2)
(f) Miscellaneous		967	(9)
		5 757	(55)
Adjustments for	(i) change in physical value of stocks	−32	—
	(ii) intermediate output	−763	(7)
	(inputs produced within UK agriculture)	4 962	48
Net input (purchases from other sectors)			
3. Capital use – depreciation and payment of rent			
	(a) plant, machinery and buildings	810	(8)
	(b) building and works	471	(5)
	Total depreciation	1 281	(12)
	(c) interest	495	(5)
	(d) net rent	98	(1)
		1 874	18
4. Labour	(a) hired	1 176	(11)
	(b) family and partners	521	(5)
		1 697	16
5. Difference between value of final output and resources accounted for in 2–4		1 848	18

income is to be maintained, more units must be produced. The farmer is thus caught in a 'treadmill' situation in which his survival depends on the application of output-increasing methods, but in which the extra output leads to downward pressure on prices, upward pressure on support costs, and a tendency for some inputs to cost more.

3 Agricultural policy

Agriculture in Britain now operates within the Common Agricultural Policy (CAP) of the European Community. This Policy provides, for most major farm products, protection from competition by the rest of the world, and, for many key items, a system of intervention purchase and export subsidy which ensures that prices within the Community cannot fall below agreed limits. Additionally, the Community provides a modest amount of aid for structural development programmes, including farm modernization, retraining and retirement provisions.

The complexity of these arrangements makes it impossible to attempt any description by commodity, but certain features can be isolated as of special relevance to this paper.

First, the Community chose to support prices at levels which are normally considerably higher than those in world markets. So long as the Community remained a net importer of the product, this caused no difficulty for its budget; a levy (which rose if world prices fell) was imposed on imports and became part of the EC's 'own resources'. Maintaining high prices at a time of developing technology has, however, transformed this situation. Increasingly, and in growing numbers of product areas, the Community now produces more than it can consume at home, at the prevailing price. However, products sold abroad can only compete if EC traders receive subsidies to enable them to buy at Community prices and sell at world prices. Thus, the costs of price support have grown. In 1973, the Policy cost some 3927 million European currency units (ECU). By 1984, it is expected to cost 16 500 million ECU (Table 6).

Second, because the Policy offers high and secure prices to farmers, it encourages each Member State to expand its own output. Provided this expansion can be achieved at less than the protected price, extra output can profitably either displace imports or add to exports. Displaced imports mean that the expenditure and employment generated by domestic demand circulate within the Member State's own economy, rather than going abroad. Additional exports may be to other Member States or to third world countries. In either case, they add to the receipts of the domestic economy. Should a subsidy be needed to bridge the gap between EC and world prices, the Member pays only his share in the marginal addition to the budget of the Community as a whole.

Table 6. Anticipated budget expenditure on price support, EC10, 1984
(Source: Commission of European Communities 1983)

	ECU million	%
Cereals	2 590	16
Rice	92	—
Sugar	1 417	9
Olive oil	773	5
Oilseeds	1 100	7
Protein products	126	1
Textile fibres and silkworms	193	1
Fresh fruit and vegetables	350	2
Processed fruit and vegetables	695	4
Wine	558	3
Tobacco	745	5
Other products (seeds, hops, etc)	55	—
Milk and milk products (after co-responsibility levy)	5 006	31
Beef and veal	1 399	9
Sheepmeat and goatmeat	351	2
Pigmeat	197	1
Eggs and poultry	128	1
Other products	327	2
	16 500	100*

*These items do not add to 100 due to rounding.

The result of externalizing the costs of expansion is seen in the behaviour of Member States towards their own agriculture. Governments help their own farmers through tax concessions, the provision of free advice, the financing of research, and many other devices. Given the existence of unexhausted and developing technological improvements, the effect is to stimulate output. The consequence is added pressure on the finances of the Community.

Third, the CAP gave more assured and higher levels of protection to most of the northern products of the Community than to most of those produced in the south. To some extent, it sought to redress this imbalance by devising a very generous regime for olive oil. Today, the enlargement of the Community to the south, to include Greece, Spain and Portugal, is already under way. These countries have many poor farmers and they will look to the CAP for aid. Even now, the potential cost of the existing olive oil regime, if it were extended to Spain, looks alarming. To provide an adequate flow of funds in relation to the need in these countries on a more comprehensive basis would further exacerbate the financial problems of the EC.

Fourth, the process of disposing of excess Community output on world markets is likely to cause rising costs both in financial and political terms. Other agricultural exporters accuse the Community of dumping products in their traditional markets. They may take retaliatory action by subsidizing their own exporters to compete with the Community. Recent tension between the Community and the USA over flour sales to Egypt indicates the type of conflict which can occur.

Finally, it is central to the future of the Agricultural Policy that the Community is nearing the limit of its financial resources. These are made up of the proceeds of customs duties and levies, plus the yield of a value added tax comprehensively applied at the level of 1%. Over the period since 1975, agricultural expenditure has grown at an annual rate of 15.5%, but the 'own resources' of the Community have only grown at 11%. As agriculture accounts for 60-70% of all expenditure, this trend threatens the solvency of the Community as a whole. Even if the bills are paid, growing agricultural expenditure reduces the ability of the EC to finance other policies of more general application in such areas as social and regional policy.

4 Future developments

It would be wrong to conclude from the present problems of the CAP that it is either likely or even desirable that the present Policy will be dismantled. Although the Policy has not provided the assured income farmers claimed or the aids to adjustment in disadvantaged rural regions needed to produce a more cohesive Community, and although it is in danger of bankruptcy, the costs of abandoning the Policy are also extremely high. Removal of the CAP would make the survival of the Community itself doubtful. Those countries who saw in the CAP a *quid pro quo* for opening their markets to industrial imports believe the advantage they receive to be their due. Many governments might be forced to make independent, possibly competitive, arrangements to sustain their own farmers. Social hardship and rural desolation are not sound vote winners. An abrupt reduction of price might compel those who remained in farming to concentrate exclusively on the narrow range of activities which remained profitable in the short term, even at the expense of a growing backlog of neglect in longer run maintenance, etc. Farmers who were forced out might well be replaced by those who pursued a more 'extractive' approach to farming, seeking to ensure a quick pay back on investment. In the process, some farm land might deteriorate into neglected rough grazing.

Such an outlook seems of doubtful political acceptability even in Britain. In other European countries, it is virtually unthinkable. However, some change in the direction of agricultural policy must take place. Despite the inconclusive character of the Athens summit, the ideas which were formulated for reform remain of interest. These may be classified in several groups.

i. Changes which effectively reduce prices to farmers, including the application of guarantee thresholds for cereals, rape and beef: arrangements which would ensure that farmers paid part of the cost of disposing of quantities produced (by the industry as a whole) beyond certain limits.

ii. Added obstacles to imports of substitute products, including, for example, voluntary agreements, taxes on products which are mainly imported, or quantitative limits imposed on imports.

iii. Quota restrictions on individual output, limiting the volume which may be produced at the supported price and imposing a levy on any excess.

iv. The introduction of discriminatory policies
   - in favour of small farms
   - in concentrating structural policy on less favoured areas.

v. The integration of social and regional policy with agricultural structural policy so as to encourage balanced economic development in designated areas.

vi. The use of direct income aids, unrelated to output, to compensate for the reductions in income which seem inevitable as a result of attempts to contain growth in output.

All these suggestions leave the basic framework of the CAP intact. They seem likely to be applied in some form within a scenario where the goal of most EC Members seems to be to make only the minimum changes required to keep the Community solvent. As a result, far from a new, clear direction emerging for policy, the future is likely to resemble the past both in terms of confused goals and in the reluctance with which adjustments will be tolerated.

It is those commodities which cost the budget the most that seem likely to be the candidates for the earliest and most severe treatment. Table 6 makes clear what these commodities are. At the top of the list is milk, next, although only half as costly, cereals, then beef and sugar. Such a logical financial progression has, however, to be placed within a political context, and effective actions in relation to milk are likely to be so politically difficult as to demand some device which eases the hardship faced by the numerous small farmers for whom dairy farming remains the principal source of income. The use of discriminatory quotas, *quantums*, which pay high prices to small producers, is favoured in some quarters. Administratively, such a device would be complex and hard to enforce. Furthermore, at a time of changing technology, it would impose an economic cost on consumers in general which would grow, even if it was not visible in budget figures. Such sustained inefficiency cannot be applauded by any who wish to conserve resources or enrich the poor.

6 Conclusions

The solutions to agriculture's current problems are unlikely to be found within agriculture itself. The applied technology which creates the obvious symptoms of stress in policy also offers the opportunity for more people to enjoy more choice, both in food and non-food items. Allowing it to be used only to increase farm output not only imposes dangerous stresses on the EC budget, but results in high economic costs as the opportunity to release resources which have higher values in other uses is lost.

Many, but not all, of those resources are rural. The changing nature of farming creates a need, too, for a changing rural society. If people in the countryside are to enjoy a full and secure life, they need new ways of earning their living which make use of rural resources. While the abrupt cessation of agricultural support could lead to rural desolation, a positive policy which attracted resources into some of these non-farming activities, including the conservation and development of wildlife, might play a positive role in reshaping the continually changing and dynamic balance which is the country life.

7 Summary

Rapid technical change in agriculture has had a major impact both on the ecology of the countryside and on the economics of farming and agricultural support policies. In Europe, the system of support employed under the CAP means that heavy costs fall on the budget of the Community when self-sufficiency is exceeded. The system also encourages Member States to encourage farmers to expand their output. The result is a growing threat to the Community's solvency. Despite this situation, farm incomes remain relatively low and are under continual pressure; depopulation continues and rural communities decline. The issue for today's policy-maker is to employ the new techniques so as to produce food at low cost, and to devise a variety of alternative activities, outside traditional agriculture, which may sustain rural community life. Today's emphasis on the value of conserving wildlife may play a positive role.

8 References

Commission of European Communities. 1982. *The agricultural situation in the Community.* Luxembourg: CEC.

Commission of European Communities. 1983. *The common agricultural policy – proposals of the Commission.* (COM (83)500 Final). Brussels: CEC.

Her Majesty's Stationery Office. 1975. *Annual review of agriculture 1974.* (Cmnd 5565). London: HMSO.

Her Majesty's Stationery Office. 1984. *Annual review of agriculture 1983.* (Cmnd 8804). London: HMSO.

(29 February 1984)

What are the main recent impacts of agriculture on wildlife? Could they have been predicted, and what can be predicted for the future?

M D HOOPER
Institute of Terrestrial Ecology, Monks Wood Experimental Station

That specific agricultural practices have had effects on wildlife has long been known. It is certainly possible to search the pre-War literature and find examples such as 'the elimination of the beautiful cowslip, green winged orchid, moonwort and adderstongue has been accomplished by the repeated use of fertilizers' (Horwood & Noel 1933), but all such examples seem to be considered as isolated rather than of general occurrence, and of local rather than national import-ance. In no part of this particular work do the authors appear deeply antagonistic to farming or the develop-ments in farming over the previous century, although such developments are described in detail in their introduction.

Now, it is only too easy to find sweeping condem-nations of most agricultural developments in almost any area (eg Paskell 1984), and it is clear that many conservationists consider British agriculture in its present form as their prime target for reform. Attitudes have thus changed very dramatically in the last 50 years, but when and why did they change?

The evidence for the time of change seems to me to indicate that it came after 1960. The early post-War conservation literature mentions agriculture, but with no significant degree of condemnation. The Ministry of Town and Country Planning (1947, see paras 132-135) discusses agriculture and predicts no important con-flicts, but rather that farming might benefit from the activities of the Biological Service (Nature Conservan-cy) that was proposed. With the benefit of hindsight, we can see that part of this opinion was based on false premises, for example that the cultivation of marginal land was uneconomic and likely to remain so for the foreseeable future. The first Annual Reports of the Nature Conservancy almost ignore agriculture, although certain interactions are noted here and there. For example, the effects of myxomatosis on grass-lands, eagles and mountain lambs are discussed, but in no way is agriculture cast as the villain. Despite the careful temperate phrasing of the Nature Conservancy Council's recent (Ninth) Report (1984a), it conveys much more an atmosphere of antagonism over SSSIs in general, and West Sedgemoor in particular.

Similar comparisons can be made with the publications of other bodies. In 1952, the Botanical Society of the British Isles (BSBI) organized a conference on *The changing flora of Britain*. One looks in vain for a mention of the pressures of agriculture in, for example, Sir Arthur Tansley's contribution (Tansley 1953). However, the BSBI conference in 1969 on *The flora of a changing Britain* gave some prominence to agricultural developments (Trist 1970; Fryer & Chancellor 1970), and assessments of their impacts on the native flora (Perring 1970).

Even as late as 1960, W H Pearsall, when speaking on the problems of nature conservation in Great Britain at the centenary celebration of an agricultural institute, felt able to cover agricultural impacts in relatively few words. He saw industrial development and urbanization as the main pressure points. Similarly, J P Savidge (in Savidge *et al.* 1963) castigates industry and urban sprawl, before mentioning only the drainage of peat mosses as the agricultural impact; together they reported the extinction of 54 species of plants from south Lancashire.

At the same time, the problems of pesticide use were emerging (Rudd & Genelly 1956) and being widely advertized (Carson 1962). The early 1960s saw several publications (eg Cramp & Conder 1961; Moore 1962) on this particular aspect, especially as it affected birds, though plants were not entirely forgotten (Yemm & Willis 1962).

The next 2 impacts, hedgerow removal and the ploughing up of pasture, first became obvious or serious, according to our viewpoint, in the next few years (Moore *et al.* 1967; Wells 1968), and at the same time began a sequence of conferences on *The countryside in 1970*.

Reviews of the situation, written from different standpoints for different audiences, also started appearing (Christian 1966; Weller 1967). The main preoccupations of the mid-1960s continue, but differences in emphasis can be found (Bonham-Carter 1971; Davidson & Lloyd 1977; Mellanby 1981). At some point in this period, the average conservationist and the average farmer became antagonists. I estimate this point around 1969-70, and suggest that the blame lies with the Silsoe Experiment and its successors.

The Silsoe Experiment (Barber 1970) attempted to bring the 2 sides together on a national scale, and subsequent attempts have been made on a local scale. While I regard those attempts as laudable and to be encouraged in every way, their success has been limited. There is no visible sign to the average conservationist that British agriculture has changed, or that the average farmer has changed, as a consequence. Some farmers may have become better conservationists, but others have become worse (very possibly not because of their personal wishes, but driven by external circumstances). Given the impacts of current farming practices, it is not surprising that an intransigent attitude has developed among conservationists. With hindsight, our expectations of immediate results from Silsoe were possibly too sanguine.

That the current impacts of farming upon wildlife are many, various, and important, and that they are more significant than forestry or building, cannot be doubted in the face of the evidence that is now accumulating. In 4 years (1978-82), 17 prime sites (204 ha) were affected by agriculture and none by forestry or building in a rural county like Shropshire (Paskell 1984). On a national scale, high percentages of important conservation areas are disappearing: 95% of herb-rich hay meadows destroyed, 80% of calcareous grasslands, 60% of lowland heaths, 50% of lowland fens, 50% of lowland woods, and 30% of upland grasslands, heaths and mires (Nature Conservancy Council 1984b).

Impacts can be ranked in a variety of ways; the statistics given above provide a ranking of sorts, and other rankings have been attempted. For flora, Perring (1970) gives natural causes as the primary impact, with land drainage a close second, arable changes (= herbicide use?) third, and ploughing up of pasture close behind in fourth place, well ahead of habitat destruction. A little later, Perring and Farrell (1977), again discussing flora, put arable weeds as most in danger, with wetland species second, implying that herbicides have been more damaging than drainage. However, the highest number of species at risk (71 out of 321) grow in lowland pasture, although only one has actually become extinct.

Such statistics are meaningful or meaningless depending upon the framework of strict definition in terms of space and of time within which they are gathered. The recent losses in Shropshire sound very bad indeed, as do the national figures, but, in the case of the figures given by Ratcliffe, we are not told either the time span over which these losses occurred or the areas involved. What did Perring (1970) mean by 'land drainage'? Was it only tile draining, or were major works on main rivers included? Also, if Perring and Farrell (1977) find arable weeds most endangered, am I right to infer damage from herbicides? Could the sources of cereal seed and seed cleaning techniques have changed over the period of time in which the arable weeds have declined?

Many such questions can be answered crudely to give a more quantitative, if still inexact, ranking of the losses of wildlife habitat and species. For example, being familiar with the terminology of habitat types used by Ratcliffe (NCC 1984b), it is possible to suggest that herb-rich hay meadows occupied 10 000 ha, calcareous grasslands 45 000 ha, lowland heaths 100 000 ha, lowland fens 12 000 ha and upland grasslands, heaths and mires 6 000 000 ha.

There must, therefore, remain only 500 ha of herb-rich hay meadows, or 4 000 000 ha of upland grasslands, heaths and mires.

An alternative method of estimating the extent of losses from a particular habitat is that the area must be increased 10-fold to double the number of species, and *vice versa* (Darlington 1957). If a habitat with 100 characteristic species is reduced in area by 90%, 50 species should still survive.

Applying such methods without discrimination to convert loss into an impact upon species can be very misleading. For example, if we accept that an average English hedge has 20 nests per km and the loss of hedges between 1946 and 1970 took place at an average rate of 7000 km each year, it is tempting to multiply 7000 by 20 to assess the loss of nesting hedgerow birds; but the result would be erroneous. Underlying assumptions imply that bird population size on farmland is limited by nest sites in hedgerows and that all hedgerows provide equivalent nest sites. Neither implication is correct. Hedges differ in provision of nest sites: big hedges with several kinds of hedgerow plant are better than pure hawthorn which, in turn, is better than hedges composed entirely of elm. The availability of nesting sites for hedgerow birds seldom becomes limiting until hedge density falls below about 30 km of hedgerow per 1000 km of land (Pollard *et al.* 1974).

Two more factors complicate the matter. First, the best hedges in terms of bird habitat tend to be those on farm boundaries and are less often removed than internal hedgerows. Birds nesting in hedges often have low reproductive success which is insufficient to replace mortality in that habitat. Populations are then maintained by immigration from nearby woods (Williamson 1969). In the long run, the loss of woodland habitat will be most serious for the many birds now found in hedges.

Hence, though we may be readily convinced that agricultural change has had great impacts upon wildlife and its habitats over the last 40 years, we have yet to measure these impacts and explore their ramifications. Even for hedgerows, which are perhaps better documented than some habitats, there are no reliable estimates of status more recent than 1972. A starting point for further research could, therefore, be a more defined, accurate, survey of land uses and the trends of change taking place.

It may be said that we already possess accurate statistics of change in land use. Since 1866, figures for major land uses have been compiled annually, and, despite doubts about certain categories (eg for woodland, see Peterken 1983), these data show the major trends in land use. They also suggest to me that most of the impacts of agriculture upon wildlife which are now decried were predictable 20 years ago.

Most current trends are long established, though not all as long as the decline in area of oats. This decline began nearly a century ago, and has continued ever since. Some crops have increased, some have decreased, and some have remained static since the Second World War. Wheat and permanent grassland have not changed very much, turnips and mangolds have decreased, and barley has increased (MAFF 1968, 1983).

More significant still are the measures of intensification. The wheat acreage may have remained static, but the yield per unit area doubled between 1946 and 1966, as did the yield of barley. Numbers of combine harvesters in Britain increased 20-fold in the same period, from 3000 to 60 000, while the regular labour force was virtually halved and has now been halved again: 900 000 in 1946, 480 000 in 1966, 233 000 in 1982. Most surprising of all, amid this tremendous increase in the yield of arable land, is the fact that livestock increased too. There were 20M sheep in 1946, 29M in 1966, and 33M now (MAFF 1968, 1983).

Additional figures showing similar trends can be collected from other sources. In England in 1946, only about 12 000 ha were drained with mole and tile drainage; in 1956, 30 000 ha were drained, and in 1966 52 000 ha (Green 1973). The trends in farming that existed nearly 20 years ago had already existed for 20 years, and have continued to the present. Those trends produced impacts which were all recognized in quality, if not in quantity, 20 years ago, so it should have been possible to predict our present state.

Because the trends have been continuous over the last 40 years, it seems simplest to assume that they will continue into the future, and that the impacts on wildlife will continue also. Nevertheless, this prognosis is not entirely certain, for what drives these trends is Government policy, which in turn depends upon public opinion, reflecting the views of the public on its environment. There is evidence that views are changing.

Wibberley (1980) charged agriculturalists with being 'willing prisoners to a set of beliefs' which he felt could be challenged. The commonly held belief that farmland has been under increasing pressure from urban development for many years has been proven false by Best (1984). The fastest loss of farmland to house building took place 50 years ago. Mills (1983) has compared French with British farming, and found the latter wanting. He is but one of a number of recent critics of financial, rather than economic, cost benefit analysis. He suggests that the farmer's benefit is at public cost. That sort of argument, however, is very often based upon wine lakes or butter mountains in the European Economic Community. At its peak, the EEC butter mountain would have fed the Community for 6 weeks. On a world scale, grain reserves are only enough to feed the world's population for 30 days.

Given that sort of statistic, it seems likely that an efficient farming system will be maintained, present trends will continue, possibly more slowly, and wildlife will feel more impacts, perhaps the more deeply for having felt them for the past 40 years.

Summary
Separate, specific impacts of agriculture upon wildlife have long been recognized by conservationists as important. Such recognition of impacts was, however, of isolated issues of local significance, often by individual conservationists with narrow interests. It was not until some time between 1960 and 1970 that conservationists as a body began to think of British agriculture as inimical to wildlife.

Two causes can be adduced. The first is that many conservationists saw impacts as important issues, and the second is that the many attempts to bring about a rapport between farming and wildlife interests produced no quick, easy solutions. As a result, conservationists' attitudes hardened.

The first important issues in the mid-1960s were the use of pesticides, ploughing up of pasture, drainage, and hedgerow removal. A little later, field sizes, monocultures, and reclamation of marginal land produced the twin problem of fragmentation and isolation. More recently still, issues such as straw burning have been raised, and the latest impact issue to receive attention has been the financial, rather than economic, basis for agricultural accounting.

All these issues are still with us to some degree, although the relative importance of each varied in time and still varies from place to place. Could they have been predicted? The answer must be 'yes'. Most major trends in British agriculture have been continuous and regular since 1945. Acreages of barley have persistently increased; oats, turnips and swedes have decreased; sheep and cattle have increased; the work force has declined; and mechanization has increased. Whether these trends continue, and whether continuation of the impacts can be predicted, depends upon the view the general public takes of agriculture as an industry. There are calls for a re-evaluation of the role of agriculture in the national scene not only from conservationists. However, given the size, and therefore inertia, in the controlling systems, the individual financial interests, and powerful political lobby represented by agriculture in Britain, these calls are unlikely to be heard and acted upon before the next century. The impacts will continue.

References
Barber, D. 1970. *Farming and wildlife: a study in compromise.* Sandy: Royal Society for the Protection of Birds.

Best, R. 1984. Are we really losing the land? *Tn Ctry Plann.,* **53,** 10–11.

Bonham-Carter, V. 1971. *The survival of the English countryside.* London: Hodder & Stoughton.

Carson, R.L. 1962. *Silent spring.* Boston, Mass: Houghton Mifflin.

Christian, G. 1966. *Tomorrow's countryside: the road to the seventies.* London: Murray.

Cramp, S. & Conder, P. 1961. *The deaths of birds and mammals connected with toxic chemicals.* (BTO-RSPB Toxic Chemical Committee Report No.1).

Darlington, P.J. 1957. *Zoogeography: the geographical distribution of animals.* Chichester: Wiley.

Davidson, J. & Lloyd, R., eds. 1977. *Conservation and agriculture.* Chichester: Wiley.

Fryer, J.D. & Chancellor, R. 1970. Herbicides and our changing arable weeds. In: *The flora of a changing Britain,* edited by F.H. Perring, 105–118. Hampton: Classey.

Green, F.H.W. 1973. Aspects of the changing environment. *J. environ. Manage.,* **1,** 377–391.

Horwood, A.R. & Noel, C.W.F. 1933. *Flora of Leicestershire and Rutland.* Oxford: University Press.

Mellanby, K. 1981. *Farming and wildlife.* London: Collins.

Mills, S. 1983. French farming: good for people, good for wildlife. *New Scient.,* **100,** 568–571.

Ministry of Agriculture, Fisheries and Food. 1968. *A century of agricultural statistics: Great Britain 1866-1966.* London: HMSO.

Ministry of Agriculture, Fisheries and Food. 1983. *Agricultural statistics: United Kingdom 1982.* London: HMSO.

Ministry of Town and Country Planning. 1947. *Conservation of nature in England and Wales: report of the Wild Life Conservation Special Committee (England & Wales),* paras 132-135. (Cmnd 7122). London: HMSO.

Moore, N.W. 1962. Toxic chemicals and birds: the ecological background to conservation problems. *Br. Birds,* **55,** 428–455.

Moore, N.W., Hooper, M.D. & Davis, B.N.K. 1967. Hedges. I. Introduction and reconnaissance studies. *J. appl. Ecol.,* **4,** 201–220.

Nature Conservancy. 1956. *Report for the year ending 30 September 1955.* London: HMSO.

Nature Conservancy Council. 1984a. *Annual report 1982-1983, 9th.* London: HMSO.

Nature Conservancy Council. 1984b. *Nature conservation in Great Britain.* Shrewsbury: NCC.

Paskell, T. 1984. Meadow mayhem. *Shrops. Wildl.,* **57,** 1.

Perring, F.H. 1970. The last seventy years. In: *The flora of a changing Britain,* edited by F.H. Perring, 128–135. Hampton: Classey.

Perring, F.H. & Farrell, L. 1977. *British Red Data Book. No. 1: Vascular plants.* Lincoln: Society for the Promotion of Nature Conservation.

Peterken, G.F. 1983. Woodland surveys can mislead. *New Scient.,* **100,** 802–803.

Pollard, E., Hooper, M.D. & Moore, N.W. 1974. *Hedges.* (New naturalist no. 58). London: Collins.

Rudd, G.L. & Genelly, R.E. 1956. Pesticides: their use and toxicity in relation to wildlife. *Bull. Dep. Fish Game St. Calif.,* no.7.

Savidge, J.P., Heywood, V.H. & Gordon, V. 1963. *Travis's Flora of south Lancashire.* Liverpool: Botanical Society.

Tansley, A. 1953. The conservation of British vegetation and species. In: *The changing flora of Britain,* edited by J.E. Lousley, 183-196. Oxford: Botanical Society of the British Isles.

Trist, P.T.O. 1970. The changing pattern of agriculture. In: *The flora of a changing Britain,* edited by F.H. Perring, 45–50. Hampton: Classey.

Weller, J. 1967. *Modern agriculture and rural planning.* London: Architectural Press.

Wells, T.C.E. 1968. Land use changes affecting *Pulsatilla vulgaris* in England. *Biol. Conserv.,* **1,** 37–43.

Wibberley, G.P. 1980. Is agriculture being given too dominant a place in British land use? *Agric. Prog.,* **55,** 98–102.

Williamson, K. 1969. Habitat preferences of the wren in English fenland. *Bird Study,* **17,** 30–96.

Yemm, E.W. & Willis, A.J. 1962. The effect of MH and 2,4-D on roadside vegetation. *Weed Res.,* **2,** 24–40.

Models for predicting changes in rural land use in Great Britain

R G H BUNCE
Institute of Terrestrial Ecology, Merlewood Research Station
R B TRANTER & A M M THOMPSON
Centre for Agricultural Strategy, University of Reading
C P MITCHELL
Department of Forestry, University of Aberdeen
C J BARR
Institute of Terrestrial Ecology, Merlewood

1 Introduction and review

In recent years, models have been used increasingly to solve problems which involve interacting factors and where changes in one parameter are linked to a series of events. Such models are necessarily simplifications of reality, yet they provide a means of manipulating large quantities of information and enable the nature and effect of the interacting forces to be more readily understood. This paper presents a review of relevant recent work on modelling changes in rural land use, and describes the experience of the authors in the field.

The first stage in developing such models is to consider the existing structure of land use and the forces maintaining such a structure. The major uses of rural land are agriculture and forestry. Some 78% of the total area of the UK is in agricultural use (Central Statistical Office 1983; MAFF 1983a) and 9% in forestry. Recently, there have been 2 main changes in the land use structure of the UK. First, the total agricultural area has fallen by some 360 000 ha over the last 10 years and, second, the area under grass and herbage has fallen by 811 000 ha over the same period (MAFF 1983a, b). The former losses have been primarily to forestry, which therefore occupies a prominent role in any consideration of future land use change, but also to urban development. To compensate for the reduction in area under grass, there has been an increase in the area of wheat and oilseed rape.

Although the MAFF census data provide detailed information on crops, the data available for GB on semi-natural habitats are fragmented. Information has been co-ordinated for many species, but, apart from specific habitats, eg lowland heaths, there has been no strategic study comparable to that by MAFF. However, the Merlewood land classification system (Bunce *et al.* 1981a) has produced categories of land use for GB which convey more information on habitats, although further subdivision and amplification are required, as exemplified by Table 1.

A further recent trend is the substantial increase in crop productivity since 1971, due, in part, to intensification of agricultural practices. These practices have been criticized by, amongst others, the Countryside

Table 1. Categories of land use recorded in the field survey, carried out in 1977–78, in 256 squares based on the 32 land classes of the Merlewood land classification system, and predicted areas for GB ('000 ha)
(For further details of categories, see senior author)

1	Perennial rye-grass ley	2244.5
2	Italian rye-grass ley	247.6
3	Rye-grass/cock's-foot ley	205.5
4	Cock's-foot ley	97.2
5	Unspecified ley	530.1
6	Cut hay/silage	258.0
7	Perennial rye-grass pasture	641.6
8	Mixed permanent pasture	953.0
9	Improved pasture	1024.3
10	Neglected pasture	624.8
11	Bent/fescue pasture	453.4
12	Mixed upland pasture	298.5
13	Rush infested	168.5
14	Bracken infested	62.2
15	Hair-grass/mat-grass	42.7
16	Heather	964.0
17	Bilberry	23.6
18	Bracken	316.7
19	Rush marshland	202.6
20	Purple moor-grass	433.0
21	Hare's-tail cottongrass	69.9
22	(Unassigned)	—
23	Herb-rich pasture	22.1
23	Ploughed/fallow	179.5
25	Derelict	83.6
26	Wheat	1112.0
27	Barley	2169.6
28	Oats	197.2
29	Sugar beet	150.0
30	Kale	47.8
31	Roots	154.1
32	Potatoes	198.4
33	Horticulture	66.2
34	Beans/peas	214.6
35	Orchards	65.7
36	Roads	340.0
37	Urban	1833.2
38	(Unassigned)	—
39	Railway	54.4
40	Cliffs/sand/mud	166.7
41	Canal/stream	84.6
42	Lake	329.3
43	Quarry/pit	51.2
44	Formal recreation areas	230.5
45	(Unassigned)	—
46	Rock	143.9
47	Hardwood copse	85.5
48	Mixed copse	9.9
49	Conifer copse	11.6
50	Hardwood shelter belt	21.0

51	Mixed shelter belt	15.2
52	Conifer shelter belt	8.5
53	Gillside wood	31.3
54	Scrub	201.3
55	Hardwood	467.5
56	Conifer woodland	1510.2
57	Mixed woodland	145.2
58	Timothy	135.7
59	Lucerne	21.2
60	Maize	40.3
61	Mat-grass	427.4
62	Mixed peatland	331.9
63	Subarctic vegetation	60.4
64	Bilberry mixture	31.9
65	Cross-leaved heath	6.1
66	Rye	6.9
67	Heath rush	6.4
68	Mixed upland grassland	171.8
69	Mixed upland moor	494.0
70	Deergrass/heather	162.7
71	Rush mixture	18.2
72	Heather/cottongrass	390.2
73	Heather/bilberry	202.8
74	Burnt	22.6
75	Parkland	27.9
76	Maritime grassland	19.3
77	Oilseed rape	46.4
78	Oats/barley	30.9
79	Salt marsh	29.2
80	New urban	182.6

Review Committee (1978). In addition, the more recent comments by Shoard (1980), Body (1982), and Bowers and Cheshire (1983) suggested that Exchequer and European Community support under the Common Agricultural Policy was largely responsible for the intensification of farming, thus encouraging public interest in the future of British agriculture and its associated impact on wildlife habitats. These concerns have also stimulated the use of models to predict the consequences of developments in agriculture and other land uses in response to macro- and micro-economic change.

The most comprehensive model of British agriculture was developed in the late 1960s to examine the effects of entry into the EC. This large-scale, aggregated linear programming (LP) model is based on more than 40 representative farm types and has proved successful in examining supply in sectors of the industry and the policy measures affecting such supply (Thomson & Buckwell 1979). However, constant revision and updating of the model with sufficiently accurate data to cover the wide range of farm types and practices are proving difficult, and the implications for wildlife have to be inferred.

The effect on British grassland of a variety of economic pressures on livestock producers was examined, using models, by Lazenby and Doyle (1981). Suggestions were made as to how these producers could survive by making better utilization of grassland, more use of clovers, and establishing more preferred grass species. The associated ecological implications were not examined.

The Centre for Agricultural Strategy (1980), when developing a strategy for the UK forest industry, needed to examine the effects on agriculture of increased plantings of forestry. It was considered feasible to replace 1M ha of upland grazings with forestry by the year 2000. The modelling exercise indicated that, if 100 000 ha of hill land were improved, then the loss of 1M ha to forestry would only reduce the breeding ewe population by 160 000, indicating that afforestation also has influences outside the actual land covered by trees.

Although there is no definitive statement on agricultural policy, projections of the future of British agriculture were made by MAFF (1979b) when preparing *Farming and the nation* (MAFF 1979a). It considered projected yields, assumptions about efficiency of resource use, alternative levels of producers' real prices, and developments in the demand for food. However, the projection of areas of crops differs somewhat in comparison with the provisional figures of the 1983 census.

At a more local level, Maxwell *et al.* (1979) developed a model to examine the potential for integrating farming and forestry, comparing the effects of different land use distributions on stock densities and economics on a local scale. Unfortunately, this model is only appropriate to conditions operating in the southern uplands of Scotland, as indicated by MacBrayne (1981). Bishop (1978) employed LP techniques to examine the interactions between land uses in Cumbria and to optimize for production. His model indicated that the area of forestry in the county could be increased by 42%, within the constraints governing land use, without having a significant effect upon farming output. Bishop incorporated assessments of conservation interest and showed how the approach could be adapted for wildlife objectives. More recently, Smith and Budd (1982) also used LP for examining forestry/farming strategies in the Sedbergh district of Cumbria. Other comparable studies have been carried out by Dane *et al.* (1977) and Miron (1976).

Apart from the models described above, other techniques such as checklists, matrices, networks and flow diagrams have been widely used in attempts to formalize intuitive assessments of future change. Occasionally, detailed studies of ecological change in particular habitats are available from which future patterns can be inferred, eg those relating to vegetation summarized by Miles (1979). Such an approach was used by Ball *et al.* (1982) to examine potential changes in the vegetation of the uplands of Britain. The rate and direction of change were predicted using explicit criteria, demonstrating the use of informed ecological opinion.

Although not specifically concerned with wildlife, the study by Ball *et al.* contains much information relevant to wildlife habitats associated with land use change.

Similarly, many of the various studies on landscape contain implicit information on habitats, although much of it is in anecdotal form.

It is also possible to transform the information on change into more specific expressions using Markov models. A general discussion of their use is given by Jeffers (1982). From the transition matrix of one state to another and the known area of each parameter, the amount of each type can be predicted over a series of time steps, as well as the expected final composition and rate. Although certain simplistic assumptions are made, eg linearity of change, such models provide an approximation of future states that are likely to be more reliable than direct extrapolation. However, the transition probabilities are critical and it is often difficult to obtain adequate information on their likely values.

There have been several recent applications of such models. Vandeveer and Drummond (1978) demonstrated their use in estimating land use change. Bellefleur (1981) has applied them to study succession and the behaviour of forest types. Markov models have also been applied in agriculture (eg by Buckwell et al. 1983), in the Scottish dairy industry, but again have not been directly applied to the present subject. Even from the brief summary above, it will be seen that such models are useful in helping to clarify the consequences of possible changes in rural land use and the associated wildlife habitats.

There is an extensive literature on the use of models in ecology. Roberts et al. (1983) and Spain (1982) give useful summaries of the present situation, and provide valuable introductions to the subject.

Although models have been used in associated studies, they have not been applied directly to the future of wildlife habitats. This lack of application is in part due to a lack of appreciation of their usefulness by conservationists, and in part to the lack of an adequate data base for developing reliable models.

2 Detailed examples
The first example is provided by a systematic model for examining the effects of competing land uses on the current pattern of land use developed during a study commissioned by the Department of Energy. This study, termed the Land Availability Study (LAS), aimed to determine the amount of land which might become available for growing trees for energy under various economic assumptions. The resultant Land Availability Model (LAM) provided a means for predicting change in land use at the site-specific level (Mitchell et al. 1983a).

The core of the LAM lay in the Merlewood land classification system (Bunce et al. 1981a; 1982). This classification of land is based on an analysis of the environmental attributes derived from maps of some 1228 km^2 squares on a grid covering GB. The analysis

results in the definition of 32 land classes. Eight randomly selected squares from each land class were used for the field survey of the land use categories given in Table 1. These 256 'fully characterized' squares are used in the analysis with the areas of land under the various categories to obtain estimates for GB (Table 1). Estimates derived in this fashion accord closely with official statistics (Bunce et al. 1982). Similarly, potential uses for land in the sample squares can be postulated and the resultant GB figures estimated. This mechanism forms the basis of the LAM, which has the advantage over other models that it provides information on areas of new land use, as well as on the types of land use which would be lost. An assessment of the environmental impact of various practices can therefore be made.

The criterion for predicting change in land use in the LAS was financial performance, ie that land use which achieved the highest net present value (NPV) over 60 years, at a given discount rate. Economic data for 1977 were used. No judgements were made as to whether the predicted land use change could be accommodated on the farm (see below).

The LAM enabled the comparison of the relative financial performance of different, actual and postulated land uses for individual areas of land in the sample squares, and provided estimates for GB of the areas of new forestry for energy, the potential production and the likely species, thus indicating possible future developments. In addition, the area and nature of displaced land use categories were given, showing that the implications of potential change can be predicted in terms of their associated habitats.

To obtain an estimate of financial performance, a series of some 140 sets of economic values was produced in order to include a range of management systems and yields for forestry. The management systems were conventional forestry for timber, forestry for energy and timber, and single stem and coppice energy plantations. Sets of NPVs were calculated for each model for a range of discount rates, timber values and assumed values of wood for fuel. Current British agricultural practice was described by, and classified into, some 40 production systems. Investigations showed that it was not possible to allocate fixed costs to particular enterprises, so, for purposes of comparison, the NPV of the enterprise gross margin over 60 years was taken. The constraints arising from national planning controls, eg nature reserves, public pressures and legal impediments to change in land use, were included by noting the significance of such constraints on each of the sample squares. Their probability of restricting forestry was used in the model, but could equally be applied to changes in agricultural practice.

The LAM enabled examination of the effects of a wide range of economic assumptions on the areas of land predicted as being available for forestry. One set of assumptions used was: to provide wood for production of pipeline gas, increasing energy prices, constant timber and agricultural costs and revenues, and a 5% discount rate.

With this example, some 4.6M ha of land were predicted to change to forestry (all with an energy component) with a potential production of some 38M dry tonnes per year of wood for energy and 28M m³/yr of timber. However, when constraints were taken into account, some 1.8M ha of land were estimated to change to forestry producing some 16M d t/yr of wood for energy and 11M m³/yr of timber (summarized by Mitchell et al. 1983a).

The incorporation of nature conservation constraints in the LAM demonstrates the way in which conflicts between development, in this case forestry, and wildlife can be assessed. The system of comparison of potential and actual uses for units of land can be readily modified to examine the likely future of wildlife habitats such as small woodlands or herb-rich grasslands. Similarly, the effects of possible changes in the countryside, eg canalization of rivers, can be examined at a strategic level. The economic implications of restricting agricultural improvements can also be assessed in comparative terms. Further, the examination of the loss of agricultural land to wood energy plantations demonstrates the way in which impacts can be predicted. Such an approach is already being used by the Highland Regional Council (Bunce et al. in press) to examine conflicts between planning constraints, nature conservation, agricultural improvement, and red deer production.

A study designed to supplement a weakness in the LAS provides a second example, in that the estimate of the potential for forestry did not consider the extent to which this was practicable on farms. The LAS was therefore extended to consider the practical and financial implications of incorporating the levels of forestry already predicted into the farm business environment using LP models of 'typical' farms (Mitchell et al. 1983b).

LP allocates scarce resources (eg land, labour and capital) amongst competing uses (eg livestock and forestry) so as to maximize or minimize some objective (eg profit or loss). The manager contemplating the introduction of forestry would have to integrate it with his current pattern. The study is therefore analogous to that of Bishop (1978).

Models for 4 'typical' farms were developed, each representative of a land class and each with farm area and fixed costs similar to the MAFF Farm Management Survey group of farms, and with equivalent geographical locations and patterns of land use. Each model selected the combination of current agricultural or possible forestry land uses that maximized farm income, subject to constraints on key resources, such as land, monthly labour and machinery, the cost of forestry contractors, and the availability of working capital.

Initially, each model reproduced the current pattern of land use on the farm, establishing the status quo. Next, the forestry (in terms of area by management system, species and yield) predicted by the LAS was inserted into the farm land use pattern, replacing any existing land use which proved less financially viable. The model was then run to examine the effects of such a change in land use on the on-farm management factors. In broad terms, the exercise confirmed that the area of forestry suggested by the LAS could be accommodated on farms, providing certain 'key' resources such as capital were available. The size of the resource required varies with farm type. If larger areas of forestry than those predicted by the LAS are allowed, then economics of scale start to take effect. In some circumstances, farm income may be increased by increasing the area under forestry. As with the previous model, although being applied for forestry objectives, a comparable approach could be used for conservation, with wildlife habitats being designated as 'key' resources.

Our third example, developed for this symposium, demonstrates the wide application of the Merlewood land classification system by using the land classes to examine the effects of different possible futures (scenarios, Table 2) on patterns of rural land use with regard to agriculture and forestry. The implications of these scenarios (listed below) were applied directly to the categories of land use given in Table 1, as, for the present purpose, it was required to assess the general changes that might result. In more detailed future studies, separate units of land should be examined from individual one km squares and combined into the land classes, as done in the LAS and by Cowie and Williams (1982). The scenarios were developed by the authors working as a multidisciplinary group, and are summarized below.

Table 2. Transfers from the land use categories of Table 1 used in the scenarios, with resultant changes over the whole of Great Britain and the proportionate changes in each category

For transfers: low = 1–5%; medium = 5–25%; high = over 26%
For GB area change: low = 0.1–0.5%; medium = 0.6–1.0%; high = over 1.1%
For % change in each land use: low = 1–5%; medium = 5–25%; high = over 26%

Transfers:

Scenario 1:	high:	18 to 14, 54 to 8
	medium:	9/10 to 7/8, 19 to 13, 11 to 10.
	low:	1–9 to 26/27
Scenario 2:	high:	none
	medium:	26–28 to 1–6, 26–28 to 77
	low:	29–31/33/34 to 1–6

Scenario 3: high: 13 to 19, 14 to 18, 16 to 69, 14/18/54 to 56, 68 to 69

medium: 8 to 9, 12/13/15/61/68 to 56, 62 to 20, 61 to 69

low: 11 to 14/54, 11 to 56, 12/15 to 70

Scenario 4: high: 10 to 18, 16 to 69

medium: 7/8 to 1, 9 to 7, 11/14 to 9, 69 to 68, 73 to 68.

low: 1 to 30/31, 18 to 14, 19 to 13, 53/54/61/68 to 9

Scenario 5: high: none

medium: none

low: 10/13 to 47, 53–55 to 56, 11/12/14–21 to 56, 61 to 56, 64/68/69/72/73 to 56

GB area change in each land use (gains in area = +; losses in area = −):

Scenario 1: high: −9, −26, −27

medium: none

low: +1, −2, −3, −4, −5, −6, +7, −8, −10, −11, +13, +14, −18, −19, −54

Scenario 2: high: +1, −26, −27

medium: none

low: +2, +3, +4, +5, +6, +29, +30, +31, +33, +34

Scenario 3: high: +16, +56, +69

medium: +9, −61

low: −8, −11, −12, −13, −14, −15, −18, +19, −20, −54, −62, −68

Scenario 4: high: none

medium: −10

low: +1, +7, +8, +9, −11, −12, −13, +14, −16, −18, −19, +30, +31, −53, −54, −61, +68, +69, −73

Scenario 5: high: +56

medium: none

low: −10, −11, −12, −13, −14, −15, −16, −17, −18, −19, −20, −21, +47, −53, −54, −55, −61, −64, −68, −69, −72, −73

% change in each land use:

Scenario 1: high: +14, +27, −54

medium: −3, −4, −6, +7, −8, −9, −10, −11, −18, −19, −26

low: +1, +13

Scenario 2: high: +1, +2, +3, +4, −26, −27

medium: +6, +30, +33

low: +29, +31, +34

Scenario 3: high: −11, −12, −13, −15, +16, +19, +56, −61, +62, −68, −69

medium: −8, +9, −14, −18, −20

low: −54

Scenario 4: high: +30, +31, −53, −54

medium: +9, −10, −11, −12, −14, −16, −18, +68, +69, −73

low: +1, +7, +8, −13, −19, −61

Scenario 5: high: +47, +56

medium: −10, −11, −12, −13, −14, −15, −16, −17, −19, −20, −21, −61, −64, −68, −69, −72, −73

low: −18, −53, −54, −55

i. *Dairying becomes less profitable*
Grasslands within enclosed land are likely to be mainly affected, as opposed to the hill land in scenarios (iii) and (iv).
(a) Higher grade grassland moves to cereals or other cash crops.

(b) Lower grade grass and herbage are likely to be improved.

ii. *Cereals become less profitable*
These changes are considered to apply mainly to the area of tillage.
(a) Cereals move to grass.
(b) Cereals move to oilseed rape or more profitable crops.

iii. *Hill subsidies are reduced*
This reduction will lead to a decline in agricultural use of the uplands and would involve subtle ecological effects, in addition to the following major changes.
(a) Pasture deteriorates in quality.
(b) Bracken invasion increases.
(c) Area of dwarf shrub vegetation increases.
(d) There is a trend toward forestry.

iv. *Hill and upland sheep become more profitable*
This scenario is the reverse of (iii) and would result in a general increase in the use of upland vegetation, with associated effects on its ecology. The changes would thus be as follows.
(a) Marginal pasture and drainage are improved.
(b) There is a trend away from conversion of agricultural land to forestry.
(c) Dwarf shrub vegetation is converted to pasture.

v. *Confidence in, and support for, forestry increase*
Changes within grassland categories were not considered likely, in comparison with the other scenarios, and thus the probable changes are as follows.
(a) Native vegetation is lost to forest.
(b) There is a general increase in coniferous forest.

The majority of transfers between the land use categories (Table 2) for the different scenarios were in the order of 5-10%. The loss to urban development, although significant in the long term, is below the level of change that can be considered by this model. The results showed some categories changing considerably, because some trends were to one land use, eg coniferous woodland (Table 2). In other examples, feedback mechanisms are operated, buffering change in land use as described by Best (1976). For example, in scenario (i), the loss of high yielding pastures to barley is compensated by the change of poorer pastures into good quality sward. It is only when a major land use category accumulates inputs from other uses that major changes occur. The complexity of feedback and the *ad hoc* nature of the present study indicate that more in-depth studies are required to obtain more reliable information on transfers between land uses. However, it is necessary to consider whether comparable patterns are followed in habitat change as some evidence suggests that change can take place very quickly. Even so, the transfers in the main crops are equivalent to the changes in recent years indicated by MAFF (1983a, b), and the change in forest area is comparable to that which has taken place over the last 10 years, suggesting that the projected changes are reasonable.

The majority of land uses incorporated in the above example were selected to demonstrate the implication for the associated semi-natural habitats, eg the changes in scenario (iii) directly affect the composition of grassland types of importance to conservation. A comparable study could be developed by identifying specific habitats, eg hedgerows and streams, and examining the implications of changes in rural land use for their occurrence, in order to assess potential national changes and critical influences on conservation. For example, the effects of stopping straw burning could be compared with peatland drainage.

As the proportions of the different categories of land use vary through the land classes, the system can be used to examine regional differences. For example, in scenario (iii), the effect on scrub is felt mainly in the downs of south-east England and in the uplands of Wales, Cumbria and Scotland. Markov models (see above) could be used with field data to investigate the implications of transfers. R. Woods (pers. comm.) has already used this method to examine the pattern of urban growth. Further developments could be made by using the technique to compare the potential of individual units of land in a similar manner to that described by Bunce et al. (1981b) and Mitchell et al. (1983a). Furthermore, the location of areas with identified changes could be examined subsequently in the field. In this way, representative areas could be selected for case studies.

3 Discussion
In general, agriculture is likely to have 2 effects on habitats. The first involves changes in practices, eg spraying, whereas the second involves changes in land use structure, eg grassland to barley, and the implications of both may be examined as described above. Forestry, although not considered directly in this symposium, is likely to have the most significant effect on wildlife habitats in the uplands (CAS 1980), and hence discussions of the likely impact of forestry in this paper are particularly relevant. In the lowlands, more diverse influences are involved, which therefore require more careful appraisal.

As stated at the outset, no adequate data base is available for the distribution and extent of semi-natural habitats in GB. Some models, for example the classic Massachusetts Institute of Technology model of economic growth, have shown the severe limitations of inadequate data. It is first necessary to design a conceptual framework and then to develop a suitable data base, as this is a prerequisite for successful prediction. The subsequent proposals follow that essential first stage.

i. Expansion of the existing data base for GB on semi-natural habitats including:
   (a) a detailed assessment of the major semi-natural habitats and land uses in GB, defined on a variety of criteria relating to vegetation and topographic factors;
   (b) a survey of farmer attitudes and beliefs in order to build dynamic elements into the *status quo* position defined in (a);
   (c) definition of past, present and future management practices and the way they are likely to affect semi-natural habitats;
   (d) the correlation of available ground truth information with remote sensing data from aerial photographs and satellites in order to investigate the potential of automation in mapping and as a further basis for modelling;
   (e) the study of key species to conservation, eg badgers and otters, as a basis for modelling threats to their existence (cf Macdonald et al. 1981).

The Merlewood land classification system provides a sampling framework for the above and various studies are planned, or in progress, to meet some of these objectives.

ii. Monitoring of habitats in order to model past development, as a basis for prediction. The essential first stage is to define the objectives of monitoring, eg loss of hedgerows. It is also necessary to record not only the target but also the underlying factors, so that the processes of change can be understood. Three main activities would be involved:
   (a) future monitoring of habitats or attributes for which previous data are available.
   (b) the use of past aerial photographs to determine changes in habitats;
   (c) the use of previous series Ordnance Survey maps to study factors such as urban growth, as a basis for predicting future patterns, as in Markov models.

iii. Identification of representative areas for case studies of particular habitats and also the incorporation of extant detailed local studies.

iv. Post-audit assessments, where checks are made against previous predictions. The land budget model discussed by the CAS (1980) is an example.

v. Simple models, as used in the LAS, can be readily applied by conservationists and have the potential of being developed to examine the effects of agricultural practice on the wildlife habitats of GB. They have the advantage of being readily understood and have been shown to reflect conventional wisdom.

vi.   Higher order models, eg Markov models, have a potential which has not yet been realized. The data collection defined above should provide sufficient data for their successful application.

These proposals are concerned with direct habitat recording, but the major force for change is primarily economic. Hence, it is important to incorporate economic factors at some stage in the modelling process, if only as a series of options of progressive severity, as the sensitivity of the systems involved is of major significance.

Models are widely used successfully in many disciplines and the discussion above shows that they have the potential for application to rural land use change. Their use could be a major factor in determining impacts and enabling conservationists to foresee threats to wildlife habitats, and, although they cannot be validated by conventional means, they are useful in exploring options.

4 Summary
The purpose of the paper is to assess the current state of the art and then to examine how appropriate models could be developed. Models, whilst being necessarily simplifications of reality, provide a means whereby the behaviour of complex systems can be understood. A review is provided of recent models used and it is concluded that, although their potential has been demonstrated in associated disciplines, directly applicable examples are not available. Three models based on the Merlewood land classification system are described in some detail, to demonstrate the feasibility and manner in which models could be developed to predict changes in land use and associated habitats in Britain. Six areas for further research were identified: expansion of the existing data base on wildlife habitats in Britain as a basis for modelling; increased monitoring of land use change; definition of representative case studies to assist in understanding the dynamics of change; the conduct of post-audit assessments of predictions; the development of simple models for use by conservationists; and, finally, the development of higher order models for predicting threats to wildlife habitats.

5 References

Ball, D.F., Dale, J., Sheail, J. & Heal, O.W. 1982. *Vegetation change in upland landscapes.* Cambridge: Institute of Terrestrial Ecology.

Bellefleur, P. 1981. Markov models of forest-type secondary succession in coastal British Columbia, Canada. *Can. J. For. Res.,* **11,** 18–29.

Best, R. 1976. The extent and growth of urban land. *Planner,* **1,** 8–11.

Bishop, I.D. 1978. *Land use in rural Cumbria – a linear programming model.* (Merlewood research and development paper no. 75). Grange–over–Sands: Institute of Terrestrial Ecology.

Body, R. 1982. *Agriculture: the triumph and the shame.* London: Temple Smith.

Bowers, J.K. & Cheshire, P. 1983. *Agriculture, the countryside and land use: an economic critique.* London: Methuen.

Buckwell, A.E., Shucksmith, D.M. & Young, D.A. 1983. Structural projections of the Scottish dairy industry using micro and macro Markov transition matrices. *J. agric. Econ.,* **34,** 57–68.

Bunce, R.G.H., Barr, C.J. & Whittaker, H. 1981a. *Land classes in Great Britain: preliminary descriptions for users of the Merlewood method of land classification.* (Merlewood research and development paper no. 86). Grange-over-Sands: Institute of Terrestrial Ecology.

Bunce, R.G.H., Pearce, M.L. & Mitchell, C.P. 1981b. The allocation of land for energy crops in Britain. In: *Energy from biomass,* edited by W. Palz, P. Chartier & D.O. Hall, 103–109. (Proc. European Community Conf., 1st, Brighton, 1980). London: Applied Science.

Bunce, R.G.H., Barr, C.J. & Whittaker, H.A. 1982. A stratification system for ecological sampling. In: *Ecological mapping from ground, air and space,* edited by R.M. Fuller, 39–46. (ITE symposium no. 10). Cambridge: Institute of Terrestrial Ecology.

Bunce, R.G.H., Claridge, C.J., Barr, C.J. & Baldwin, M.B. In press. An ecological classification of land – its application to planning in the Highland Region, Scotland. In: *Land and its changing uses: an ecological appraisal,* edited by F.T. Last. London: Plenum Press.

Central Statistical Office. 1983. *Annual abstract of statistics 1983.* London: HMSO.

Centre for Agricultural Strategy. 1980. *Strategy for the UK forest industry.* (CAS report no. 6). Reading: CAS, University of Reading.

Countryside Review Committee. 1978. *Food production in the countryside – discussion paper.* London: HMSO.

Cowie, J.D. & Williams, A. 1982. *The application of the land classification of ITE to the MAFF Hills and Uplands Study.* (R & D Resource Planning Report RD/RP/L). Pinner: Ministry of Agriculture, Fisheries and Food, Land and Water Service.

Dane, C.W., Meadow, N.C. & White, J.B. 1977. Goal programming in land use planning. *J. For.,* **75,** 325–329.

Jeffers, J.N.R. 1982. *Modelling.* London: Chapman & Hall.

Lazenby, A. & Doyle, C.J. 1981. Grassland in the British economy – some problems, possibilities and speculations. In: *Grassland in the British economy,* edited by J.L. Jollans, 14–50. (CAS paper no. 10). Reading: Centre for Agricultural Strategy, University of Reading.

MacBrayne, C.G. 1981. *Towards closer integration of farming and forestry in the uplands of Great Britain.* MSc thesis, University of Aberdeen.

Macdonald, D.W., Bunce, R.G.H. & Bacon, P.J. 1981. Fox populations, habitat characterization and rabies control. *J. Biogeogr.,* **8,** 145–151.

Maxwell, J.J., Sibbald, A.R. & Eadie, J. 1979. Integration of forestry and agriculture – a model. *Agric. Syst.,* **4,** 161–188.

Miles, J. 1979. *Vegetation dynamics.* London: Chapman & Hall.

Ministry of Agriculture, Fisheries and Food. 1979a. *Farming and the nation.* (Cmnd 7458). London: HMSO.

Ministry of Agriculture, Fisheries and Food. 1979b. *Possible patterns of agricultural production in the United Kingdom by 1983.* London: HMSO.

Ministry of Agriculture, Fisheries and Food. 1983a. *Annual review of agriculture 1983.* (Cmnd 8804). London: HMSO.

Ministry of Agriculture, Fisheries and Food. 1983b. *Agricultural statistics, United Kingdom 1982.* London: HMSO.

Miron, J.R. 1976. *Regional development and land use models and overview of optimisation methodology.* (Research memorandum RM-76-20). Laxenburg: International Institute for Applied Systems Analysis.

Mitchell, C.P., Brandon, O.H., Bunce, R.G.H., Barr, C.J., Tranter, R.B., Downing, P., Pearce, M.L. & Whittaker, H.A. 1983a. Land availability for production of wood energy in Great Britain. In: *Energy from biomass*, edited by A. Strub, P. Chartier & G. Schleser, 159–163. (Proc. European Community Conf., 2nd, Berlin, 1982). London: Applied Science.

Mitchell, C.P., Thompson, A.M.M. & Tranter, R.B. 1983b. Trees on farms – a source of fuel. In: *Strategies for family-worked farms in the UK*, edited by R.B. Tranter, 239–243. (CAS paper no. 15). Reading: Centre for Agricultural Strategy, University of Reading.

Roberts, N., Andersen, D., Deal, R., Garrett, M. & Shaffer, W. 1983. *Introduction to computer simulation: the systems dynamics approach*. Reading, Mass: Addison-Wesley.

Shoard, M. 1980. *The theft of the countryside*. London: Temple Smith.

Smith, R.S. & Budd, R.E. 1982. *Land use in upland Cumbria: a model for forestry/farming strategies in the Sedbergh area*. (Research monographs in technological economics no. 4). Stirling: University of Stirling.

Spain, J.D. 1982. *BASIC microcomputer models in biology*. Reading, Mass: Addison-Wesley.

Thomson, K.J. & Buckwell, A.E. 1979. A micro-economic agricultural supply model. *J. agric. Econ.*, **30**, 1–11.

Vandeveer, L.R. & Drummond, H.E. 1978. The use of Markov processes in estimating land use change. *Tech. Bull. Okla. agric. Exp. Stn*, no. T148.

Trends in mechanization in the lowlands

D B DAVIES
Agricultural Development and Advisory Service, Ministry of Agriculture, Fisheries and Food, Cambridge

1 Introduction

Large-scale mechanized farming has only developed since the 1930s. Between 1930-58, the number of tractors in UK agriculture increased 33-fold from about 12 000 to over 400 000 (MAFF 1930-82). Over the same period, the number of working horses fell by a factor of 8 to about 100 000 (see Figure 1). From 1958-83, the number of tractors increased only slightly, while the working horse became a museum piece. This dramatic change in sources of energy for agriculture was associated with substantial changes in the countryside, some, but by no means all, caused by this mechanical revolution.

2 Energy available on UK farms

Excluding crop drying, most energy on UK arable farms is consumed in the cultivation of the land. Presumably, therefore, changes in tractor numbers and power available mainly reflect changes in land management. Table 1 classifies wheeled tractor numbers by horse power (HP) and horse power per hectare for the post-War period. Since the initial rise in tractor numbers, there was a substantial increase in tractor power on farms, and this increase is probably continuing. In 1962, only 0.9 HP was available per ha; by 1972, this figure had nearly doubled to 1.5, and in the following decade to 1982 there was yet another

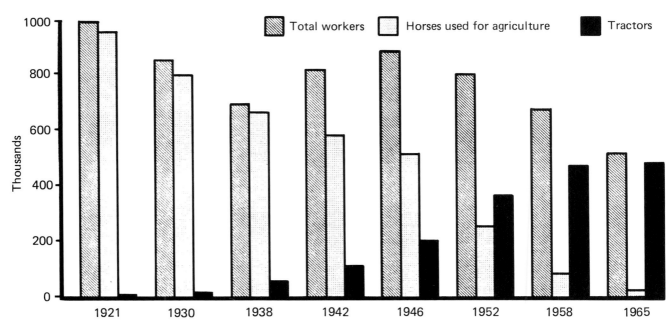

Figure 1. Labour, horses and tractors in Great Britain, 1921–65

Table 1. Wheeled tractors in England and Wales (Source: MAFF 1930–82)

HP	1942	1962	1972	1982
<10	90 260	355 140	60 260	12 706
10–50			217 900	169 695
50–80			107 360	162 263
80–107			7 160	57 088
107–134				11 085
>134				4 002
Total	90 260	355 140	392 680	415 839
HP/ha	0·25	0·9	1·5	2·7

Table 3. Sizes of holdings in the UK, 1942–52

	>120 ha	>200 ha	Total number
1942	14 884		536 613
1962	17 326		460 084
1972	20 891	7 820	311 981
1982		14 539	261 144

doubling to 2.75 HP per ha. Most of this increased power per unit area of land resulted from the increasing size of tractors and ever larger machinery.

Why have UK farmers invested in larger machinery? The following factors together account for this trend.

i. A diminishing labour force, which approximately halved between 1960 and 1981 (Table 2), needed to be replaced.

ii. Larger farms allowed more effective use of larger tractors and machinery.

iii. A steady increase in the size of UK holdings since 1945 (Table 3) was also important in the purchase of larger tractors, if not in the increased power per unit area of land.

iv. The relatively high profitability of arable farming also allowed farmers to invest more money to compensate for adverse seasons.

v. Perhaps most important of all were changes in cereal production. Cereals replaced grass on many traditional clay-land pastures in the midlands and southern England, and, in consequence, power requirement in these areas increased sharply.

vi. In addition, the autumn demand for power on cereal farms intensified as:
   (a) more than one half of the spring barley area was replaced by winter barley;
   (b) cereal systems intensified, reducing the area of spring break crops on medium and clay land;
   (c) modern higher yielding cereal varieties needed earlier sowing to exploit their yield potential.

3 Larger tractors, larger fields

The quest for higher cultivation work rates to improve productivity of labour inevitably led to larger fields in many parts of arable England and Scotland. Sturrock *et al.* (1978) examined the relationship between field size, work rate and implement widths (Figure 2). If we accept their assumptions, there is a 'minimum' field size for each width of implement below which work rate is substantially reduced. For primary cultivation tools such as ploughs and cultivators, and also for combine harvesters, which usually lie within the 1-6 m width range, there is little advantage in field size exceeding 20 ha. However, for seed bed cultivation, rolling and spraying, much larger width machinery is employed and 'minimum' field size rises to 40 ha or more. This reasoning shows clearly why farmers in most parts of arable Britain have increased the sizes of fields and why pressure for yet larger fields may continue, if average tractor size increases in the future.

Table 2. Agricultural manpower in the UK in 1960 and 1981

	1960	1981
Total regular workers	645 000	232 000
Workers/100 ha	5·5	1·9

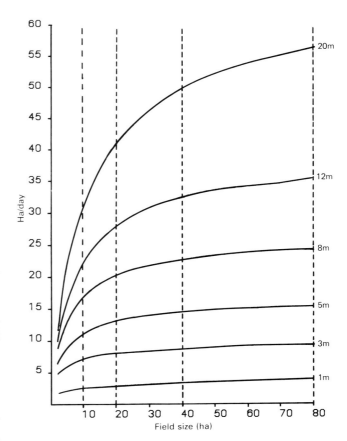

Figure 2. Increase in work rate due to larger fields, and wider implements (Source: Sturrock et al. 1978)

4 Changes in cultivation system

Greater intensity of autumn cropping and earlier drilling in autumn have been achieved partly by increased mechanization and also by streamlined cultivation systems. Use of cultivators rather than ploughs, shallow cultivations (less than 10 cm), and zero tillage have all contributed towards more work in autumn. By 1980, about one third of the country's cereal crop (autumn plus spring) was established by such systems, and the figure was as high as two-thirds in clay-land areas of eastern England. Straw burning is a necessary part of these streamlined systems, both through time saving and through avoiding the loss of yield associated with surface and shallowly incorporated straw. If the practice of straw burning declines substantially, farmers will need to make extra overall investment in tractor power and in other machinery.

Since 1980, there has been a return from reduced cultivation systems towards ploughing and deeper cultivation. This change was brought about partly because of grass weed problems, but also because of the development of better cultivation equipment.

5 Other changes in arable farming

Other important developments in arable farming over the last 5 years include the following.

5.1 Drainage

An important requirement of mechanized agriculture is adequate control of water tables in slow draining land. Otherwise, the risk of low bearing capacities becomes unacceptable and soil physical conditions and crop yield suffer. This interaction between water regime of land and mechanized agriculture has been a major factor in stimulating improved field drainage in the UK.

5.2 Cereal yields

National average yields of cereals (Figure 3) have risen at a substantially faster rate than previously, thereby increasing the amount of crop residues incorporated and the quantities of straw burnt. To support these yields, fertilizer applications, particularly of nitrogen, have increased, but there is no indication that efficiency of fertilizer nitrogen use in terms of crop yield response has diminished over the same period. Both the evidence of higher yields and similar nitrogen use efficiency suggest that inherent soil fertility, ie the ability of land to sustain yields, has not been impaired by current practices.

5.3 Expansion of cereals

Higher profitability of cereals relative to grazing livestock enterprises during the last decade has inevitably resulted in an expansion of the cereal area at the expense of the grass. Between 1976-82, the area of cereals grown in England rose by about 10% to 3.37M ha, largely at the expense of grass. Although high cereal prices were a factor in this switch, improved efficiency of grassland production was equally important. Table 4 shows that the increase in cereal area

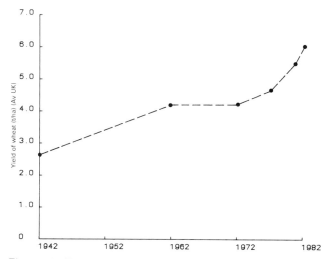

Figure 3. Trends in wheat yields (UK)

occurred not only in the more traditional livestock counties such as Hereford and Somerset, but also in traditional arable counties such as Cambridgeshire.

5.4 Tramlines

Another significant change has been the almost universal switch to tramline cereal growing, ie the use of permanent narrow lanes through crops from drilling to harvest. This method confines compaction to these uncropped wheelings, and incidentally ensures greater accuracy of pesticide and fertilizer applications.

6 Mechanization and wildlife habitats

6.1 Hedgerows

Changes in field size and the consequent changes in length of hedgerows and other field boundaries have long been recognized as having implications for wildlife habitats. Perhaps as important as field size is the quality of hedgerows. In areas without grazing livestock, only game conservation, protection from exposure, and concern for wildlife encourage good hedge maintenance.

6.2 Straw disposal

Straw burning seems likely to have significant implications for wildlife habitats compared with other forms of disposal. Where standards of burning are poor and unacceptable by current codes, damage to habitats can be extensive, but whether well managed burning has any other than fairly transient effect on above-

Table 4. Changes in cereal and grass area (ha) in selected English counties

County	1976		1982	
	Cereals	Grass	Cereals	Grass
Buckinghamshire	50 000	74 000	56 000	64 000
Cambridgeshire	167 000	33 000	182 000	25 000
Hereford & Worcestershire	77 000	188 000	90 000	176 000
Lancashire	20 000	147 000	21 000	145 000
Northumberland	63 000	153 000	76 000	145 000
Somerset	33 000	215 000	40 000	209 000

ground habitats perhaps needs debating within this seminar. By depriving soil fauna of a source of food in the form of straw, burning may reduce some populations (but see Edwards 1984). Incorporation of straw at current levels of crop production has long-term implications for levels of humified organic matter in the soil; current models suggest that, although effects would be small in the short term, ie decades, organic matter levels should double after one or 2 centuries of incorporation. The influence of such changes on the soil fauna and flora, and on wildlife which use them as a source of food, may be highly significant.

6.3 Soil physical fertility

It is a popular belief that large tractors, and larger field machinery in general, inevitably cause more compaction which is harmful to land and to crop production. With the exception of the minority enterprises of root crops and vegetables, there is no evidence to support this view. The evidence available suggests that perhaps the opposite is true.

6.3.1 Yields of cereals and production from grass have constantly risen in recent years. Although this improved yield does not directly exclude the possibility of increased soil structural damage, it does indicate that changes in soil structure/compaction have not been important limitations to yield. Indeed, increased mechanization on farms has been an important factor in supporting and servicing increased production.

6.3.2 Awareness of the importance of improved soil management amongst arable farmers is now greater than in previous decades. This awareness has been translated into improved management in practice, for example use of tramlines, earlier autumn cultivations, and better land drainage.

6.3.3. Large improvements in the design of soil engaging implements have allowed farmers to achieve optimum soil conditions for crop growth more efficiently.

6.4 Erosion

Wherever arable agriculture is practised, there is a potential problem both for farmers and the natural environment through soil erosion by water. This process occurs naturally in all sloping landscapes to a greater or lesser extent. It is only when loss exceeds the rate at which soil can be produced by weathering and other natural processes that agricultural production is at risk. In Britain, the rate of loss by erosion has been slow historically and only a small minority of farmers have had to take control measures. To investigate whether current farming practices are causing increased losses, the Soil Survey of England and Wales, in conjunction with ADAS, started to survey water erosion in 1981. Aerial photography is used to identify fields subject to erosion in a number of transects through areas of England and Wales where soil/site factors predispose the land to movement.

Field visits are then made to eroded fields to estimate quantities of soil lost and other relevant information. At the end of 5 years, we should be in a position to say to what extent agriculturally significant erosion is occurring in England and Wales, and whether factors such as field size, cropping and/or cultivation system are involved. Early results suggest that arable farming in areas previously considered too marginal for arable crops may be particularly at risk.

7 Conclusion

From the evidence available, it seems probable that the direct effects of increased mechanization, as distinct from the indirect effects, on the land and countryside have had little, if any, influence on wildlife habitats, either beneficial or adverse, despite the mechanical revolution of the last 50 years.

8 Summary

UK agriculture has been completely mechanized since the 1930s. During the last decade, tractor numbers have not risen substantially but power per hectare has doubled. Increased sizes of tractors and machinery have inevitably led to larger fields and fewer hedges.

There have also been substantial changes in methods of cultivation, as the pressures of intensive autumn cereal cropping have led to reduced cultivation methods supported by straw burning. The development of higher yielding cereal varieties and the use of increased power per unit area of land have necessitated improved standards of field and arterial drainage to provide better soil bearing capacity for machinery.

In general, there is no indication that increasing tractor power and machinery weight have adversely affected soil fertility. However, this is probably not the case on some of our lowland soils growing higher than normal proportions of root crops and vegetables. Problems may also arise in areas marginal for cereals into which these crops have spread. The soil is more at risk to physical damage in places with slow draining clays on upland margins, and also where drainage/structure problems may arise. In addition, cultivation of land in sloping landscapes, whether marginal or not, inevitably leads to soil loss by water erosion. ADAS and the Soil Survey are currently monitoring erosion losses annually with the aid of aerial photography, and, if erosion losses are found to be higher than acceptable in some areas, there may well be implications for wildlife as well as for agriculture.

In eastern England, straw burning has become a necessary expedient of intensive autumn cereal production, with presumably important implications for wildlife above and below the ground. If straw incorporation becomes widespread, the organic cycle of arable soils will be greatly altered by the large quantities of organic substrates introduced. The significance of this change could be large for the soil fauna and flora, and for the wildlife which rely on them.

9 References
Edwards, C.A. 1984. Changes in agricultural practice and their impact on soil organisms. In: *Agriculture and the environment,* edited by D. Jenkins, 56–65. (ITE symposium no. 13). Cambridge: Institute of Terrestrial Ecology.
Ministry of Agriculture, Fisheries and Food. 1930-82. *Agricultural statistics: United Kingdom.* London: HMSO.
Sturrock, F.G., Cathie, K. & Payne, T.A. 1978. Economics of scale in farm mechanisation. *Occ. Pap. Camb. Univ. agric. Econ. Unit,* no. 22.

Drainage for agriculture

J MORRIS, P B LEEDS-HARRISON, A M RYAN & T M HESS
Silsoe College, Silsoe, Bedford

1 Introduction

Whilst water is essential for agricultural crop production, too much water can restrict crop growth and limit cropping activities. The basic aim of agricultural drainage is to alleviate or prevent the problems caused by excess water in order to facilitate more productive agriculture.

The agricultural drainage problem may be due to coastal or fluvial flooding, and/or the presence of seasonally or permanently high water tables. Poor drainage due to flood inundation often calls for river re-channelling and embanking works. Where poor drainage is due to waterlogging, the preoccupation is with improving arterial watercourses, installing piped under-drainage, and introducing other measures such as subsoiling which improve the movement of water in the soil.

This paper, in very general terms, considers the objectives, methods and value of agricultural drainage, and concludes with a discussion of research priorities to improve drainage decision-making, with particular reference to achieving a satisfactory compromise between agricultural and environmental objectives.

2 Drainage objectives

Figure 1 summarizes the principal benefits of improved drainage for grass and arable enterprises. They can be generalized in terms of improvements in the

ARABLE LAND

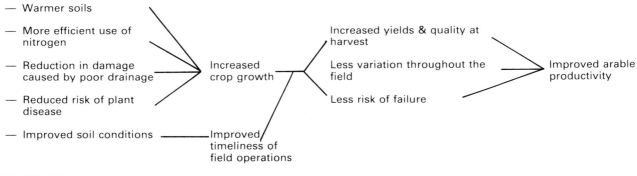

GRASSLAND

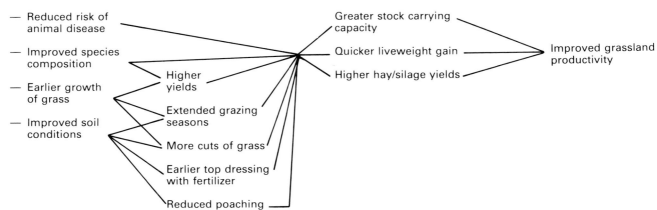

Figure 1. The benefits of improved drainage for arable and grassland uses

soil/plant/water growing environment and in the 'trafficability' of soils which allow more timely access for field activities, together with a reduction in crop damage caused by poor drainage.

Adequate drainage is essential for a favourable crop growth environment. British agriculture is mainly rain-fed and depends on the changing seasonal soil water regime. In winter, rain far exceeds evapotranspiration, resulting in high soil water contents. Soils are brought to a condition in which soil in the unsaturated zone above the water table is holding as much water as it can against gravity. This is called field capacity. On well drained sites, further rain infiltrates, passes down through the profile, and drains away. On poorly drained sites, water contents rise and may reach saturation or result in standing water at the surface. In summer, rainfall continues at roughly the same average level. It is overtaken, however, by evapotranspiration which increases through the spring and dries the soil in the root zone. Water contents remain below field capacity until evapotranspiration tails off again in autumn (see Smith & Trafford 1976).

Crop yields are influenced by the soil/plant/water conditions at the start of the growing season in spring. Early leaf expansion encourages a greater net interception of solar radiation through the summer, which ultimately increases yields. Early growth, however, depends on aeration of the soil. Only with adequate aeration can soil temperatures rise, roots expand, and gases be exchanged between roots and the atmosphere. On well drained sites, aeration is not a constraint upon leaf growth, which accelerates in response to rising temperatures and lengthening days. Wet sites have poor aeration in spring and lag behind in their response so that potential production is lost. One purpose of field drainage is, therefore, to fulfil the crop's initial aeration requirement in spring.

Improved drainage, by alleviating inundation by floodwaters and/or removing excess storm rain during the growing season, can also reduce crop damage and yield depression. The timing and duration of inundation and waterlogging largely determine the degree of detriment. In winter, for instance, when crop growth is minimal, grass and cereals can tolerate severe waterlogging, and grass may not be greatly affected by inundation. In summer, however, waterlogged soils are quickly exhausted of available oxygen, and resultant anoxic conditions may starve and damage the plant if allowed to continue even for a few days. Drainage measures need to be sufficient to remove water rapidly and limit the period of inundation or waterlogging.

Most research into crop response to drainage has measured soil wetness in terms of depth to water table and related yields to this parameter (Visser 1958). Researchers have identified the best compromise between aeration requirements and the need for water supply to roots in summer by capillary action. Generally, the need is to control water table height between some summer minimum and winter maximum. Visser considered the combination of mean winter and summer levels which minimized yield depression (Bon 1968). Whilst results varied between soil types, grass yields were only slightly depressed (<5%), provided that winter levels did not rise above 25-40 cm below the surface and summer levels did not fall below 70-110 cm.

A more comprehensive approach to crop response has related yield depression to the number, duration and severity of incursions of water table level above a specified critical level. A depth of 30 cm has been selected as the basis for a SEW_{30} index (Sieben 1964) used to evaluate the degree of waterlogging. SEW_{30} is the number of cm-days when the water table exceeds 30 cm; a 4-day incursion within 15 cm of the surface gives an index of 60 cm-days. SEW_{30} has been shown to have a linear relation to the percentage yield depression.

In the UK, Trafford (1974) reviewed the experimental results of the effects of high water levels on crop yield. He concluded that the limited experimental data suggested a wide difference between the tolerance of individual crops and between different dates and durations of flooding or waterlogging. Trafford (1972) had earlier reviewed the evidence in the literature for increased yield due to drainage, admitting that, whilst the evidence was scanty, some benefit was reported in most cases.

Recent work in the UK continues to examine the seasonal changes in soil/plant/water relationships and the implications for drainage design. For instance, winter wheat shows considerable tolerance to winter waterlogging, and, whilst capable of recovering from isolated waterlogging events in the growing season, suffers more than proportionally if waterlogging recurs. The work concludes, however, that water table control to 0.5 m is adequate, provided incursions above this level are very brief (Cannell & Belford 1982).

With respect to 'trafficability', improved drainage can significantly increase the number of days on which the soil is fit for traffic or the use of soil engaging implements. Soil strength and load bearing capacity vary inversely with soil water content and the height of the water table. By increasing the number of workdays available, better drainage reduces the risk of untimeliness for critical operations such as seed bed preparation, and fertilizer/pesticide/herbicide/fungicide applications. A special feature of agricultural operations is their sensitivity to timing; delay often means a loss of potential yield.

In many respects, requirements for working the soil or moving equipment may impose stricter drainage conditions than the crop itself, particularly given the move to larger and more sophisticated farm machinery, and the need to avoid undue soil compaction and structural degradation.

In grassland systems, improved drainage can reduce poaching liability and allow earlier access for grazing livestock, thereby exploiting the spring flush. The ability to apply nitrogen to grass early in the spring is a major benefit of improved drainage.

Research into drainage and 'trafficability' has proceeded on 2 broad fronts. First, agricultural engineers have been concerned with the relationship between soil wetness and field travelling or working conditions, whether this be the load bearing capacity of the soil or the effectiveness of soil engaging implements such as cultivators or seed drills. Effort has been directed at the factors that determine field work-days for particular soil/plant/water/machinery combinations, and the importance of drainage treatment in this context (eg Godwin & Spoor 1977; Spoor & Godwin 1979; Jarvis 1977). Second, consideration has been given to assessing the value of improved timeliness of operation arising from an increase in the number of field work-days (Smith 1972; Armstrong 1977). American researchers, in particular, have attempted to assign monetary values to the timeliness benefits of field drainage (Wendte *et al.* 1978).

3 Drainage methods

3.1 Drainage design

The object of drainage design is to control the water table within the limits that allow optimum agricultural production. The benefits and level of control have been outlined in the previous section. To achieve them, the arterial and field drainage of the agricultural catchment must be considered together as a whole. At this stage, a distinction should be made between the drainage of *wet land* and *wetland* (Leitch 1982). Drainage of *wet land* is the removal of excess water from the soil profile by the lowering of water tables through ditches and field under-drainage. This type of drainage is most common in the United Kingdom. Drainage of *wetland* is the creation of an arterial drainage system which allows flood alleviation and the removal of standing water. In the United Kingdom, responsibility for arterial drainage principally falls on the Water Authorities, various Internal Drainage Boards, and Local Authorities. Drainage design in terms of flood routing and channel design is based on rational design techniques using the statistical evidence of flood returns. The Natural Environment Research Council (1975) outlines these techniques.

Field drainage, however, which involves ditches and piped under-drainage, is essentially a traditional art based on experience of local soils and conditions. At field level, there may be many contributory factors to a drainage problem. Although excess winter rain (ie that rain which falls in excess of evaporative demand) may cause many problems, foreign water from higher in the catchment may be a major cause of problems; and water tables in lowland and riverine areas can be kept high by seepage from a highland carrier. Rational drainage design can be accomplished by seeking solutions to the equations which describe the movement of water in the soil. Such approaches are used elsewhere, notably in the Netherlands where several equations for drainage design at field level have been developed.

The control of a rain-fed water table by tube drains is shown in Figure 2. Midway between the drains, the water table rises to its maximum giving a minimum potential root zone. It can be shown that the maximum height of the water table above the drain level (H_m) is a function of the depth of the aquifer (D_o), the spacing of the drains (L), the hydraulic conductivity of the subsoil (K), and the steady state re-charge by rainfall to the water table (q). Where the hydraulic conductivity of the soil is low, the presence of a water table may not be so significant as the low infiltration rate of water into the subsoil. Soils of this type very often have a perched water table in the topsoil layers. Such a perched water table is just as much a problem to agricultural production as the true groundwater problem.

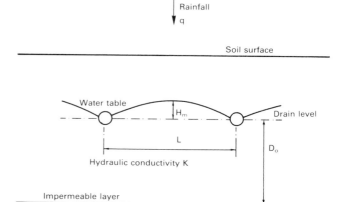

Figure 2. Water table control by field under-drainage

3.2 Drainage criteria

Rational drainage design aims to control the water table by finding a suitable drain spacing and depth for the expected rainfall and measured soil properties using solutions to mathematical relationships which describe Figure 3. It is possible to determine the hydraulic conductivity of soil *in situ* and to ascribe a representative value to a given site. These values will depend on soil texture and, more importantly, on soil structure. Table 1 shows the range of values expected for different textured subsoils. The required height of the water table over the drains may be decided, based on the depth of the drain and the position to which the water table is to be controlled. The most difficult parameter to measure in many cases is the depth of the aquifer below the drain. Calculated drain spacings are very sensitive to this parameter at small values.

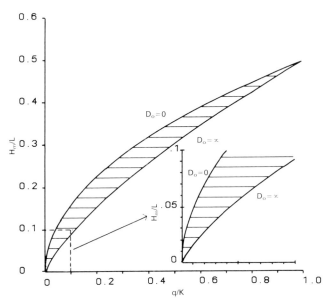

Figure 3. *Relationship between variables for field drainage design*

Table 2. Flood frequency standards suggested by ADAS (1979)

Land potential	Desirable standard mid-March/mid-Nov	Minimum acceptable standard 'whole year'
Very high	Essentially no flood risk	1 in 100 years
High	1 in 25 years	1 in 10 years
Medium	1 in 10 years	1 in 5 years
Low	1 in 5 years	1 in 2 years
Very low	1 in 3 years	1 in 1 year

Table 1. Ranges of hydraulic conductivity for various soil textures (Source: ADAS 1982)

Hydraulic conductivity Ranges for soil textures	Range m/day	Class
C	0·01–0·1	Very slow
ZyC	0·1–0·3	Slow-Mod
SC CL ZyCL	0·3–1·0	Moderate
SL	1·0–10·0	Mod-Rapid
Pt S	10	Very rapid

C — Clay	ZyCL — Silty clay loam	
SC — Sandy clay	SL — Sandy loam	
CL — Clay loam	S — Sand	
ZyC — Silty clay	Pt — Peat	

However, all these values relate to physically measurable site-specific parameters and are considered not to vary.

A figure for the steady state rainfall must be chosen from rainfall statistics. Drainage intensity will be based on the value chosen. Conventionally, as with desirable design flood frequency standards for arterial drainage, the value chosen is based on the risk and consequence of the drainage design not meeting its criteria for water table control. By choosing a longer return period, the drainage intensity is increased. For arterial drainage, the Ministry of Agriculture, Fisheries and Food recommends the design flood return frequencies shown in Table 2. For most field crops, return periods of 1 in 2 years to 1 in 5 years are commonly chosen. A return period of 1 in 10 or more would normally only be chosen for high-value short-term horticultural crops. In practice, rain events are discrete and water tables fluctuate.

The rate of lowering of the water table following an event will depend on the same physical parameters of the site which determine its storage capacity, the drain spacing and the effective porosity of the soil. The more intense the drainage, the more rapid will be the draw down of the water table. Water tables will only be lowered to drain level so that over-drainage need not be a problem. However, evaporative demands and natural deep drainage may lower the water table beyond this level. Over-drainage in the more permeable soils may be a problem in summer where the arterial systems allow water levels to fall. In these situations, irrigation may be needed to prevent water stress to the crop.

In clay soils in which the permeability is very low, intensive drainage is needed to control water tables. In the UK, much use is made of unlined mole drains which allow such intensive drainage. This method of drainage can control water tables in the subsoil and perched water tables in the topsoil. However, not all clay soils are suitable for mole drainage and for these soils closely spaced tube drains may be an alternative, although this solution is likely to be expensive. The criterion for perched water table control on mole drained situations is to remove the excess water from the topsoil within 24 hours of a rainstorm, and is based on the need to prevent excessive wetting of the unlined mole channel which can rapidly deteriorate under these conditions.

Mole drains are normally placed at a depth of 0.5-0.6 m below the soil surface and so can control a water table in the subsoil to that depth. Lined drains are generally placed at depths which range from 0.8-1.5 m depending on the soil type, the machine used to install them and the available outfall. A generally accepted outfall criterion for field drains is that there should be 0.15 m freeboard at the outfall, although submerged outfalls will not necessarily prevent adequate drainage.

The maintenance of the ditch system which provides the outfall for the drains is of major importance. Theobald (1958) reported that the majority of drainage failures were caused by choked ditches and blocked outfalls to the field drains. This situation indicates the importance of ditch maintenance which has to be carried out on a regular basis, ie every 2-3 years, to allow the drainage system to meet its design potential.

3.3 Drainage modelling

Models based on the physical equations which describe soil water movement can be used to describe the soil moisture regime. Typically, such models will predict the fluctuation of the water table under a given rainfall and evapotranspiration regime. As such, they are a valuable tool for the drainage engineer and researcher. Many models are currently allowing the effect of various drainage options to be assessed.

The task of the drainage design engineer is to provide a drainage system within the constraints imposed by the cropping and trafficability considerations, but also within a cost constraint. The importance of drainage in terms of the potential returns needs to be considered carefully against its cost.

4 Drainage value

4.1 Potential benefits

To the farmer, drainage works are worthwhile if the extra benefits attributable to improved drainage are greater than the extra costs, both in absolute terms and relative to other investment opportunities. Evaluating the drainage investment involves a financial assessment of both the pre- and post-drainage situation for the 'benefit' area. In some cases, the impact of drainage may extend beyond the area in benefit, in which case the evaluation will need to adopt a whole-farm perspective.

The general approach to evaluating drainage investment is to compare the 'without drainage project' with the expected (or actual) 'with drainage project' situation. The method identifies the difference in pre- and post-drainage enterprise gross margins (value of output less direct costs of seeds, fertilizers, etc) and subtracts any changes in fixed costs (labour, machinery, buildings) necessary to exploit the drainage benefits. The resultant net return, expressed as an annual cash flow, can then be discounted against the capital and maintenance costs of the drainage works. Generally, the greater the constraint imposed by poor drainage, the greater the financial attraction of alleviation.

The factors affecting the net agricultural benefit of improved drainage are summarized in Figure 4. The net benefits may be manifested in a number of ways.

i. *The reclamation case.* In areas where drainage is so poor as to exclude agricultural use, the benefits of drainage are obvious, being measured in terms of the net output of new activities.

ii. *Improved production from existing land uses.* Reducing inundation and waterlogging will improve the yields of existing crop/livestock systems along the line previously described, as well

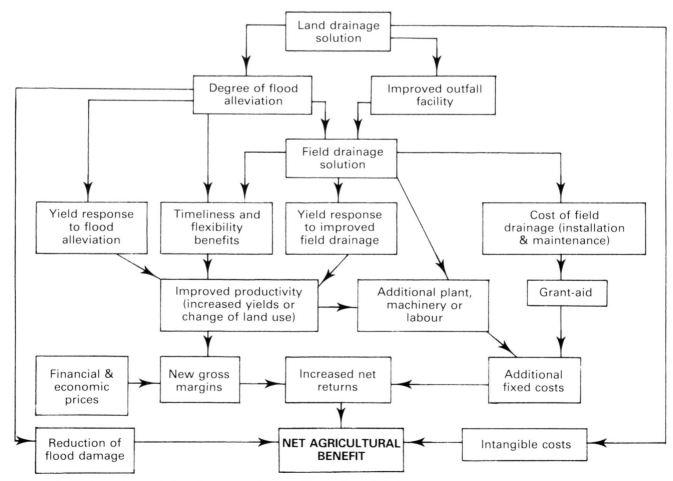

Figure 4. Factors determining the net agricultural benefits of drainage

as facilitating the use of inputs to increase yields, such as chemical fertilizers. Grass production is one example. Improved drainage can extend the grazing season, enable and justify more N fertilizer use, improve sward composition, increase the energy and digestibility value of grass, facilitate more efficient grazing and conservation practices, and lead to higher livestock yields, higher stocking rates and increased profitability. For arable cropping, increased production can take the form of a move to higher yielding but drainage sensitive crop species or varieties.

iii. *Change in land use.* Improved drainage may enable the introduction of a previously infeasible but financially attractive land use or enterprise type. For example, the change may be from summer grazing on indigenous pasture to the intensive grazing of improved leys, from permanent pasture to an arable/ley rotation, or from one form of arable cropping to another, possibly including roots and horticultural crops. The shift to a more intensive system will depend on the extra degree of protection afforded. In many cases, land use change may require the installation of field drains in addition to flood alleviation works.

iv. *Reduced costs.* Drainage improvements can effect a saving in production costs through a reduction of flood damage costs and improved working conditions which can provide labour and machinery economies.

v. *Benefits to the whole farm.* Where drainage improvement incorporates a large proportion of the farm, there may be indirect benefits for activities on other parts of the farm. For instance, increased stocking rates on improved and more accessible lowland pastures may release upland areas for arable production whilst maintaining herd size. Alternatively, increased output from previously unproductive wet land could justify or necessitate large capital investments (eg farm machinery, buildings) previously infeasible.

5 Discussion

In the context of drainage investment appraisal, as far as the private farmer is concerned, the decision to drain will depend on the ratio of extra outputs to extra inputs, expressed in prevailing financial farm gate prices, net of relevant taxes and subsidies.

There is considerable debate at present whether resource allocations made on this basis are economically rational, particularly as prevailing market prices may not reflect the real economic value placed by society on additional production or resource use. For instance, it is argued that the current EC Common Agricultural Policy over-values the real worth of producing more farm produce for surplus, and that producers do not meet the full cost of grant-aided drainage works. Furthermore, where improved agriculture results in environmental loss, these 'external' opportunity costs are not given adequate recognition in the appraisal procedures which are essentially financial and production oriented. Largely in response to pressure from non-farm land uses/users, there has been a move to incorporate economic ('shadow') pricing and environmental impact analyses in future drainage scheme proposals.

A decisive factor in the potential value of any proposed agricultural land drainage scheme is the rate and nature of uptake of the potential benefits by farmers in response to improved drainage opportunities. Whether farmers intensify production, change land use, and/or invest in field drainage depends on a host of technical, psychological, social and economic factors which will include such variables as the nature of the potential benefit, soil type, farming system, farmer age, expertise, preference and risk attitude, farm size, tenure status, and financial status. To date, no satisfactory method has been found to predict the uptake of potential drainage benefits, and estimates have relied on a vague mixture of local knowledge and farmer statements of intent in response to questionnaires. It is apparent, however, that many farmers, for a variety of reasons, do not exploit the full potential of their farms. Fertilizer N used on grass, for instance, is probably less than one third of 'recommended' rates, and stocking rates concomitantly lower. Those concerned with conserving the rural space, farmers included, may well express relief that this is the case, without necessarily being able to explain it. Work at Silsoe College, however, involves the ex-post evaluation of selected land drainage schemes within the Severn-Trent region, with a view to measuring benefit uptake and explaining the factors which account for variations in farmer response.

6 Drainage and related research: the way forward

This section considers the need for further research to guide practical drainage decision-making, particularly as it may affect environmental matters.

The practical usefulness of past research into drainage needs and effectiveness has in many cases been limited by the restrictive conditions and resources imposed on researchers. It is very difficult to disentangle the effect of extraneous variables, particularly weather, on experimental drainage sites, and it is not easy to simulate the conditions that prevail within the real farm system, notably the effect of extra work-days on eventual yields. Laboratory experiments involving lysimeters (soil tanks) cannot adequately reflect the benefits of 'trafficability' and timeliness. Consequently, many of the data available are difficult to interpret for drainage purposes. The peculiarities of UK weather and soil water regimes mean that overseas data, with the exception of those from the Netherlands, are not easily applicable.

The priority for research is thus with integrated systems to examine the impact of drainage as one of a number of variable inputs to the farming system, along with environmental (soil) factors, fertilizer use, mechanization, grazing management. This challenge is currently being taken up by researchers from the Field Drainage Experimental Unit at Brimstone Farm (Oxon), where the role of alternative drainage treatments is being studied in the context of other non-drainage activities, notably alternative cultivation systems. The latter work is supported by lysimeter (soil tank) experiments at Letcombe Laboratory (Oxon) to consider, amongst other things, the fate of nitrogen under different drainage conditions.

The Grassland Research Institute's North Wyke (Devon) site is examining the responses of grass production and grazing livestock performance to various drainage scenarios in heavy clays. The relationships between nitrogen use and energy from grass, and between poaching and grass utilization are extremely critical for productive grassland systems, and the impact of drainage on these relationships is now being given the attention it deserves.

With respect to trafficability, the research priority lies in determining the criteria that define 'work-days' for given environmental, crop and activity combinations. Once this has been done, the drainage design parameters that can reasonably achieve these conditions can be determined.

In view of the growing competition for land as a resource, priority needs to be given to assessing the value of agricultural versus other rural land uses. This assessment includes the potential benefits attributable to drainage, the alternative drainage methods to achieve stated potential benefits, a more economically rational basis for valuing potential benefit, a more confident basis for predicting farmer uptake, the cost to agriculture of keeping environmental impact within acceptable limits, and the consequences of retaining natural water levels.

In many respects, the kind of data base, techniques and expertise developed for designing and justifying agricultural drainage are applicable, in principle, to designing and justifying measures to protect or create wetland sites. For instance, much research effort has examined soil/plant/water regimes for productive agriculture. The same principles could be applied to describe these regimes for agriculturally non-productive species. In this way, the sensitivity of natural species to changes in soil water regimes could be assessed, particularly in relation to changes proposed for agricultural purposes. It would also be possible to identify environmental engineering and management methods which could create or retain the desired soil/plant/water habitat conditions in the way that agricultural engineers address drainage for agriculture problems. Furthermore, selected aspects of the cost-benefit procedures used for justifying land drainage could be employed to assess the value of wetland conservation, not only in terms of estimating the real value of agricultural output foregone, but also the value of (non-priced) services flowing from these sites. To give an example, Silsoe College has recently undertaken a preliminary investigation into the feasibility of wetland creation/retention in generally drained areas for CIRIA (1984). This study showed that hydrological/engineering/economic principles and methods could equally apply to conserving, as opposed to removing, particular drainage conditions.

The Hill Farming Research Organisation has undertaken research into the tolerance of the various species making up grass swards to increasing soil wetness, including those which are not agriculturally productive (Rogers *et al.* 1974). If the drainage engineer is to take account of species not favoured for agricultural purposes, the identity and environmental needs of valued species must be made known to him. It will then be necessary to evaluate the responses of these species to changes in soil water regimes. This would require close collaboration between agricultural engineers and ecologists.

Finally, particularly for the wider countryside, it is relevant to emphasize that it is not the drainage *per se* that places greatest pressure on the environment. The conflict between environment and agriculture arises from the intensification of the latter, with the move from traditional, environmentally gentle, low input-low output systems to technologically sophisticated and synthetic, high input-high output systems. As yet, very little is known about the trade-off between agricultural efficiency and environmental impact, and the extent to which a compromise is possible or desirable. In situations where additional farming inputs are subject to diminishing marginal returns, and where financial values do not reflect economic benefits and costs, the difference between 'improved' traditional and high intensity farming systems may be more apparent than real. Identifying this difference would provide a more informed basis for policy-making in the agriculture versus the environment debate.

7 Summary

This paper discusses in very broad terms the objectives, methods and value of drainage for agricultural purposes. The basic objective of agricultural drainage is to alleviate or prevent the problems caused by excess water, whether these are due to inundation or waterlogging. The potential benefits of improved drainage relate to an improvement of soil water regimes, a reduction in crop damage, and an improvement in the capacity of the soil to carry machines and animals. Drainage research has particularly concentrated on soil/plant/water relationships with a view to optimum drainage design.

Agricultural drainage design aims to control flooding and water table levels within acceptable limits. Whilst much of field drainage design remains a traditional art, there are theoretical and practical criteria which incorporate crop and environmental parameters and provide a rational basis for drainage design.

The value of improved drainage to the farmer is generally viewed in the context of the farm as a business. The benefits are mainly in terms of an intensification or change in land use and farming practices. Whilst the farmer is concerned with financial profitability, there is considerable debate at present as to whether grant-aided drainage investments are 'economically' rational once hidden subsidies are removed. Whilst improved drainage is often a pre-requisite for improved farming, it is often the changes in farming practice which follow drainage rather than drainage *per se* which have the greatest environmental impact.

The main research needs concerning drainage and the environment are as follows.

i. *Agricultural benefits of drainage.* There is a need for ongoing monitoring and evaluation of the actual and potential benefits of improved drainage in the context of whole-farm situations.

ii. *Environmental impact of drainage.* Many of the techniques developed for identifying desirable soil water regimes for agricultural species are equally applicable for describing the requirements of agriculturally non-productive species.

iii. *Agricultural intensification versus the environment.* A crucial issue in the debate is the extent to which farming and the environment are competitive. Research is needed into the trade-off between agricultural 'efficiency' and environmental impacts, which would enable an assessment of the environmental loss associated with a given agricultural gain.

These 3 research priorities call for multidisciplinary inputs. The latter 2 topics require an understanding of the inter-relationships between agricultural drainage and the environment, and need the collaborative effort of both agriculturalists and ecologists.

8 References

Agricultural Development and Advisory Service. 1982. *The design of field drainage pipe systems.* (Reference book 345). London: HMSO.

Agricultural Development and Advisory Service. 1979. *Getting down to drainage. Arterial drainage and agriculture.* (Advisory leaflet 736). Pinner: Ministry of Agriculture, Fisheries and Food.

Armstrong, A.C. 1977. Field drainage and field work days: results from a national experiment. *Agric. Eng., 32,* 93-94.

Bon, J. 1968. The influence of a rise of the groundwater table on crop yield. In: *Determination of the optimum combination of water management systems in areas with a microrelief. Tech. Bull. Inst. Ld Wat. Mgmt Res.,* no. 56. 89-104.

Cannell, R.W. & Belford, R.K. 1982. Crop growth after transient water logging: advances in drainage. *Proc. ASAE Nat. Drainage Symposium, 4th, Chicago, 1982,* 163-170.

Construction Industry Research and Information. 1984. *The retention of wetlands: lowland areas generally drained by gravity.* (CIRIA project RP318). Bedford: Silsoe College.

Godwin, R.J. & Spoor, G. 1977. Soil factors influencing work days. *Agric. Eng., 32,* 87-90.

Jarvis, R.H. 1977. The effects of timeliness of soil-engaging operations on crop yield. *Agric. Eng., 32,* 84-86.

Leitch, J.A. 1982. *Economics of prairie land drainage.* (ASAE Winter Meetings Paper 82-2543). Chicago: American Society of Agricultural Engineers.

Natural Environment Research Council. 1975. *Flood studies report.* 5 vols. London: NERC.

Rogers, J.A., King, J. & Davies, G.E. 1974. The problem of waterlogged soil. *Rep. Hill Fmg Res. Org., 1971–73,* 86-94.

Sieben, W.H. 1964. *Het verband tussen onwatering en opbrengst bij de jonge Zavelgronden in de Noordoostpolder.* (Van Zee tot Land, no. 40). Zwolle, Netherlands: Willink.

Smith, L.P. 1972. The effect of weather, drainage efficiency and duration of spring cultivations on barley yields in England. *Outl. Agric., 7,* 79-83.

Smith, L.P. & Trafford, B.D. 1976. *Climate and drainage.* (Technical bulletin 34). London: HMSO.

Spoor, G. & Godwin, R.J. 1979. Soil deformation and sheer strength characteristics of some clay soils at different moisture contents. *J. Soil Sci., 30,* 483-498.

Theobald, G.H. 1958. Reconditioning of old drains. *J. Proc. Instn Br. agric. Engrs, 14,* 24-32.

Trafford, B.D. 1972. The evidence in literature for increased yield due to field drainage. *Tech. Bull. Field Drain. Exp. Unit, Agric. Dev. Advis. Serv.* no. 72/5.

Trafford, B.D. 1974. Soil water regimes—what is known, the work which is in hand and suggestions for progress. *Tech. Bull. Field Drain. Exp. Unit, Agric. Dev. Advis. Serv.* no. 74/13.

Visser, J.H. 1958. De Landbouwwaterhuishouding in Nederland. *Rapp. Comm. Onderz. LandbouwWaterhuish. ned. TND,* no. 1, 231.

Wendte, L.W., Drablos, C.J.W. & Lembke, W.D. 1978. The timeliness benefit of subsurface drainage. *Trans. ASAE, 21,* 484-488.

Changes in agricultural practice and their impact on soil organisms

C A EDWARDS
Rothamsted Experimental Station, Harpenden

1 Introduction

During the Second World War, there was great pressure to increase food production. Since then, agriculture has intensified greatly, partially due to economic pressures and Government subsidies, and more recently because of support from the European Economic Community. Some results of this intensification and pressure for higher crop yields have been the much greater use of (i) inorganic fertilizers, (ii) pesticides, (iii) development of new shallower methods of cultivation, (iv) increasing monoculture, (v) larger sizes of fields, (vi) precision drilling of some crops to a stand, (vii) burning of cereal straw and stubble after harvest, and (viii) short-term leys instead of old pasture for grass production.

The soil supports a vast array of living organisms ranging from tiny bacteria, protozoa and micro-organisms to nematodes, molluscs, earthworms, symphylids, millipedes, centipedes, mites, springtails, thrips, beetles, ants, caterpillars and fly larvae. Some of these are pests, others are predators or parasites of other animals, but probably the majority contribute to the breakdown of organic matter and its incorporation into the soil structure. The activities of all these organisms are interlinked intimately so the influences of various agricultural practices on them are usually complex.

Many soil organisms derive their nourishment either directly or indirectly from the organic matter present in soil. Many of the newer agricultural practices, such as the use of inorganic fertilizers, direct drilling with no cultivation, precision drilling and straw burning, tend to decrease the amounts of organic matter in soil and so have a strong indirect effect on populations of soil organisms.

It is very difficult to assess the effects of agricultural practice on micro-organisms either accurately or meaningfully, so most of the discussion will concentrate on the influence of these practices on soil inhabiting invertebrates.

2 Effects of fertilizers

As animal production has become increasingly specialized and intensified, the availability of animal wastes as organic sources of nitrogen (N), phosphorus (P), and potassium (K) has diminished. Organic manures are bulky in terms of their nutrient content. In relation to their economic value as nutrient sources, they are also costly to transport when the animals are a long way from crops. Hence, the use of inorganic fertilizers, particularly as sources of nitrogen, has increased rapidly. In 1975, about 100 000 tonnes of nitrogen as artificial inorganic fertilizer were applied to agricultural land in Great Britain (Royal Commission on Environmental Pollution 1979).

There is some information in the scientific literature on the effects of organic fertilizers on soil invertebrate populations (Morris 1922, 1927; Franz 1953; Sauerlandt & Marzusch-Trappmann 1962; Edwards & Lofty 1969, 1975a, 1982; Edwards *et al.* 1976; Curry 1976; Cotton & Curry 1980).

The data on the effects of inorganic fertilizers on the soil fauna are even sparser (Franz 1953; Hrynuik 1958; Mayer-Krapoll 1963; Huhta *et al.* 1967, 1969; Edwards & Lofty 1975a, 1982; Edwards *et al.* 1976). An excellent overall review of the effects of organic manures and inorganic fertilizers on the soil fauna was published by Marshall (1977).

Among these publications there are conflicting reports on the effects of organic fertilizers on soil invertebrate populations. Huhta *et al.* (1967, 1969), Abrahamsen (1970), and Axelsson *et al.* (1973) investigated the effects of between one and 3 annual applications of inorganic fertilizers on numbers of different soil inhabiting invertebrates in pine forests. Huhta *et al.* reported that 90 kg/ha of N, P, K fertilizer decreased numbers of invertebrates for up to a year; thereafter, there was an increase, particularly in populations of enchytraeids and springtails. Abrahamsen (1970) studied the effects of 100, 400 and 1600 kg/ha of nitrogen (urea) on invertebrate populations, and also reported an initial decrease, but some of his results were conflicting. Axelsson *et al.* (1973), in a much more thorough investigation, demonstrated clearly that, when pine woodland was treated in 3 consecutive years with 60, 60 and 40 kg/ha of ammonium nitrate or 180, 180 and 120 kg/ha of this fertilizer in the same years, there were decreases in populations of some soil inhabiting invertebrates, especially mites, springtails and enchytraeid worms, compared with those in untreated plots, which corresponded with the level of nitrogen applied. Numbers of almost all groups of micro-arthropods were decreased by the largest doses of nitrogen.

Edwards and Lofty (1975a, 1977) reported the effects of several nitrogenous-based fertilizers on the invertebrate fauna of grassland (Park Grass, Rothamsted) that had received the same annual fertilizer treatments for 118 years. Three doses of nitrogen had been used (48,

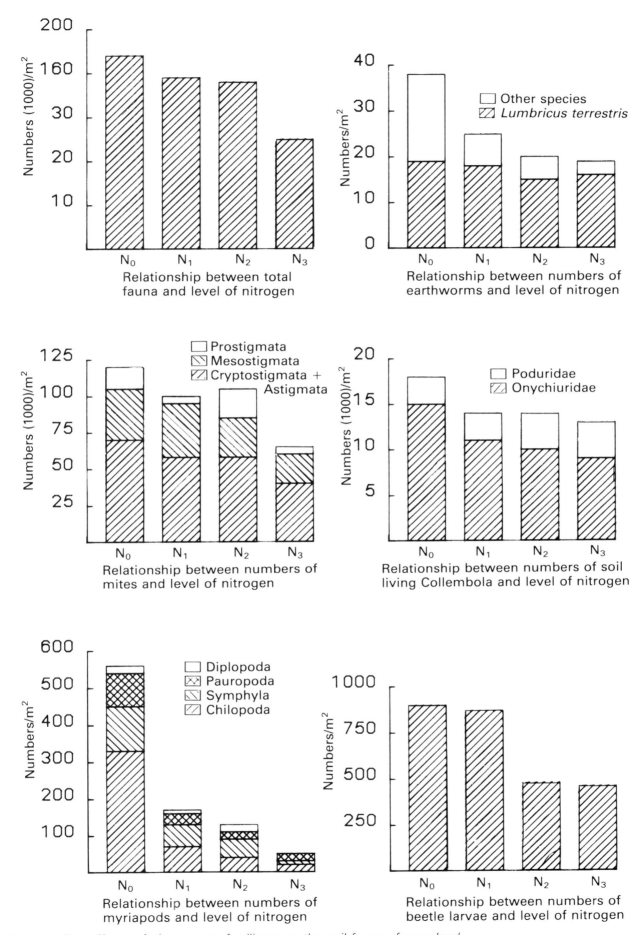

Figure 1. The effects of nitrogenous fertilizers on the soil fauna of grassland
(N_0 = no nitrogen; N_1 = 48 kg N/ha; N_2 = 96 kg N/ha; N_3 = 145 kg N/ha)

96 and 145 kg/ha). The resultant decreases in numbers of the total invertebrate fauna, earthworms, enchytraeid worms, myriapods, mites, springtails and beetle larvae, were inversely proportional to the dose of nitrogen that had been applied (Figure 1). Very few other data are available relating to the effects of inorganic fertilizers on the invertebrate fauna of grassland.

In arable soils, Hrynuik (1958) reported that various combinations of inorganic nutrients increased populations of nematodes, enchytraeid worms, insects, springtails and mites. Muller (1957) found that mite populations in arable soils increased after application of inorganic fertilizers. Edwards and Lofty (1982) reported that earthworm populations in a field where wheat had been grown since 1843 (Broadbalk, Rothamsted) were correlated directly in size with the amount of inorganic fertilizer applied annually since the start of the experiment (Figure 2). In experiments in wheat and maize fields, Artemjeva and Tatilova (1975) found that N, P, K fertilizers increased numbers of micro-arthropods both in crop rotations and monoculture.

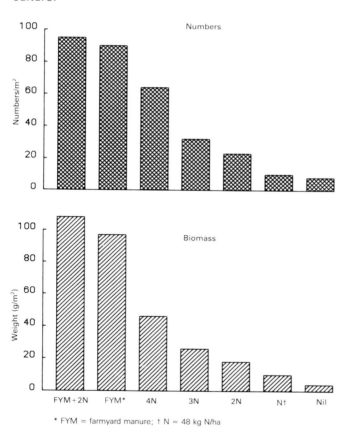

* FYM = farmyard manure; † N = 48 kg N/ha

Figure 2. Effects of long-term treatments with organic and inorganic fertilizers on earthworm populations in plots growing continuous cereals since 1843 (Broadbalk)

To summarize:

i. where there is abundant organic matter such as in grassland or forest soils, nitrogenous fertilizers tend to depress invertebrate populations;

ii. in arable soils where there is much less organic matter, nitrogenous fertilizers seem to increase invertebrate populations, probably because the increased crop residues that are left on the soil after harvest provide food for these animals.

Many more data are needed to confirm these conclusions.

3 Effects of pesticides

The use of pesticides in agriculture has been increasing steadily during the last 4 decades. New synthetic herbicides and insecticides were introduced first, but more recently there has been increasing use of fungicides. The Royal Commission on Environmental Pollution (1979) reported sales of herbicides in the UK as £140M, of insecticides as £35M and of fungicides as £15M. These chemicals are biocides with different degrees of specificity in their toxicity to soil animals; they have considerable potential for causing harm to life in the soil.

Most *herbicides* are sprayed on to crops or applied directly to soil, and soil organisms in agricultural land are exposed to large quantities of these chemicals. Fortunately, most herbicides are not very toxic to invertebrates that live in the soil (Edwards 1970, 1978; Edwards & Thompson 1973; Thompson & Edwards 1974; Madge 1981). Exceptions are monuron and TCA which can affect soil animals at very large doses, and DNOC which is very toxic to some groups of soil animals but is little used now. Only the triazine herbicides such as simazine have shown much direct toxicity to the soil fauna.

However, herbicides can exert quite considerable indirect effects on soil living invertebrates. When weeds are killed by herbicides, there is a brief flush of decaying organic matter which may provide food for soil detritivores, but the long-term effect is to diminish the amounts of organic matter in soil and consequently decrease overall populations of soil inhabiting invertebrates.

As *insecticides* are designed to kill animals, it is to be expected that effects on some of the soil fauna could be quite drastic. Although a few of them have a broad enough spectrum of activity to cause an overall depression of invertebrate populations, most exert a selective action and affect some invertebrate groups much more than others. Every insecticide differs in its effects and selectivity, so their influences can be summarized only very generally; even a small difference in chemical structure may change their effects drastically.

The organochlorine insecticides are well known for their persistence, particularly in soil, and for their potential to be taken up into the tissues of organisms. None of them has really drastic effects on populations of soil inhabiting invertebrates, overall numbers being only rarely decreased by more than 50%. Usually, drastic decreases in numbers of one group of invertebrates are associated with increases in populations of invertebrates in other groups that fill the same ecological niche but which are not susceptible to the insecticide. Typically, DDT is very toxic to predatory mites which feed mainly on Collembola. As these springtails are not very susceptible to DDT, they usually increase in numbers dramatically (Figure 3) (Edward & Thompson 1973).

The main ecological hazard of organochlorine insecticides is that they may be taken up into the tissues of earthworms, slugs, and larger arthropods such as beetles. When large numbers of these are eaten by vertebrates, they may kill the animal that eats them or other animals higher up the trophic food chain.

Organophosphate insecticides are much less persistent than organochlorines, and even more variable in their effects on populations of invertebrates living in soil. They tend to upset the delicate ecological balance that exists between soil organisms. These upsets may cause decreases in populations of some invertebrates and quite dramatic increases in others (Figure 4). An

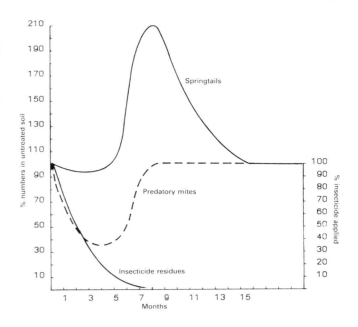

Figure 4. The relationship between residues of insecticides in soil and the numbers of predatory mites and springtails

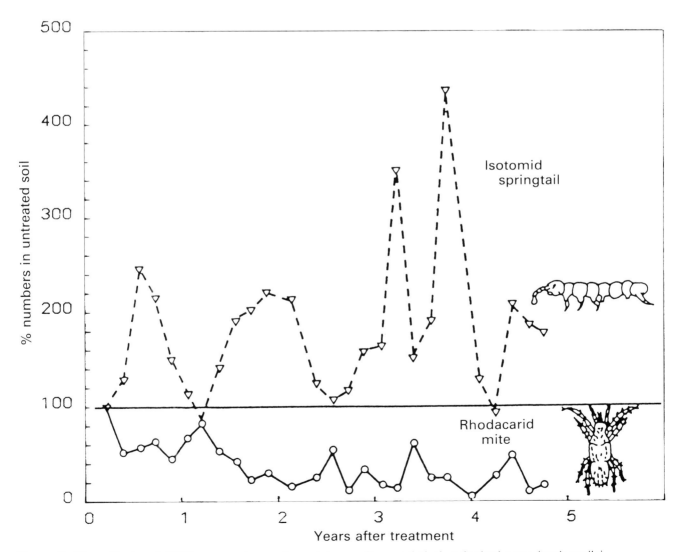

Figure 3. The effects of DDT on numbers of predatory mites and their principal prey (springtails)

interesting feature of their effects is that populations that are changed a great deal may still be affected after the last residues of the chemical causing the effect have disappeared. In general, organophosphate insecticides do not have drastic overall effects on the soil fauna. Carbamate insecticides tend to be rather more persistent and to have a more broad spectrum influence. They have much more drastic effects on soil inhabiting invertebrate populations than most other insecticides. In particular, they are very toxic to earthworms.

Nematicides are the most toxic of all pesticides to the soil fauna. Those nematicides with a fumigant action are the most dramatic of all, a single treatment with a nematicide such as DD or metham sodium killing almost all the animals in soil. When this happens, it may take as long as 2 years for populations of some invertebrates to recover, although the chemical residues may disperse after a week.

Fungicides are applied as seed dressings, soil fumigants or foliar sprays, all of which can leave residues in soil or on the soil surface. Very few fungicides are toxic to soil inhabiting invertebrates, but the carbendazim fungicides such as benomyl or methyl thiophanate, which are increasing rapidly in use, can kill earthworms and arthropods.

Pesticides tend to be most toxic to active animals which are often those that prey on other animals (Figure 5). As the more active invertebrates pass through soil or over the soil surface, they come into contact with the pesticide residues and accumulate a larger dose than more sluggish animals that often live in the deeper soil.

Micro-organisms
Nematodes (Nematoda)
Molluscs (Mollusca)
Earthworms (Oligochaeta)
Springtails (Collembola)
Woodlice (Isopoda)   increasing
Symphyla   susceptibility
Most mites (Acarina)
Millipedes (Diplopoda)
Centipedes (Chilopoda)
Other insects (Insecta)
Predatory insects
Predatory mites
Pauropoda

Figure 5. Relative susceptibility of soil invertebrates to chemicals

Pesticide residues are usually larger near to the soil surface which becomes contaminated by fall-out from aerial spraying that misses its target. Invertebrates living on or near to the soil surface are therefore at much greater risk than those living in deeper soil layers; most pesticide residues remain in the top 10 cm of soil, even if the soil is cultivated several times. Soil is an extremely effective filter so that only small quantities of the more soluble pesticides leach into the deeper soil layers.

Although we now know many of the general principles governing the effects of pesticides on the soil fauna, it is still necessary to screen each pesticide that may reach soil in appreciable quantities, for its possible effects on soil inhabiting invertebrates.

4 Effects of cultivations
The traditional method of cultivating soil has been the use of deep ploughs which invert the soil to a depth of about 20 cm, followed by a light surface working with disks or harrows to provide a seed bed. This is a very drastic treatment for the soil fauna because the inversion transfers soil inhabiting invertebrates which normally live in the top 5-10 cm of the soil profile to a depth of 20 cm where they may become trapped. Moreover, deep living invertebrates such as earthworms and insect larvae are brought to the soil surface where they may desiccate on the surface or be eaten by birds. It is common to see large numbers of birds following a deep plough. There is good evidence that deep ploughing can decrease populations of invertebrates in soil by at least 50% (Edwards & Lofty 1969, 1975b) (Figure 6).

The effects of deep ploughing a 300-year old pasture on the different groups of soil inhabiting invertebrates are illustrated in an experiment at Rothamsted. The old pasture was cultivated in different ways before re-seeding with grass for 8 years. One group of plots was deep ploughed, rolled, disked 5 times, harrowed, rolled and re-seeded; others were deep ploughed, disked twice, rolled and re-seeded; these treatments were termed 'least' and 'most' cultivations respectively. The cultivations were compared with plots left undisturbed, and the populations of invertebrates in the different treatments were assessed every spring and autumn. Although there were fluctuations in populations of the different groups of invertebrates, the cultivations clearly decreased numbers of most groups of invertebrates, and particularly those of cryptostigmatid, parasitic and predatory mites, surface living springtails and symphylids (Figure 7). The differences in populations of invertebrates in the most and least cultivated plots were not great, although the numbers of invertebrates in the undisturbed plots were very much larger than in either of the cultivated plots (Edwards 1970).

Since about 1960, there has been a strong trend away from traditional ploughing to shallower cultivations, often with no inversion; these methods include shallow tine or chisel ploughing. The extreme expression of this trend is the practice of avoiding cultivations altogether. A broad spectrum herbicide such as

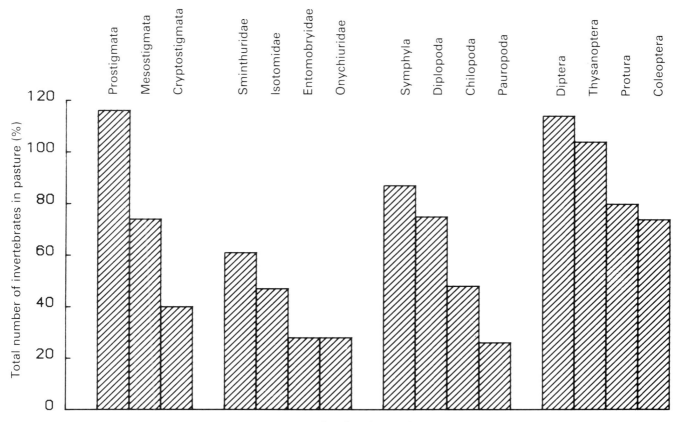

Figure 6. Effect of ploughing pasture on numbers of soil arthropods

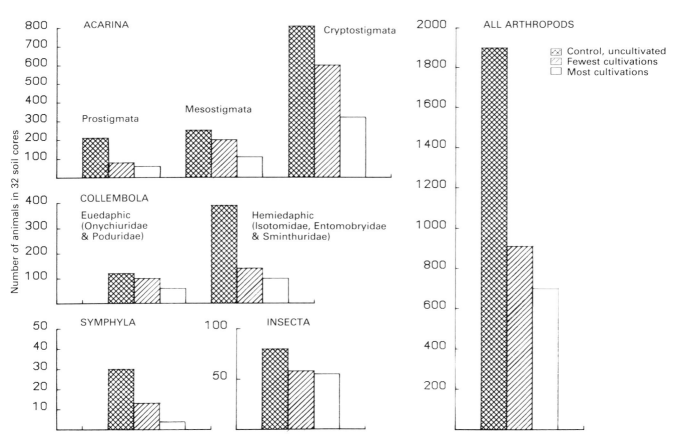

Figure 7. Effect of cultivating and re-seeding old pasture on soil arthropods

paraquat is used to kill all existing crops and vegetation, followed by sowing the next crop with a specially designed seed drill that causes little disturbance to the soil. This method is called direct drilling and has become increasingly popular in recent years in the UK, Europe, North America, and parts of Africa.

The effects of direct drilling on the soil fauna have been investigated extensively at Rothamsted in 6 specially designed field experiments, in 6 experiments laid down by MAFF, and in 14 fields on a large farm in Sussex. Populations of most groups of invertebrates were much larger in plots or fields that had been direct drilled than in those that were ploughed. Numbers in plots that were cultivated only shallowly with a chisel plough were closer to those in direct drilled plots than those in ploughed plots. Direct drilling particularly favoured populations of those invertebrates that contribute to the breakdown of plant organic matter, and these animals become increasingly important in soil which has not been ploughed. Attacks by some pests, such as wireworms, leatherjackets and some other insects, particularly slugs, tended to be considerably greater in direct drilled plots than in ploughed ones.

When soil is not ploughed, invertebrates, and particularly earthworms, are the main agents in maintaining soil structure, aeration and drainage. Earthworms can turn over very large quantities of soil annually and are the animals which take down organic matter from the soil surface and mix it into the lower layers of soil. The effects of drilling the same fields for 8 consecutive years were studied on 3 sites by Edwards and Lofty (1975b, 1982) (Figure 8). They showed that earthworm populations were between 17 and 37 times greater in direct drilled than in ploughed plots after 8 years of both treatments. Populations in chisel ploughed plots were intermediate between those in ploughed and direct plots. The differences were greatest for the deep burrowing species of earthworms, *Lumbricus terrestris* and *Allolobophora longa*, probably because they live in permanent burrows. However, even with continuous direct drilling, there was still a tendency for earthworm populations to decrease with time, probably because the amount of organic matter in the soil falls off after repeated direct drilling, without the plough to take the organic matter down into the soil. Inoculating earthworms into soils with sparse natural populations (although direct drilled for a number of years) increased yields of cereals significantly (Edwards & Lofty 1980).

There seems little doubt that, if the trend to less cultivation continues, the importance of the soil fauna in maintaining soil fertility will become crucial. There is an urgent need for more research of the kind that so far has been confined to the work at Rothamsted.

5 Effects of straw burning
Since 1970, the practice of burning the stubble and surplus straw in cereal fields has increased greatly in

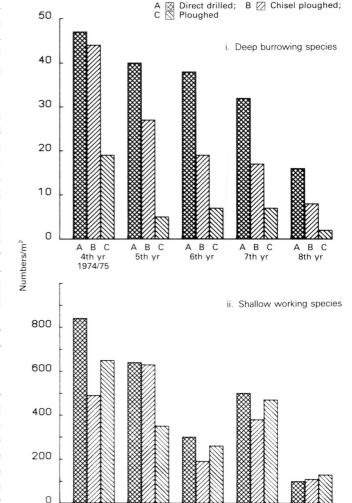

Figure 8. Effects of long-term cultivations on earthworm populations—Boxworth. (i) Deep burrowing species; (ii) shallow working species

the UK. In most years, straw on about 1.2M ha, or about one half of the total, is burned in England and Wales (Vickerman 1974). Considering the general public concern and the extensive publicity and discussion that have occurred about straw burning, there has been surprisingly little research into its ecological effects.

In 2 long-term field experiments at Rothamsted, the effects of straw burning on the soil fauna were compared with those of other methods of straw disposal. Four treatments were compared: (i) baling and removal, (ii) spreading straw evenly over the field, (iii) burning straw spread in this way, and (iv) burning straw where it fell in the stubble rows (Edwards & Lofty 1979a, b) (Figure 9). The burning seemed to have little effect on those invertebrates that spend all their lives in soil. The flame passed rapidly over the surface and did not heat the soil sufficiently to kill invertebrates living in the surface soil. However, there were very drastic effects on the surface living fauna, particularly

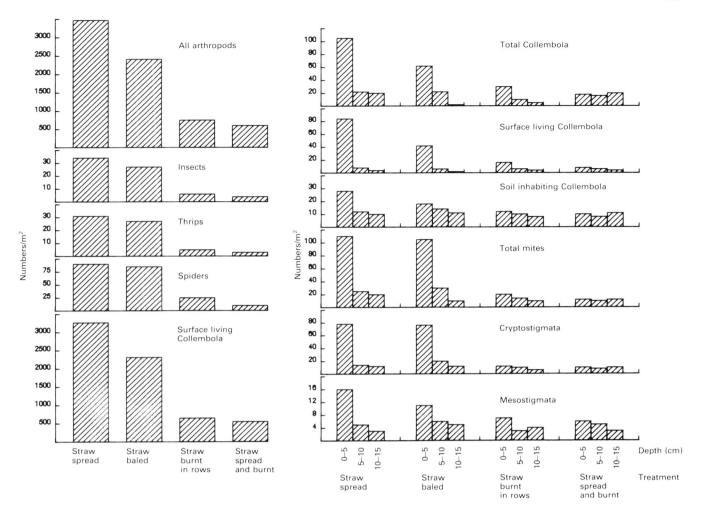

Figure 9. Vertical distribution of soil micro-arthropods 3 months after straw removal (soil samples)

some mites, springtails, spiders, millipedes and beetles. Moreover, these animals took some time to recover their numbers because the straw provided an effective refuge or habitat for them.

The greatest effect of straw burning on the soil fauna was indirect and depends upon the gradual decrease in availability of organic matter in fields burnt off repeatedly. Although there was no obvious direct effect of burning on populations of earthworms, the removal of straw has drastic effects on populations of the deep burrowing species such as *Lumbricus terrestris*, which was virtually eliminated by repeated burning in one experiment (Figure 10). The changed organic matter seemed to have little effect on the shallow working species of earthworms such as *Allolobophora chlorotica* and *A. caliginosa*.

Considerably more research would be needed to clarify all the effects of straw burning on the diverse forms of invertebrates with greatly different habits that live in agricultural soils.

6 Effects of crop rotations
Since the Second World War, there has been an increasing trend to shorter and simpler rotations of crops, and even towards the continuous growing of a single crop, particularly a cereal. There is virtually no information on how different crop rotations influence populations of soil inhabiting invertebrates. Only for pests such as nematodes do we have much idea of how populations of a particular pest build up when a crop is grown in a close rotation or in monoculture. Another example is the establishment of pygmy mangold beetle when sugar beet is grown in consecutive years. In a pilot study at Rothamsted, it was shown that the continuous growing of cereals tended to favour increases in the soil fauna as a whole, more than growing root crops or legumes.

Our lack of knowledge on the effects of monoculture on the soil fauna is unfortunate. If this practice continues and becomes more common, it is important to know (i) whether it encourages the build-up of pest populations more than that of their parasites and predators, and (ii) how populations of those invertebrates that influence the turnover of organic matter are affected.

7 Conclusions
Considering the many different changes in agricultural practices during the last 4 decades, there is a surprising dearth of information as to how these changes have affected the soil fauna that play such

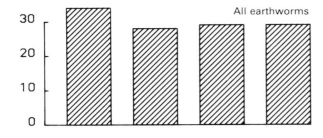

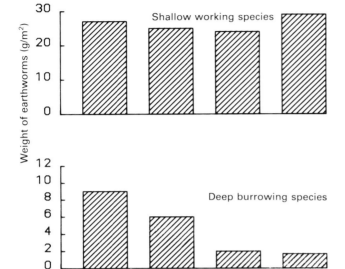

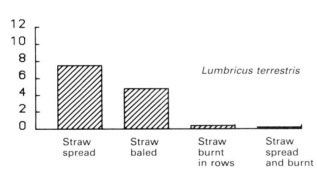

Figure 10. Biomass of earthworms 4 months after the third successive year of straw removal

important roles both as crop pests and in maintaining soil fertility. Probably this lack of research reflects our lack of fundamental knowledge of soil biological processes and of the ecology of soil organisms. The most important area for research seems to be studies into how different forms of organic matter affect the soil fauna. With this fundamental knowledge, it would be much easier to predict how existing and future changes in agricultural practice might affect this group of animals.

8 Summary
Agricultural practice has changed greatly in the last 50 years and some of the changes favour soil organisms, but, as many of them decrease the amounts of organic matter in soil, the overall tendency is for lower populations.

Fertilizers
With intensification of agriculture, there has been a drastic change from the use of organic to inorganic fertilizers. This change has tended to decrease the diversity and size of populations of most groups of soil invertebrates, particularly earthworms. There is some evidence of a compensatory effect, as increased crop yields tend to leave more plant residues behind to provide food for soil invertebrates.

Pesticides
Since the Second World War, increasing amounts of synthetic pesticides have been used. Herbicides have little direct effect on soil invertebrates, but influence the availability of organic matter. Except for the carbendazim-based compounds, fungicides are not toxic to invertebrates but may influence microbial populations. Insecticides tend to upset the delicate balance between groups of invertebrates and create upsurges in populations of some species. Organochlorine insecticides are not very toxic to soil invertebrates, but tend to depress overall populations. Organophosphate insecticides are more selectively toxic, depressing populations of some invertebrates at the expense of others. Carbamates are more harmful to most groups of invertebrates. Contact and fumigant nematicides have drastic effects on all species from which they may take more than a year to recover.

Cultivations
With the current trend towards less cultivation, ranging through rotovation, deep ploughing, subsoiling, shallow ploughing, chisel ploughing to direct drilling with zero cultivation, there is a strong tendency for the decreased cultivations to favour populations of most invertebrates. Numbers may be several times larger in direct drilled than in deep ploughed soil. With less cultivation, there tends to be a greater stratification of the soil fauna.

Straw burning
About 50% of UK cereal straw is burnt in the field, either left in rows or spread. The actual burning usually has little effect other than on surface living invertebrates, but populations of invertebrates are decreased because of the decrease in available organic matter.

Rotations
The trend from diverse rotations towards monoculture has been very marked in recent years. Different crops influence populations of soil invertebrates in different ways, so the effects of complex rotations are difficult to assess. However, with monoculture or limited rotations, a predominance of cereals tends to favour soil invertebrate populations, whereas root crops tend to be associated with smaller numbers.

Precision drilling
The accurate drilling of crops such as sugar beet or vegetables tends to obviate the need for singling and leaves less plant residues available as food for soil invertebrates.

Needs for further research

There has not been extensive research into the effects of agricultural practices on soil organisms. Probably, this reflects our lack of fundamental knowledge of soil biological processes and the ecology of soil organisms; moreover, research in this field is laborious and time-consuming. The first research priority is support for fundamental work on soil biology, with particular reference to agriculture. An important area of research which is directly or indirectly involved with agricultural practices is the study of the influence of different kinds of organic matter on populations of soil organisms in agricultural soils.

9 References

Abrahamsen, G. 1970. Forest fertilization and the soil fauna. *Tidsskr. Skogbr.*, **78**, 296-303. (In Finnish).

Artemjeva, T.I & Tatilova, F.G. 1975. Soil microfauna changes under the influence of various fertilizers. In: *Progress in soil zoology*, edited by J. Vanek, 463-467. Hague: Junk.

Axelsson, B., Lohm, U., Lundkvist, H., Persson, T., Skoglund, J. & Wiren, A. 1973. Effects of nitrogen fertilization on the abundance of soil fauna populations in a Scots pine stand. *Rapp. Uppsatser Inst. Växtekologi Marklara*, no. 14.

Cotton, D.C.F. & Curry, J.P. 1980. The effects of cattle and pig slurry fertilizers on earthworms (Oligochaeta, Lumbricidae) in grassland managed for silage production. *Pedobiologia*, **20**, 181-188.

Curry, J.P. 1976. Some effects of animal manures on earthworms in grassland. *Pedobiologia*, **16**, 425-438.

Edwards, C.A. 1970. Effects of herbicides on soil fauna. *Proc. Br. Weed Control Conf., 10th*, 1052-1061.

Edwards, C.A. 1975. Effects of direct drilling on the soil fauna. *Outl. Agric.*, **8**, 243-244.

Edwards, C.A. 1978. Pesticides and the microfauna of soil and water. In: *Pesticide microbiology*, edited by I.R. Hill & S.J.L. Wright, 603-622. London: Academic Press.

Edwards, C.A. & Lofty, J.R. 1969. The influence of agricultural practice on soil micro-arthropod populations. In: *The soil ecosystem*, edited by J.G. Sheals, 237-247. London: Systematics Association.

Edwards, C.A. & Lofty, J.R. 1975a. The invertebrate fauna of the Park Grass Plots. I. Soil fauna. *Rep. Rothamsted exp. Stn 1974*, **2**, 133-154.

Edwards, C.A. & Lofty, J.R. 1975b. The influence of cultivation on soil animal populations. In: *Progress in soil zoology*, edited by J. Vanek, 399-407. Hague: Junk.

Edwards, C.A. & Lofty, J.R. 1977. The influence of invertebrates on root growth of crops with minimal or zero cultivation. In: *Soil organisms as components of ecosystem*, edited by U. Lohm & T. Persson, 348-356. (Ecological bulletin no. 25). Stockholm: Swedish Natural Science Research Council.

Edwards, C.A. & Lofty, J.R. 1979a. Effects of straw burning on the soil fauna. *Papers, Conf. Straw Utilization, 4th, Oxford, 1978*, 45-51.

Edwards, C.A. & Lofty, J.R. 1979b. The effects of straw residues and their disposal on the soil fauna. In: *Straw decay and its effect on disposal and utilization*, edited by J. Grossbard, 37-44. Chichester: Wiley.

Edwards, C.A. & Lofty, J.R. 1980. Effects of earthworm inoculation upon the root growth of direct drilled cereals. *J. appl. Ecol.*, **17**, 533-543.

Edwards, C.A. & Lofty, J.R. 1982. Nitrogenous fertilizers and earthworm populations in agricultural soils. *Soil. Biol. Biochem.*, **14**, 515-521.

Edwards, C.A. & Thompson, A.R. 1973. Pesticides and the soil fauna. *Residue Rev.*, **45**, 1-79.

Edwards, C.A., Butler, C.G. & Lofty, J.R. 1976. The invertebrate fauna of the Park Grass Plots. II: Surface fauna. *Rep. Rothamsted exp. Stn, 1975*, **2**, 63-89.

Franz, H. 1953. Der Einfluss verschiedener Düngungsmassnahmen auf die Bodenfauna. *Angew. PflSoziol.*, **11**, 1-50.

Hrynuik, J. 1958. Wplyw wieloletniego nawozenia na dorbna faune glebowa. *Roczniki glebozn.*, **7**, 231-234.

Huhta, V., Matli, N. & Valpas, A. 1967. Effect of silvicultural practices upon arthropod, annelid and nematode populations in a coniferous soil. *Ann. zool. fenn.*, **4**, 87-143.

Huhta, V., Matli, N. & Valpas, A. 1969. Further notes on the effect of silvicultural practices upon the fauna of coniferous forest soil. *Ann. zool. fenn.*, **6**, 327-334.

Madge, D.S. 1981. Influence of agricultural practice on soil invertebrate animals. In: *Biological husbandry*, edited by B. Stonehouse, 79-98. London: Butterworths.

Marshall, V.G. 1977. *Effects of manures and fertilizers on soil fauna: a review.* (Special publication no. 3). Harpenden: Commonwealth Bureau of Soils.

Mayer-Krapoll, H. 1963. Der Einfluss einer Düngung mit Handelsdüngemitteln auf die Kleinlebewelt forstlich genutzer Boden. *Phosphorsäure*, **23**, 179-205.

Morris, H.M. 1922. The insect and other invertebrate fauna of arable land at Rothamsted. *Ann. appl. Biol.*, **9**, 282-305.

Morris, H.M. 1927. The insect and other invertebrate fauna of arable land at Rothamsted. *Ann. appl. Biol.*, **14**, 422-464.

Muller, G. 1957. Prüfung der Beziehungen zwischen mineralischer Düngung und Bodenleben. *Dt. Landwirt.*, **8**, 24-31.

Royal Commission on Environmental Pollution. 1979. *Seventh report: Agriculture and pollution.* London: HMSO.

Sauerlandt, W. & Marzusch-Trappmann, M. 1962. Einige Probleme der biologischen Untersuchung der Ackerboden. *Z. Pfl-Ernähr. Düng. Bodenk.*, **97**, 216-224.

Thompson, A.R. & Edwards, C.A. 1974. Effects of pesticides on nontarget invertebrates in freshwater and soil. In: *Pesticides in soil and water*, edited by W.D. Guenzi, 341-386. Madison, Wis: Soil Science Society of America.

Vickerman, G.P. 1974. The effects of strawburning on invertebrates. In: *Strawburning and its effect on wildlife*, 7-11. Fordingbridge: Game Conservancy.

The environmental implications of current pesticide usage on cereals

P I STANLEY* & A R HARDY†
*Ministry of Agriculture, Fisheries and Food, Slough
†Ministry of Agriculture, Fisheries and Food, Tolworth

1 Introduction

The scale of cereal production in the UK and the increasing use of pesticides on cereals make it important that the environmental implications of the current cereal production systems are thoroughly investigated and understood. Pesticides may have direct effects on wildlife by primary poisoning, or indirect effects by, for instance, affecting the food supply of a species. This paper discusses the potential for the current pesticide usage on cereals to cause indirect effects on the 'pest' and 'beneficial' arthropod species associated with cereal crops. The direct effects on wildlife of pesticides used on cereal crops and, in particular, of the use of cereal seed treatments are reviewed elsewhere (Hardy & Stanley 1984).

In 1983, cereal crops in the United Kingdom accounted for approximately 4M ha of the total tillage of 5.1M ha (MAFF 1983). The total area of wheat planted was a record 1.7M ha. The area of barley planted was 2.1M ha; this figure represents a small decrease from the area planted in recent years, but the trend towards winter barley has continued with, for the first time, more barley being sown in the autumn than in the spring.

Since the late 1940s, the average yield of winter wheat has risen from just over 2 tonnes/ha to approximately 4.5 t/ha in the mid-1970s (Gough 1977). This increase was achieved through changes in the crop production systems, including the development of high yielding and disease resistant varieties and the increasing use of fertilizers and pesticides.

When considering the environmental implications of pesticide usage, it is artificial to isolate the effects of pesticide usage from the overall effect of the farming system, as the pesticide usage and farming practices are interdependent. For instance, the availability of effective herbicides has allowed reduced cultivation and zero tillage to be practised which, although advantageous in reducing soil erosion, moisture loss and soil compaction, may increase the disease and pest risks from soil-borne or crop debris-borne pathogens, and so increase the need for pesticides.

It is also necessary to consider the characteristics of the cereal ecosystem when assessing the environmental effects of pesticide usage and, in particular, when considering the indirect effects of pesticides on the 'pest' and 'beneficial' arthropods associated with cereal crops. There is a fundamental difference between the ecosystems represented by perennial crops typified by apple orchards and annual crops such as cereals (Way 1978). Characteristic pest species have evolved to exploit the range of different ecosystems of which the extremes are represented by the stable apple orchard habitat and the notably unstable annual cereal ecosystem. It is the difference in the ecology of these pest species that demands and allows different pest control strategies to be employed in these contrasting crops.

The perennial crop habitat contains a range of long-lived plant species and insects which have limited ability for multiplication and movement. It is recognized that the repeated application of pesticides to perennial crops, particularly insecticides, within a growing season can seriously disturb the arthropod relationships and lead to pest resurgence. The heavy pesticide usage in the past on crops such as cotton and in apple orchards led to serious pest resurgence. Ripper (1956) summarized the information available on the effects of pesticides on arthropod populations and cited many examples where the use of pesticides on perennial crops had created pest problems by reducing the populations of predatory mites and bugs which were the natural enemies of species which then achieved pest status.

In contrast to the orchard ecosystem, agricultural practices for growing cereals provide a barren habitat suitable for invasive species of plants and insects to colonize. The bare soil is receptive to the numerous and widely distributed seeds from 'weed' plants, and the stark monoculture crop is an easy target for plant feeding insects such as aphids. The invading insects themselves are preyed upon by similarly invasive predatory species. The non-crop plant species and the invasive insects have a number of features in common, including rapid multiplication and movement into and out of crops which allows rapid colonization. The plant feeding insect species have a short-lived and mobile life style and frequently cause serious damage to host crop plants. The characteristics of the species present in cereal crops suggest that it would be inherently more difficult for pesticide usage on cereals to lead to pest resurgence problems than in perennial crops.

There is no published evidence from the UK or elsewhere that pesticide usage on cereals has yet caused significant indirect effects on the arthropod predator-prey relationships resulting in pest resurgence. The demonstration of such an effect would be technically difficult, unless it occurred on a large scale. However, the above account of the differences between the cereal ecosystem and the perennial crop ecosystem is over-simplified and does not take into account factors such as the scale of the cropping area being treated with pesticides or the effect of the increasing routine use of some pesticides on cereals. Therefore, the major research question concerning the use of pesticides on cereals that requires answering is whether the current cereal production systems which rely to a considerable extent on pesticide usage could lead to long-term indirect problems involving, for instance, pest resurgence. Such problems would have serious consequences for both agriculture and conservation.

2 Cereal growing systems and pesticide usage in the United Kingdom

In this paper, we consider the growing system for winter wheat and the possible environmental effects of pesticides used on winter wheat. This emphasis on winter wheat is a reflection of the large area grown and the tendency for winter wheat in the past to receive more pesticide applications than other cereal crops. However, the change to autumn rather than spring sown barley has resulted in the barley growing system becoming similar to the winter wheat system. Pesticide use on winter barley now resembles the use on winter wheat.

The outstanding feature of winter wheat production has been the continuing annual increase in yield of about 2% since 1945, following many decades when yields remained relatively static (MAFF 1968). It is suggested that approximately half of this increase in yield has been due to the effect of improved varieties, and the remainder to a range of innovations including improvements in the application and timing of fertilizers and the exploitation of pesticides (MAFF 1980). The introductions of various pesticide treatments have contributed to the increase in yield. The first increase in yield resulted from the introduction in the late 1930s of organomercurial seed treatments to control a wide range of seed-borne diseases. The next major advances came in the 1950s, with the large-scale use of gamma-HCH to control wireworms and organochlorine insecticide seed treatments to control the wheat bulb fly (Gough & Woods 1954). Blackman and Roberts (1950) demonstrated that the use of herbicides to control weeds in wheat crops could increase the yield by over 20%, and, since that time, the use of herbicides to control broad-leaved weeds has been routine. In recent years, selective herbicides have been introduced to combat serious infestations of grass weeds and wild-oats.

The MAFF Pesticide Survey Group, since its inception in 1965, has carried out surveys of pesticide use on agricultural and horticultural crops generally through personal visits to growers to collect data. The use of pesticides on cereals was studied in 1974 and 1977, and the information for winter wheat is presented in Table 1. These data represent the pattern of pesticide use over the total area planted and demonstrate the average pesticide use on winter wheat. However, the use of pesticides on winter wheat varies from minimal applications to crops grown on land that is marginal for winter wheat where the farmer uses low inputs and is satisfied with relatively lower yields, to the more intensive applications by farmers on high grade land aiming for yields in excess of 10 t/ha. This range of pesticides usage is shown in Table 2, which provides information from the 1977 survey on the number of chemicals and spray rounds applied to winter wheat crops. Table 1 shows that the average pesticide use on winter wheat in 1977 was approximately 4 applications per crop, but Table 2 indicates that, whilst 47% of the crop received 4 or less chemicals and 86% received 8 or less chemicals, a small proportion (13%) received between 9 and 18 different chemicals. The larger number of chemicals applied to a small percentage of the crop generally resulted from the 'spot treatment' of parts of fields with a range of herbicides to combat local serious infestations of certain weeds.

Table 1. The use of pesticides on winter wheat in England and Wales
(Source: Sly 1977; Steed et al. 1979)

	1974	1977
Total area grown ('000 ha)	1139	1025
Area of crop treated ('000 ha)		
Insecticides	108	518
Insecticide seed treatments	758	555
Fungicides	94	377
Fungicide seed treatments	1066	912
Herbicides	1793	1647
Molluscicides	59	28

Table 2. The number of (i) spray rounds and (ii) chemicals applied to winter wheat in 1977
(Source: Steed et al. 1979)

i.	Number of spray rounds										
	0	1	2	3	4	5	6	7	8	9	10–14
% of crop	—	2	10	18	23	17	8	5	6	9	8

ii.	Number of different chemicals							
	0	1–2	3–4	5–6	7–8	9–10	11–13	18
% of crop	—	9	38	26	13	8	3	2

There have undoubtedly been changes in the use of pesticides on cereals since the 1977 survey, and the Pesticide Survey Group has recently conducted another survey, but the results will not be available until the spring of 1984. An indication of pesticide use on cereals during the crop year 1981-82 is provided by the survey information based on pesticide sales published by the British Agrochemicals Association (BAA 1983). This survey indicates that, whilst the average use of herbicides and insecticides has remained relatively constant, there has been a 5-fold increase in the use of foliar application of fungicides.

The increase in area of winter wheat and winter barley grown and the substantial increase in pesticide usage reflect the economics of grain production in recent years. With the greatly increased prices for cereals, it is now possible for farmers to achieve satisfactory profits on these crops (Nix 1978), and this has provided the incentive to increase yields. However, with the prospect of satisfactory profit margins and the commitment of increased inputs, farmers are increasingly prepared to exploit pesticides to protect the crop and insure the financial return.

The winter wheat production system is still evolving, and there has been a number of recent changes in husbandry which have influenced the need to control pests, diseases and weeds. A major factor that has influenced pesticide usage has been the earlier drilling of winter wheat in the autumn. Early drilling has a number of advantages. In particular, it can lead to higher yields, it allows the plants to be well established before adverse weather conditions are likely to occur, and it also avoids the need for the farmer to drill the crop later in the autumn when the soil condition may prevent him from cultivating the land. The earlier sowing results in the crop being more vulnerable to slug damage in early autumn, to autumn attack by aphids which may transmit barley yellow dwarf virus (BYDV), and to damage during the early spring by the yellow cereal fly.

Winter wheat is also susceptible to damage from the wheat bulb fly early in spring, from various aphids during the summer, and from wireworms and leatherjackets. Pesticide treatments are available to combat all these pests. Early sowing in autumn also favours the introduction and development of diseases. Mildews and rusts can survive on volunteers from a previous crop and infect the newly emerged, early sown crop. The warm weather in early autumn also favours the development and spread of most leaf diseases. The recent substantial increases in the rates of nitrogen fertilizer applied to winter wheat which have contributed to increases in yield have also increased the susceptibility of the crop to leaf diseases. The use of varietal resistance is still the most effective means of minimizing crop loss through diseases, but a wide range of fungicides is now available to combat the individual diseases and fungicide use has substantially increased in recent years. A large area of winter wheat and winter barley now receives foliar fungicide applications in addition to fungicide seed treatments. Farmers apply fungicides either on the basis of regular inspection of the crop to detect the onset of disease, or on a routine prophylactic basis, or by a combination of both approaches.

Routine prophylactic applications have been increasingly adopted by farmers, especially in winter wheat and winter barley, to simplify disease control in their crop management system. The overall use of herbicides has not changed dramatically in recent years, but a number of new selective herbicides has been introduced to combat the increasingly serious infestations of grass weeds and wild-oats in cereal crops. Another innovation has been the use of a herbicide application shortly before harvest to combat weeds in the standing crop. This simplifies weed control following harvest and allows earlier drilling of the next crop.

3 Current research on environmental effects of pesticides
The financial benefits of using pesticides on cereals can be clearly demonstrated (Graham-Bryce *et al.* 1980), but these must be considered in relation to any adverse environmental effects. Potential adverse effects include the development of resistance to pesticides by pest species and damage to non-target organisms in the crop, and particularly to predators, parasites, and pathogens that could exert some control over the populations of pest species.

Although, intrinsically, the use of insecticides on cereals could lead to the development of resistance in, for instance, aphid species, there is no evidence that this is a current problem. Workers are aware of the possibility and a range of monitoring studies is in progress to detect the occurrence of resistance. The development of fungal resistance to fungicides has been encountered and fungicide programmes are now designed to discourage the development of resistant strains. For instance, the application of the same or related fungicides in autumn and spring to control the eyespot fungus is discouraged as it favours the development of resistant strains.

The potential for damage to non-target organisms, with a resultant loss in biological control, has been considered since the early demonstration of the effects of pesticides in reducing biological control in perennial crops such as apple orchards. Cereal crops in the United Kingdom contain a rich flora and fauna, with almost infinite possibilities for interdependence between the plant and arthropod species present. There may be hundreds of species of predatory insects which could, for example, influence aphid populations. Aphid predators include aphid-specific predators such as the ladybird and hoverfly, whose populations tend to increase when aphids occur in large numbers, and also many species of polyphagous predator that will prey on aphids but also take other prey. It is likely that these polyphagous predators, which include many spiders, mites, beetles, beetle larvae, and earwigs, could influence aphid populations in the cereal crop even when the aphid density is low. However, the aphid-specific predators probably only exploit the excessive numbers of aphids present in aphid outbreaks.

Pesticide use can influence predators in a range of direct and indirect actions. Croft and Brown (1975) reviewed the direct response of arthropod natural enemies to insecticides, but it must be appreciated that fungicides and herbicides can also have a major influence on these species. Fungicides could affect the population level and reproduction of some polyphagous predators either by direct toxicity or through removal of the fungal food supply (Vickerman & Sotherton in press), and could also decrease the action of pathogenic fungi on aphids and other pests. Herbicides, by removing weeds found in cereal crops, can influence the populations of species that are dependent on particular weed species at some stage in their life cycle. It can be appreciated that establishing the influence of pesticide use in cereals on the level of biological control exerted on pest species is remarkably difficult, and requires the commitment of substantial resources to multidisciplinary and long-term studies.

Although there have been several studies of the effects of pesticide use on particular insect predator/pest relationships in field crops (Dunning et al. 1975), the only study encompassing the whole cereal ecosystem is the Joint Cereal Ecosystem Project which has been conducted since 1970 by the Game Conservancy, supported by the Agricultural Research Council (Potts 1977). This study started as a monitoring project to investigate the population levels in cereal crops of the insect prey items which are necessary food items of young partridges, if chick survival is to be adequate to maintain populations. However, the study has widened to become an extensive monitoring study of the insect fauna of cereals. Since 1970, cereal fields in the 62 km^2 west Sussex study area have been sampled each year in the third week of June using a portable Dietrick vacuum insect sampler (D-vac). On average, about 100 cereal fields have been sampled each year, and the insects present in the samples have been identified and counted. In addition, since 1972, D-vac samples have been taken at intervals of 7-10 days between March and October from cereal fields on 3 farms in the study area to provide more detailed information on the timing and duration of increases in the insect fauna.

The study has indicated changes in the abundance of individual species or groups in the study area and, in particular, there has been a downward trend in the insects preferred by the partridge chicks (Potts 1977; Vickerman 1982) and in the abundance of various polyphagous predators (Vickerman 1980). The insects preferred by partridge chicks tend to be associated with the weeds found in cereals, and over the study period the weeds have declined in abundance through the use of herbicides and different husbandry techniques.

This pioneering study is yielding information on the relative abundance of a large number of insects in cereals. Although trends in abundance have been identified over the study period, the significance of changes is not yet known, particularly as it is necessary to isolate declines due to the farming system from cyclical changes in insect populations.

Assessing the causes of any changes in abundance on the study area is complicated by the changes in the farming system that have taken place over the study period. For example, the cropping pattern has changed with more winter wheat and winter barley; husbandry techniques have changed with more direct drilling and less under-sowing of cereal crops; and there have been marked changes in pesticide use. In particular, there has been a substantial increase in the use of foliar fungicides; new herbicides have been introduced to control grass weeds; aphicides were used on a large scale for the first time in 1975, 1976 and 1977; and the use of chemicals to control slugs and leatherjackets has increased. The Joint Cereal Ecosystem Project has stimulated a range of subsidiary research projects, including studies on the effects of pesticides on insects (Sotherton 1982a; Vickerman 1977), on the ecology of individual species in the insect fauna (Sotherton 1980, 1982b), and on the value of field boundaries and hedgerows as over-wintering sites for predatory insects (Sotherton 1983).

Serious infestations of the grain aphid Sitobion avenae developed in cereals in 1975, 1976 and 1977, and led to the large-scale use of aphicides. Although similar infestations have not been experienced during the last 6 years, the problems in 1975, 1976 and 1977 stimulated research into whether decline in biological control had contributed to the infestations. Chambers et al. (1983) monitored numbers of cereal aphids inside and outside cages designed to exclude aphid-specific predators. This study, which was conducted in a field of winter wheat in 1976, 1977 and 1979, indicated that peak aphid numbers in the cages were higher than outside and occurred at a different time. Although it was not possible to rule out a subtle effect of the caging technique itself on the aphid numbers, it was concluded that predation was likely to be the major cause of the differences observed in aphid numbers within and outside the cages.

The role of predators in controlling cereal aphid populations is being investigated using a computer simulation model which will utilize the cereal aphid data collected during the Joint Cereal Ecosystem Project (Carter 1983). Unravelling the role of predators, particularly polyphagous predators, in controlling cereal aphid population is a central requirement if we are to understand the significance of the effect of pesticides on non-target insects. However, the incidence of aphid outbreaks will be influenced by a range of factors in addition to pesticide usage. These factors include the greater vulnerability of the cereal plants both intrinsically and through the effects of fertilizers, and the larger areas of winter wheat and winter barley being grown which will influence the development of infestations.

The results of the *Joint Cereal Ecosystem Project,* the pattern of pesticide use on cereals in recent years, and the recognition by the Agricultural and Development Advisory Service (ADAS) of the desirability of encouraging the sensible use of pesticides to reinforce rather than replace natural control processes led ADAS to embark on a multidisciplinary project at the end of 1981 to compare both the economic and ecological implications of different pesticide use strategies in intensive winter wheat production. Farmers will only adopt systems using lower pesticide inputs if it can be demonstrated that the systems are financially and agriculturally viable in both the short and long term. An important part of the project is to compare the total cost and the practical management and operational problems of maintaining the different pesticide use strategies.

The 3 pesticide use strategies that will be studied are a high *insurance* pesticide input, involving the routine use of a range of pesticides but similar to the input adopted by farmers seeking maximum yields; a *reduced* pesticide input, where the decision to apply a pesticide is made on the basis of regular pest and disease monitoring by ADAS regional staff, and weed assessment by staff of the Weed Research Organization (WRO) to determine when damage thresholds are exceeded; and an *integrated* approach, where, again, the pesticide use will be based on monitoring to determine pest, disease and weed levels in relation to thresholds. In addition, changes in husbandry will be exploited to minimize the need for pesticide applications.

As an important objective is to isolate the effect of varying the pesticide input from other farming operations and influences, the husbandry operations will be identical, as far as possible, on the insurance and reduced treatment areas. The study, which will continue for 7 years, occupies 133 ha of the Boxworth Experimental Husbandry Farm (EHF) in Cambridgeshire. During the first 2 years, all 3 treatment areas received the pesticide regimes currently employed on the farm, and the flora and fauna both within the crops and in adjacent hedgerows and non-crop habitats have been monitored to establish base-line data on the populations. In addition, this period has been used to test the husbandry operations which are required by the project.

Ideally, farming operations on the treatment areas would be carried out simultaneously. However, this is not possible, and therefore individual fields in each area have been matched with a corresponding field in each of the other 2 areas; husbandry operations, including drilling, harvest, straw disposal, etc, will be completed on each group of 3 fields, before moving to the next group of 3 fields. This approach will result in there being at least one field in each area where the effect of variations in the timing of husbandry operations will not be important.

The contrasting pesticide regimes on the 3 areas commenced in the autumn of 1983 and will continue for 5 years. As far as is practicable, the study areas will be maintained in winter wheat for the duration of the study, but oilseed rape will feature as a break crop on a 5-year rotation. One field in each of the 3 areas will be kept in continuous winter wheat. The study is being conducted in a practical farm situation and, as the practices and husbandry techniques adopted are generally representative of commercial cereal growing, the experimental design does not include an area receiving no pesticide application.

The *insurance* treatment area consists of 4 fields occupying 67 ha which will receive a routine proramme of pesticides. This programme will include treatments to control slugs prior to drilling, fritfly at drilling, fritfly and aphids in the autumn, cereal and grass flies in winter and aphids in summer. Fungicides will be applied to control eyespot, *Septoria*, mildew, rusts, *Botrytis*, and *Alternaria*, according to crop. Herbicide treatments may include pre-sowing, early post-emergence, and spring applications of wide spectrum herbicides for broad-leaved weeds and grasses, a wild-oats herbicide and pre-harvest wide spectrum treatments.

Principally, the same pesticides will be used on the *reduced* area which consists of 3 fields occupying 45 ha. Each field in the reduced area will be considered independently and pesticides will only be applied if pests, diseases and weeds attain threshold levels.

The *integrated* area consists of 3 fields occupying 21 ha, and the treatment decisions will again depend on pests, diseases and weeds attaining threshold levels. Husbandry operations will be adopted that reduce the need for pesticides, and may include deep cultivation, later sowing date, and higher seed rate; in addition, the cereal variety will be selected on the basis of disease resistance rather than yield characteristics.

For each area, the cost of seeds, fertilizers and pesticides will be recorded and each agricultural operation will be costed. The time required by ADAS regional staff and WRO staff to monitor for pests, diseases and weeds (to provide the basic information on which pesticide application decisions will be taken) will also be included in the costs of the reduced and integrated areas. At harvest, the yield and quality of grain from each field will be determined. A replicated plot trial will be conducted on the insurance treatment area to compare the effects on yield of the insurance and reduced pesticide treatments and of a minimal pesticide treatment.

The environmental studies being conducted by research staff from ADAS, WRO and Cambridge and Southampton Universities have been designed to monitor as many taxonomic groups of flora and fauna as possible. Wide-ranging studies are being carried out by University staff, including a detailed investigation of the relationship between major cereal pests, particularly aphids, and their fungal parasites, parasitoids and predators. A second entomology project involves monitoring the abundance of a wide range of fauna, and aims to investigate the life histories and dynamics of important polyphagous predators. The 2 entomology projects will be complementary and will include sampling all the study fields and adjacent habitats throughout the year using vacuum sampling, pitfall trapping, and a range of other techniques. University staff are also studying the distribution, population dynamics, movement and feeding ecology of small mammals on the 3 study areas, and these studies will be closely linked to the entomology projects.

Monitoring studies of weed populations are being conducted by WRO staff. Each field will be surveyed in the summer using selected gridded co-ordinates to count the established population of major grass weeds and to measure the seed crop. Repeat surveys will be made in the late autumn and spring and detailed estimates of weed populations will also be made using transects running from the study fields into adjacent non-crop habitats.

ADAS staff are studying the feeding ecology and breeding success of resident insectivorous birds, and are also monitoring some taxonomic groups not covered by other studies. The chemical fate of selected pesticide applications will be followed in detail using chemical analysis to quantify the residue levels both in the crop and in adjacent habitat in order to interpret the results of the other monitoring studies.

4 Conclusions and research priorities

From first principles, it would appear to be desirable for decisions on pesticide use to be governed by the monitoring of the pests, diseases and weeds and the use of threshold levels. However, it must be appreciated that this approach will only be widely adopted if it can be demonstrated that it is financially and agriculturally viable. To reduce unnecessary pesticide applications and to improve the timing of essential applications, ADAS provides a weekly intelligence service on pests and diseases. Cereal pests and diseases are monitored throughout the growing season, and information on their incidence and severity is available from ADAS locally and also through the national press and the radio. The availability of this pest and disease monitoring intelligence helps the cereal farmer to make sensible and confident decisions on pesticide usage.

The *Joint Cereal Ecosystem Project* and the ADAS research programme at the Boxworth EHF are investigating the possible effects of current pesticide usage on non-target flora and fauna. It should be emphasized that both the development of improved pest and disease management programmes for cereals and the identification of the environmental implications of pesticide usage on cereals depend on a thorough knowledge of the basic ecology and dynamics of the various species present in the cereal ecosystem. At the present time, the ecology and population dynamics have only been documented for a small number of species, and there is a major research requirement for further detailed studies of species associated with the cereal crop. Detailed studies both of the biology and behaviour of individual species, including a life table approach to identify significant mortality at different developmental stages, and of the interactions between pests and predators/parasites are required under controlled conditions, where the effects of pesticides can be separated from the influences of other farming practices. In particular, further studies of polyphagous predators, which include many species of beetles, spiders, mites, earwigs, centipedes and harvestmen, would be valuable.

5 Summary

In 1983, cereal crops in the United Kingdom accounted for approximately 4M ha, out of a total tillage area of 5.1M ha, and the pattern of pesticide use on cereals makes it important that the environmental implications of the current cereal production systems are thoroughly investigated and understood. Recent developments in cereal production technology and pesticide usage are discussed in relation to the complete farming system. The major research priority identified is to establish whether the current cereal production system which relies to a considerable extent on pesticide usage could lead, in the long term, to indirect effects on the level of biological control in the cereal crop, and hence contribute to pest, disease and weed problems. Current research in the UK aimed at elucidating the environmental implications of pesticide use on cereals is discussed, and details of the recent research programme initiated by MAFF are presented.

6 References

Blackman, G.E. & Roberts, N.A. 1950. The control of annual weeds in winter wheat. *J. agric. Sci., Camb.,* **40,** 62-69.

British Agrochemicals Association. 1983. *Annual report and handbook 1982–83.* London: British Agrochemicals Ltd.

Carter, N. 1983. Modelling the effects of predators on cereal aphid populations. *Annu. Rev. Game Conservancy, 1982,* no. 14, 38-42.

Chambers, R.J., Sunderland, K.D., Wyatt, I.J. & Vickerman, G.P. 1983. The effects of predator exclusion and caging on cereal aphids in winter wheat. *J. appl. Ecol.,* **20,** 209-224.

Croft, B.A. & Brown, A.W.A. 1975. Responses of arthropod natural enemies to insecticides. *A. Rev. Ent.,* **20,** 285-335.

Dunning, R.A., Baker, N.N. & Windley, R.F. 1975. Carabids in sugar beet crops and their possible role as aphid predators. *Ann. appl. Biol.,* **80,** 125-128.

Gough, H.C. 1977. Pesticides on crops—some benefits and problems. In: *Ecological effects of pesticides,* edited by F.H. Perring & K. Mellanby, 7-26. (Linnean Society symposium series no. 5). London: Academic Press.

Gough, H.C. & Woods, A. 1954. Seed dressings for the control of wheat bulb fly. *Nature, Lond.,* **174,** 1151-1153.

Graham-Bryce, I.J., Hollomon, D.W. & Lewis, T. 1980. Pest and disease control in cereals: a research viewpoint. *Jl R. agric. Soc.*, **141**, 131-139.

Hardy, A.R. & Stanley, P.I. 1984. The impact of the commercial agricultural use of organophosphorus and carbamate pesticides on British wildlife. In: *Agriculture and the environment*, edited by D. Jenkins, 72-80. (ITE symposium no. 13). Cambridge: Institute of Terrestrial Ecology.

Ministry of Agriculture, Fisheries and Food. 1968. *A century of agricultural statistics: Great Britain 1866–1966.* London: HMSO.

Ministry of Agriculture, Fisheries and Food. 1980. *Winter wheat husbandry and growing systems.* (Booklet 2291). Pinner: MAFF.

Ministry of Agriculture, Fisheries and Food. 1983. *June 1983 agricultural returns for the United Kingdom.* (Press Notice no. 235). Pinner: MAFF.

Nix, J. 1978. *The economics of growing wheat and barley, 1977–80 and recent trends.* (Farm Business Unit, Occasional paper no. 1). Wye: Wye College, University of London.

Potts, G.R. 1977. Some effects of increasing the monoculture of cereals. In: *Origins of pest, parasite, disease and weed problems,* edited by J.M. Cherrett & G.R. Saga, 183-202. Oxford: Blackwell Scientific.

Ripper, W.E. 1956. Effects of pesticides on balance of arthropod populations. *A. Rev. Ent.*, **1**, 403-438.

Sly, J.M.A. 1977. *Review of usage of pesticides in agriculture and horticulture in England and Wales, 1965–1974.* (Pesticide Usage Survey report no. 8). Pinner: Ministry of Agriculture, Fisheries and Food.

Sotherton, N.W. 1980. *The ecology of* Gastrophysa polygoni *(L.) (Coleoptera: Chrysomelidae) in cereals.* PhD thesis, University of Southampton.

Sotherton, N.W. 1982a. Effects of herbicides on the chrysomelid beetle *Gastrophysa polygoni* (L.) in the laboratory and field. *Z. angew. Entomol.*, **94**, 446-451.

Sotherton, N.W. 1982b. Observations on the biology and ecology of a chrysomelid beetle *Gastrophysa polygoni* (L.) in cereal fields. *Ecol. Entomol.*, **7**, 197-206.

Sotherton, N.W. 1983. Field boundaries and beneficial insects. *Annu. Rev. Game Conservancy, 1982*, no. 14, 35-37.

Steed, J.M., Sly, J.M.A., Tucker, C.G. & Cutler, J.R. 1979. *Arable farm crops 1977.* (Pesticide Usage Survey report no. 18). Pinner: Ministry of Agriculture, Fisheries and Food.

Vickerman, G.P. 1977. The effects of foliar fungicides on some insect pests of cereals. *Proc. Br. Crop Prot. Conf. Pests Dis.*, **1**, 121-128.

Vickerman, G.P. 1980. Important changes in the numbers of insects in cereal fields. *Annu. Rev. Game Conservancy, 1979*, no. 11, 67-72.

Vickerman, G.P. 1982. Changes in the insect fauna of cereals. *Annu. Rev. Game Conservancy, 1981*, no. 13, 43-47.

Vickerman, G.P. & Sotherton, N.W. In press. Effects of some foliar fungicides on the chrysomelid beetle *Gastrophysa polygoni* (L). *Pestic. Sci.*

Way, M.J. 1978. Integrated pest control with special reference to orchard problems. *Rep. E. Malling Res. Stn, 1977*, 187-204.

The impact of the commercial agricultural use of organophosphorus and carbamate pesticides on British wildlife

A R HARDY* & P I STANLEY†
*Ministry of Agriculture, Fisheries and Food, Tolworth
†Ministry of Agriculture, Fisheries and Food, Slough

1 Introduction

Pesticide use has steadily increased in the UK over the last 25 years and has made a major contribution to increased agricultural production during this period. While the total home and export pesticide market in 1948 represented (at 1982 prices) some £70M, by 1982 this had risen to a total of £542M, with home pesticide sales equalling export sales (BAA 1983). During this period, there have been extensive changes in the range of pesticides and formulations used as new compounds and application techniques have been developed. At the same time, some older compounds which caused environmental problems were phased out and withdrawn.

Since 1957, the commercial introduction of agricultural pesticides into the United Kingdom has been controlled under the Pesticides Safety Precautions Scheme (PSPS) (MAFF 1979). Under this non-statutory agreement between the Government and the pesticide industry, safety of any pesticide formulation is assessed to the operator, to the consumer of treated crops or processed food, and to the environment. The approach to safety evalution adopted by the PSPS is a stepwise progression through a testing programme designed to demonstrate any potential hazards, to understand the underlying mechanism of toxic action, and to identify and assess any risks in relation to the intended use of the pesticide. Principles behind tests for environmental risk assessment are reviewed elsewhere (Bunyan & Stanley 1979; Stanley & Hardy 1983). Validated data are submitted by a manufacturing company to the PSPS for assessment and, when safety in use is demonstrated, a pesticide formulation is cleared for commercial use according to agreed label recommendations.

It is necessary to monitor the early years of commercial introduction of a new pesticide to provide reassurance that the predictions of environmental safety based on limited field experience are supported in wider use. In the UK, this monitoring is done by ADAS of MAFF which investigates any suspected poisoning of wildlife on farmland thought to involve pesticides. The results of investigations since 1964 form the basis of the current paper.

We exclude the deliberate mis-use of pesticides, including organophosphates and carbamates, which has been documented by Brown *et al.* (1977), Cadbury (1980) and Hamilton *et al.* (1981). This reprehensible and illegal use of toxic chemicals is chiefly aimed at killing wildlife species which conflict with game-rearing interests. It is non-selective and some 60 vertebrates have been recorded as victims (Cadbury 1980). In most cases, it is not considered to result in a significant impact on wildlife populations, except for the scarcer birds of prey, eg the red kite and golden eagle, where loss of individuals may have serious impact on small populations with low recruitment.

We distinguish between 'direct' effects, resulting from the immediate toxicity of a particular compound, and 'indirect' effects, normally arising from changes in habitat or food supply brought about by pesticides (Bunyan & Stanley 1983). This paper is principally concerned with 'direct' effects of pesticide use. (For a discussion of indirect effects, see Stanley & Hardy 1984.) The hazard to non-target wildlife from a pesticide depends both on the intrinsic toxicity of the compound and the degree of exposure in the field. The latter is determined by many factors, including the formulation and the method and timing of application. The impact of the commercial usage of organophosphorus and carbamate compounds is therefore reviewed according to formulation as the hazard varies fundamentally with the method of application. Most of the information on pesticide usage and wildlife incidents comes from England and Wales, but, where relevant, reference is made to information from elsewhere.

2 Pesticide usage

Since 1965, the MAFF Pesticides Survey Group has surveyed the use of pesticides in major agricultural and horticultural crops every 4-5 years. Some results from the last complete cycle of surveys are shown in Tables 1 and 2 to indicate the estimated annual usage during 1975-79 (Sly 1981).

Table 1. Annual usage of pesticides in agriculture and horticulture, England and Wales, 1975–79 (Source: Sly 1981)

	Treated area ('000 hectares)	Tonnes active ingredient
INSECTICIDES, MOLLUSCICIDES, ACARICIDES		
Organochlorines	146·3	165·9
Organophosphorus	976·1	534·1
Carbamates	509·5	314·0
Total	1718·3	1606·8
SEED TREATMENTS	3751·7	590·9
FUNGICIDES	2252·9	2336·1
HERBICIDES	7829·3	11145·4
DEFOLIANTS	41·1	8781·9
OTHERS (growth regulators, soil sterilants, fumigants)	203·2	1038·1
TOTAL	15798·3	25499·9

Herbicides and fungicides are the most widely used pesticides, but, from their intrinsic toxicity, insecticides have greater potential direct effects on non-target wildlife. Estimated usage figures for the periods 1971-74 and 1975-79 changed little in the overall level of organochlorine pesticide use. However, the organochlorine compounds now shown to have caused environmental problems have been or are being phased out and replaced by less persistent alternatives (see below). The use of organophosphorus compounds increased principally through applications to control aphids on cereals (Sly 1981). A 6-fold increase

Table 2. Annual usage of organophosphorus and carbamate pesticides in agriculture and horticulture, England and Wales 1975–79 (Source: Sly 1981)

		Treated area ('000 hectares)	Tonnes active ingredient
SEED TREATMENTS	Organophosphorus	86·8	19·4
	Carbamate	203·4	0·4
TOTAL SEED TREATMENTS		3752·7	590·9
SPRAYS	Organophosphorus	908·6	410·6*
	Carbamate	336·7	107·4
GRANULES	Organophosphorus	66·5	123·5
	Carbamate	130·9	197·3
SLUG PELLETS	Carbamate	41·9	9·2
TOTAL SPRAYS, GRANULES, PELLETS			
	Organophosphorus	975·1	534·1
	Carbamate	509·5	314·0
TOTAL PESTICIDE TREATED AREA		15798·3	25499·9

*Available usage figures do not distinguish between granular and spray applications of chlorpyrifos and chlorfenvinphos

in area treated with other insecticides, acaricides and molluscicides reflects the introduction and wide use of carbamate compounds, chiefly pirimicarb, aldicarb and methiocarb. The more recent agricultural development of the synthetic pyrethroids has also contributed to increased insecticide use.

Forty per cent of the annual tonnages of organophosphorus and carbamate compounds used in agriculture and horticulture are applied as seed treatments on cereals, which account for one third of the total agricultural cropped area in England and Wales (Sly 1981). The latest available survey figures indicate the extent of organophosphorus and carbamate pesticide use (Table 2). A wide range of different chemicals is available for use. Sly (1981) lists 40 organophosphorus and 11 carbamate compounds in use during 1975-79.

3 Seed treatments

In the eastern counties of Scotland and England, winter wheat is liable to attack from the wheat bulb fly, probably the most serious insect pest of winter wheat in Great Britain (MAFF 1973a). Effective cereal seed dressings were developed to control this pest in the mid-1950s with the introduction of the cyclodiene insecticides, aldrin, dieldrin and heptachlor. Since then,

seed dressings have been widely used to combat various soil-borne pathogens and insect pests using both fungicides and insecticides. The advantage of this technique is the optimal positioning of the chemical to protect the developing seedling from pest or fungal attack without the need for additional farming operations. Unfortunately, many grain eating birds exploit small cereal grains on arable farmland in late autumn and winter, and the treatment of their potential food with toxic insecticides has led to problems associated with a number of compounds.

Suspected wildlife poisoning incidents thought to involve agricultural chemicals have been investigated by MAFF at Tolworth and elsewhere since 1964. After local field investigation by regional officers, casualties are examined at Veterinary Investigation Centres, with detailed laboratory studies to identify and confirm pesticide involvement, to monitor the introduction of new pesticides and the commercial use of existing pesticides, and to identify any significant environmental effects. The findings are submitted to the PSPS in order that, where necessary, action can then be taken to prevent recurrence. Details are published regularly (MAFF 1973b, 1975, 1978, 1981a, b, c, 1982, 1983a). Tables 3 and 4 give the number of

Table 3. Vertebrate wildlife incidents in England and Wales investigated by MAFF attributed to the agricultural use of organophosphorus and carbamate pesticides

Years	64	65	66	67	68	69	70	71	72	73	74	75	76	77	78	79	80	81	82	Totals
SEED TREATMENTS																				
Organophosphorus																				
Chlorfenvinphos							1	2		1	2	3	3			4		5	3	24
Carbophenothion												1				1	1	1	2	6
																				30
SPRAY TREATMENTS																				
Organophosphorus																				
Triazophos																		1		1
Fonofos																	1			1
Malathion															1					1
Dememton-S-methyl								1		1				1						3
Haloxon														1						1
Phosphamidon									1		1									2
Dimethoate											1									1
																				10
GRANULAR APPLICATIONS																				
Organophosphorus																				
Disulfoton																	1	1	2	4
Carbamate																				
Aldicarb								1		1	13	1	2	2						20
Oxamyl											1									1
Carbofuran																			1	1
																				26
PELLETED MOLLUSCICIDE																				
Methiocarb																1	1			2
																			Total	72
Total number of incidents investigated	48	24	14	27	83	17	24	50	36	96	110	139	171	143	204	192	193	239	201	Totals 2011
Total involving pesticides	13	6	5	12	19	7	16	32	15	49	40	61	82	46	80	62	91	127	93	856

Table 4: Vertebrate wildlife incidents in England and Wales investigated by MAFF attributed to the agricultural use of organochlorine insecticides

Years	64	65	66	67	68	69	70	71	72	73	74	75	76	77	78	79	80	81	82	Totals
SEED TREATMENTS																				
Dieldrin	6	4	3	7	9	2	10	18	4	24	10*	18	5*							120
SPRAY TREATMENTS																				
DDT/DDE	1	1	2	5	5	2		2	6	5	7*	4	14*	1		1			2	58
Endrin		1			1	1	1		1	1										6
Heptachlor epoxide	6																			6
Chlordane					1															1
PCB											1									1
																				192
Total number of incidents investigated																				
	48	24	14	27	83	17	24	50	36	96	110	139	171	143	204	192	193	239	201	2011
Total involving pesticides																				
	13	6	5	12	19	7	16	32	15	49	40	61	82	46	80	62	91	127	93	856

*Includes an incident where residues of more than one compound were identified

wildlife incidents investigated by MAFF since 1964 attributed to the commercial use of organochlorine, organophosphorus, and carbamate pesticides. Incidents where deliberate mis-use of pesticides is involved are excluded from the Tables, but are included in the total number of incidents investigated.

Persistent cyclodiene insecticides used as seed treatments caused the deaths of large numbers of granivorous birds, particularly wood pigeons, as early as 1956 (Turtle et al. 1963), but without a significant effect on their populations. However, predatory birds were also killed through eating prey poisoned by dieldrin, leading to declines in, for example, sparrowhawks and peregrines. Mammal casualties included badgers (Jefferies 1969) and foxes (Taylor & Blackmore 1961), but without population declines in these or other predatory species (Jefferies & Pendelbury 1968). A voluntary ban was introduced in 1962 (Sanders 1961) to restrict the use of cyclodiene insecticides to autumn sown grain only, when the danger of wheat bulb fly attack is real, and by 1967 this restriction had been largely achieved. In 1969, it was further recommended that the remaining agricultural uses of these organochlorine compounds be continuously reviewed and that they should be withdrawn when suitable less persistent alternatives were available (Anon 1969). Aldrin and dieldrin were withdrawn as cereal seed treatments in 1975. This measure was effective in preventing further wildlife incidents (Table 4), although some residual treated grain was apparently used in 1976. Monitoring by ITE showed a significant drop in the levels of dieldrin in predatory birds, including sparrowhawks, kestrels and barn owls, after 1975 (Cooke et al. 1982).

The phasing out of the environmentally unacceptable organochlorine seed treatments was made possible by the introduction of 2 less persistent organophosphorus compounds, carbophenothion and chlorfenvinphos, to control wheat bulb fly. These new pesticides showed considerable variation in toxicity between species, which is characteristic of the organophosphorus insecticides (Stanley & Bunyan 1979). Carbophenothion seed treatments resulted in a series of poisoning incidents of geese in the early 1970s (Table 5) (Stanley & Bunyan 1979). The first recorded incident involved the death of approximately 500 greylag geese in Scotland (Bailey et al. 1972), and a further series of incidents in winter 1974-75 again involved significant numbers of grey geese (Table 5) in Scotland and on Humberside (Hamilton & Stanley 1975; Hamilton et al. 1976). Carbophenothion treated grain was again identified as the common cause in all cases, either where treated grain left on the surface had been consumed or where germinated seedlings had been uprooted under wet conditions. The results of laboratory toxicity tests with 5 species of geese showed that the grey geese (Anser) were more susceptible to poisoning from carbophenothion than the Branta geese, ie the Canada goose (Jennings et al. 1975; MAFF 1978).

Seeds dressed with carbophenothion appeared to present an unacceptable hazard to wintering grey geese in the UK. Some 1500 birds had died (Table 5) when steps were taken to prevent such casualties. In 1975, most (85%) of the world population of pink-footed geese which wintered in Britain, and most wintering greylag geese (65% of the world population) were found in Scotland, with others in Lancashire, Humberside and around the Wash.

Carbophenothion was therefore voluntarily withdrawn from use in Scotland in 1975; and, in wheat bulb fly areas frequented by wintering wildfowl in Humberside and around the Wash, farmers were advised to use an alternative insecticide, chlorfenvinphos. These steps eliminated further significant problems until winter 1982-83. However, in February 1979, 300 brent geese died of carbophenothion poisoning in Essex. In this case, treated grain was accidentally put out for the birds to feed on during severe winter weather (Stanley & St. Joseph 1979). A small incident in Cambridgeshire in November 1980 involved a feral flock of geese feeding on newly sown wheat fields. Relatively more

Table 5. Deaths of wintering wildfowl in the UK attributed to the consumption of winter wheat treated with carbophenothion

Date	Locality	Species involved	Number of dead birds*	
October 1971	Perthshire	Greylag goose	500	(Source: Bailey *et al.* 1972)
November 1974	Angus	Greylag goose	325	(Source: Hamilton & Stanley 1975)
December 1974	Perthshire	Greylag goose	46	(Source: Hamilton & Stanley 1975)
December 1974	Perthshire	Greylag goose	56	(Source: Hamilton & Stanley 1975)
December 1974	Perthshire	Greylag goose	24	(Source: Hamilton & Stanley 1975)
January 1975	Humberside	Pink-footed goose	243	(Source: Hamilton & Stanley 1975)
October 1975	Fife	Pink-footed goose	298	(Source: Hamilton *et al.* 1976)
February 1979	Essex†	Brent goose	300	(Source: Stanley & St. Joseph 1979)
November 1980	Cambs	Greylag goose (feral)	6	(+ 7 sick)
		Canada goose	2	
November/Dec. 1982	Angus	Greylag goose	33	(Source: Hamilton pers. comm.)
November 1982	Norfolk	Brent goose	85	
		Canada goose	21	(+ 1 sick)
		Pink-footed goose	4	
December 1982	Norfolk	Berwick's swan	22	
		Whooper swan	2	

*Based on the number of dead birds found, which may under-estimate the total number of birds involved
†No treated seed sown in the area but evidence suggests that treated grain was accidentally put out for geese to feed on

greylag geese than Canada geese died of carbophenothion poisoning, although the flock consisted of greater numbers of Canada geese (MAFF 1982).

Two further incidents occurred in early winter 1982-83. In November, at least 110 geese were found dead on the Norfolk coast (Table 5). They had grazed very wet fields previously sown with carbophenothion treated grain, and had uprooted germinated wheat seedlings and eaten treated seed coats which would not normally be available to them. In the second incident, some 25 swans, principally Bewick's together with a few whooper swans, died of carbophenothion poisoning on the flooded Ouse Washes at Welney after feeding on whole treated grain exposed on the wet surface of nearby fields. These swans were already conditioned to feeding on grain through being fed daily at a local refuge. Increased advice to farmers, in those areas where wintering wildfowl are at risk, by both MAFF and conservation organizations should prevent further incidents.

In view of the potential acute toxicity to vertebrates of both carbophenothion and chlorfenvinphos, farmers are advised that no seed dressed with either compound should be sown after the end of December, when gamma-HCH treated grain should be used.

Wood mice were studied on newly sown winter wheat fields during several field trials conducted by MAFF to assess the environmental hazards of different insecticidal seed treatments (MAFF 1981b). Results obtained in the field were interpreted by reference to laboratory studies with wild mice. In mice trapped on a field newly drilled with chlorfenvinphos treated grain, measurements of plasma esterases revealed depressed activity which correlated with residues of chlorfenvinphos detected in their gut contents (Westlake *et al.* 1980). Residues and inhibition were greater in mice trapped on the field, where they had been exposed to

surface grain, than in mice trapped in adjacent woodland. Whereas chlorfenvinphos residues on surface grain and in mice declined rapidly after drilling, carbophenothion in a separate trial was shown to be more persistent (Bunyan & Stanley 1979; Westlake *et al.* 1982a). Residues were detected in mice for up to 4 months after drilling. Prolonged inhibition of esterase activity was demonstrated in mice trapped on the field (Westlake *et al.* 1982b), and was considered to have been due to continued exposure to the pesticide. This persistence of carbophenothion is a contributory factor to the environmental problems seen with geese from the use of grain treated with carbophenothion.

In contrast to carbophenothion, the use of chlorfenvinphos as a seed treatment has never presented environmental risk to wintering wildfowl. However, early laboratory toxicity studies demonstrated a 9-fold difference between the toxicity of chlorfenvinphos to pigeons and to quail (Bunyan *et al.* 1971). It was predicted that, under certain conditions, for example food shortage, the use of grain treated with chlorfenvinphos could present a risk to pigeons, an apparently sensitive species. Indeed, since 1971 in a series of incidents, feral pigeons were found to be poisoned by chlorfenvinphos (Table 3). However, in view of the large-scale use of chlorfenvinphos and the relatively small number of incidents involving ubiquitous and, in some cases, pest species, this is not considered to be an environmentally significant problem.

In view of their higher intrinsic toxicity to vertebrates, carbamate compounds have not been widely introduced as cereal seed treatments. The experimental use of bendiocarb as a seed treatment on winter wheat was demonstrated to present an unacceptable hazard to birds, largely pheasants, even after a relatively clean drilling operation which left very little grain on the surface (MAFF 1981b). Bendiocarb has been successfully introduced as a commercial treatment for maize seed to control fritfly. MAFF conducted a surveillance exercise on 12 sites in 1978 where treated maize was commercially drilled. Although a small number of rooks died, the risk was assessed as acceptable, taking into account the intended scale of use and the abundance of the species concerned. No wildlife incidents have since been identified to have arisen from the commercial use of bendiocarb.

4 Spray applications
Compared with seed treatments, the direct risk of poisoning wild vertebrates by spray applications is considerably reduced, and spray applications have usually led to fewer environmental problems. However, the use of DDT, a persistent organochlorine insecticide, led to great contamination of wildlife and residues still persist, although the agricultural uses of DDT will have been withdrawn at the end of 1984. Heavy use of this persistent chemical in orchards after its introduction in the late 1940s resulted in the delayed deaths of many thrushes, particularly blackbirds, not directly following spray operations but in spring from the later mobilization of accumulated residues (Bailey *et al.* 1974). Various raptors accumulated residues along food chains and suffered declines in the early 1950s (Ratcliffe 1967; Newton 1979, 1984). Mammals appear better able to metabolize DDT (Bunyan *et al.* 1972), and fewer problems were recorded.

In contrast, the considerable use of commercial spray applications of organophosphorus pesticides has led to few direct effects on vertebrates (Tables 2 & 3). The isolated incidents investigated did not reveal ecologically significant problems, in general because of low application rates and reduced exposure to wild vertebrates. The species most likely to be at risk are those able to graze sufficiently on freshly treated crops to obtain a lethal dose. Most incidents where organophosphorus compounds were found to be involved were associated with pigeons. Geese were involved once (about 30 greylags in Norfolk (MAFF 1983)). Post-mortem examination revealed that they had consumed cereals and grass, had inhibited brain esterase enzyme activity and gut residues of triazophos which had been sprayed nearby to control fritfly on winter cereals. The experimental aerial application of fenitrothion in Scotland, an organophosphorus insecticide used to control larvae of the pine beauty moth, resulted in decreases in brain esterase activity in small forest birds (Hamilton *et al.* 1981a). This effect has also been demonstrated in Canada (Busby *et al.* 1983), but did not appear to result in direct mortality. The longer term ecological implications of exposure are under study. Aerial treatments on such a scale may present a hazard to aquatic drainage systems (Morrison & Wells 1981).

The consequences to wild vertebrates of sublethal exposure to organophosphorus pesticides sprayed on to field crops are largely unknown and long-term effects have not been identified. This question requires research. As part of current MAFF research associated with cereals (Stanley & Hardy 1984), resident insectivorous birds are being studied to monitor field exposure in wild birds feeding on treated crops. Chemical fate studies of selected organophosphorus insecticide applications will include biochemical measurements in adult and nestling birds, together with assessments of reproductive success.

Pirimicarb and carbaryl are the only 2 carbamate insecticides available as spray formulations. Though widely used, pirimicarb has not led to environmental problems in vertebrates. Bird repellency properties have been attributed to the non-systemic insecticide methiocarb, particularly in North America where it is used to protect ripening crops. Experimental applications to cherries in a Kent orchard for the purpose of preventing depredation by starlings demonstrated no unacceptable risk to bird or mammal species surveyed (MAFF 1982). Significant, but transient, biochemical changes were detected in resident orchard birds, but no apparent effects on survival were found.

Beneficial insects are at risk from the field application of insecticides, especially when the sprayed crop is attractive to pollinating insects such as honeybees (Needham *et al.* 1966; Stevenson *et al.* 1978). Problems can be avoided by careful selection of pesticide formulation and time of application, together with close liaison between spray operator and beekeepers.

The area of winter oilseed rape grown in the UK has increased 4-fold in the last 5 years, and it is now the third largest arable crop in the UK (MAFF 1983b). When in flower, this crop is attractive to honeybees but suffers damage from cabbage seed weevil and brassica pod midge. Most confirmed pesticide poisoning incidents involving bees are associated with oilseed rape from late May to mid-June after flowering (MAFF 1983a). The optimal time for pest control is at petal fall, but uneven crop growth from pest damage or environmental stress may result in delayed, patchy flowering which maintains the attractiveness of the crop. The introduction of the organophosphorus pesticide triazophos resulted in a number of bee incidents, and aerial applications were stopped in 1976 due to the unacceptable hazard to bees. Application from high ground clearance machinery has caused incidents, though less than 1% of bee colonies in rape growing areas have been affected. The spring use of the carbamate spray carbaryl in orchards where bees are important pollinators presents occasional problems, especially in 1982 in Essex. Mild spring weather may have encouraged early bee activity, increasing the risk of exposure to this pesticide (MAFF 1983a). Honeybees are useful indicators, particularly because they return to their hive where mortality can be detected. No corresponding information is available on possible mortality of wild pollinators (eg *Bombus* spp.), and research on this is required.

Some 'non-insecticide' pesticides can have detrimental effects on non-target species. The carbamate fungicide benomyl kills earthworms when applied as a spray, and has been used near airports to reduce attractiveness to birds which present hazards to aircraft (Tomlin *et al.* 1981).

5 Granular applications

Toxic carbamate insecticides were introduced in granular formulations to the UK in the mid-1970s. Aldicarb, highly toxic to mammals and birds (Bunyan & Jennings 1976), was the first to be used for incorporation when planting potatoes or sugar beet. Trials showed that the worst hazard arose from the ingestion of non-incorporated granules by ground feeding birds after drilling. Moribund earthworms containing aldicarb residues were also found on the soil surface (Bunyan *et al.* 1981).

In 1975 and 1976, incidents investigated by MAFF involved the deaths of up to 100 birds, principally black-headed gulls, following recent drilling of potatoes and sugar beet crops (MAFF 1978). A common feature was that the granules had been applied on wet soil where they were sometimes left exposed for a considerable time before rotavation. Apparently, gulls had eaten aldicarb either as granules or in contaminated earthworms. In consequence, the application machinery was improved to minimize chances of leaving granules on the surface, and farmers were advised of the hazard. This problem was successfully overcome, and granular carbamate insecticides are now used widely to protect vegetable crops with a high degree of environmental safety (Table 3).

Isolated deaths of gamebirds have been attributed to the use of disulfoton granules under dry conditions (Table 3). Considering the scale of use of granular organophosphates, these are ecologically insignificant. However, routine investigation of all suspected poisoning incidents by MAFF continues.

6 Miscellaneous formulations

Methiocarb is widely used as a pelleted molluscicide for autumn control of slugs and snails in cereals and other crops. Only 2 wildlife incidents have ever been proved to involve methiocarb (Table 3), both with pheasants found dead near newly treated cereal fields. This is insignificant when the scale of use of methiocarb is considered.

Veterinary treatments of domestic stock with organophosphorus pesticides can occasionally present a hazard to wildlife. Famphur, a warble fly treatment in cattle, has killed birds in several incidents. Magpies, in UK and USA, and small birds have been affected, with brain esterase inhibition and famphur residues in gizzard contents; most dead birds were found near cattle yards a few days after the treatment (Felton *et al.* 1981; Heinz *et al.* 1979). Hill and Mendenhall (1980) showed that predatory birds eating prey poisoned by famphur would be at risk from secondary poisoning. Occasionally, the treatment of horses with antihelminthics has resulted in the death of insectivorous birds which had fed around the faeces of the treated animals.

7 Conclusion and research priorities

The scale of current pesticide use and the introduction of new compounds demand vigilance to identify and remedy the direct and indirect effects on wildlife (Bunyan & Stanley 1983). The comparatively small number of direct wildlife problems associated with the commercial introduction of new pesticides in the last few years is encouraging and reflects the rigorous testing for potential environmental hazards that compounds undergo during development. Application methods, where the potential exposure of wildlife suggests the possibility of environmental risk, must be constantly monitored under commercial conditions. Where problems are identified, these must be adequately studied to understand the underlying processes. As technology improves, newly developed formulations will need careful assessment. The introduction of slow release, micro-encapsulated formulations may reduce the hazard to vertebrate wildlife. However, attention should be paid to those bird species considered to be most at risk and whose gizzard grinding action may rupture micro-capsules, thus increasing the toxicity of the formulation. The characteristic variation in toxicity between species shown by organophosphates (Stanley & Bunyan 1979) underlines the need for constant vigilance for susceptible species.

Although direct mortality of honeybees is investigated by MAFF to identify pesticide involvement and allow remedial action where possible, no information is available on risks to other wild bees. More research is required in order to measure impact on pollinators in general (see also Stanley & Hardy 1984).

While evidence is available from the effective surveillance which indicates that current pesticide usage is not having an unacceptable direct effect on mammal and bird populations (Bunyan & Stanley 1983), the same evidence is not available for the potential effect of sublethal exposure to pesticides. Understanding is poor of the biological implications of demonstrated exposure, eg transient inhibition of esterase enzyme activity. Further research is required, as new techniques are developed, to determine the effects of individual exposure in the field to carbamate and organophosphorus pesticides in order to assess the consequences at both the individual and population level. Current studies by MAFF at Boxworth (Stanley & Hardy 1984), using insectivorous birds as a model to measure exposure to pesticide applications to cereals, should provide further relevant data (Bunyan & Stanley 1979). There is, however, considerable scope for further research.

8 Summary

Organophosphorus and carbamate pesticides are applied to a total of 5.2M spray ha of agricultural and horticultural crops in England and Wales each year. Direct effects of pesticide use on wildlife are reviewed with reference to the results of investigations of suspected poisoning incidents conducted by MAFF since 1964. Environmental problems are considered according to formulation type as the risk of exposure to non-target wildlife varies with application method. Deaths of wildlife attributed to the use of seed treatments, sprays and granular formulations are described, together with steps taken to reduce or prevent further incidents occurring. The phasing out of organochlorine pesticides and their replacement by less persistent alternatives have substantially reduced the hazard to non-target wildlife species from direct poisoning. The need to monitor the commercial introduction of new pesticides and the use of existing pesticides is stressed in order to identify environmental problems which may require remedial action. Attention is drawn to areas requiring further research to increase understanding of the direct impact of pesticides on non-target wildlife.

9 References

Anon. 1969. *Further review of certain persistent organochlorine pesticides used in Great Britain.* London: HMSO.

Bailey, S., Bunyan, P.J., Hamilton, G.A., Jennings, D.M. & Stanley, P.I. 1972. Accidental poisoning of wild geese in Perthshire, November 1971. *Wildfowl*, **23**, 88-91.

Bailey, S., Bunyan, P.J., Jennings, D.M., Norris, J.D., Stanley, P.I. & Williams, J.H. 1974. Hazards to wildlife from the use of DDT in orchards. II. A further study. *Agro-ecosystems*, **1**, 323-338.

British Agrochemicals Association. 1983. *Annual report and handbook 1982-83.* London: British Agrochemicals Ltd.

Brown, P.M., Bunyan, P.J. & Stanley, P.I. 1977. The investigation and pattern of occurrence of animal poisoning resulting from the misuse of agricultural chemicals. *J. forensic Sci. Soc.*, **17**, 211-221.

Bunyan, P.J. & Jennings, D.M. 1976. Carbamate poisoning. Effect of certain pesticides on esterase levels in the pheasant *Phasianus colchicus* and pigeon *Columba livia. J. agric. Fd Chem.*, **24**, 136-143.

Bunyan, P.J. & Stanley, P.I. 1979. Assessment of the environmental impact of new pesticides for regulation purposes. *Proc. Br. Crop Prot. Conf. Pests Dis., 10th*, 881-891.

Bunyan, P.J. & Stanley, P.I. 1983. The environmental cost of pesticide usage in the United Kingdom. *Agric. Ecosyst. Environ.*, **9**, 187-209.

Bunyan, P.J., Jennings, D.M. & Jones, F.J.S. 1971. Organophosphorus poisoning: a comparative study of the toxicity of chlorfenvinphos (2-chloro-1-(2′, 4′-dichlorophenyl)-vinyl diethyl phosphate) to the pigeon, the pheasant and the Japanese quail. *Pestic. Sci.*, **2**, 148-151.

Bunyan, P.J., Townsend, M.G. & Taylor, A. 1972. Pesticide-induced changes in hepatic microsomal enzyme systems. Some effects of 1,1-di(p-chlorophenyl)-2,2,2-trichlorethane (DDT) and 1,1-di(p-chlorophenyl)-2,2-dichlorethylene (DDE) in the rat and Japanese quail. *Chemico-biol. Interactions*, **5**, 13-26.

Bunyan, P.J., Van Den Heuvel, M.J., Stanley, P.I. & Wright, E.N. 1981. An intensive field trial and a multi-site surveillance exercise on the use of aldicarb to investigate methods for the assessment of possible environmental hazards presented by new pesticides. *Agro-ecosystems*, **7**, 239-262.

Busby, D.G., Pearce, P.A., Garrity, N.R. & Reynonds, L.M. 1983. Effect of an organophosphorus insecticide on brain cholinesterase activity in white throated sparrows exposed to aerial forest spraying. *J. appl. Ecol.*, **20**, 255-263.

Cadbury, C.J. 1980. *Silent death. The destruction of birds and mammals through the deliberate misuse of poisons in Britain.* Sandy: Royal Society for the Protection of Birds.

Cooke, A.S., Bell, A.A. & Haas, M.B. 1982. *Predatory birds, pesticides and pollution.* Cambridge: Institute of Terrestrial Ecology.

Felton, C.L., Brown, P.M., Fletcher, M.R., Stanley, P.I., Quick, M.P. & Machin, A.F. 1981. Bird poisoning following the use of the warble fly treatments containing famphur. *Vet. Rec.*, **108**, 440.

Hamilton, G.A. & Stanley, P.I. 1975. Further cases of poisoning of wild geese by an organophosphorus winter wheat seed treatment. *Wildfowl*, **26**, 49-54.

Hamilton, G.A., Hunter, K., Ritchie, A.S., Ruthven, A.D., Brown, P.M. & Stanley, P.I. 1976. Poisoning of wild geese by carbophenothion treated winter wheat. *Pestic. Sci.*, **7**, 175-183.

Hamilton, G.A., Hunter, K. & Ruthven, A.D. 1981a. Inhibition of brain acetylcholinesterase activity in songbirds exposed to fenitrothion during aerial spraying of forests. *Bull. environ. Contam. Toxicol.*, **27**, 856-863.

Hamilton, G.A., Ruthven, D.A., Findlay, E., Hunter, K. & Lindsay, D.A. 1981b. Wildlife deaths in Scotland resulting from misuse of agricultural chemicals. *Biol. Conserv.*, **21**, 315-326.

Heinz, G.H., Hill, E.F., Stickel, W.H. & Stickel, L.F. 1979. Environmental contaminant studies by the Patuxent Wildlife Research Center. In: *Avian and mammalian wildlife toxicology*, edited by E.E. Kenaga, 9-35. (ASTM Special technical publication no. 693). Philadelphia: American Society for Testing and Materials.

Hill, E.F. & Mendenhall, V.M. 1980. Secondary poisoning of barn owls with famphur, an organophosphate insecticide. *J. Wildl. Mgmt*, **44**, 676-681.

Jefferies, D.J. 1969. Causes of badger mortality in eastern counties of England. *J. Zool.*, **157**, 429-436.

Jefferies, D.J. & Pendelbury, J.B. 1968. Population fluctuations of stoats, weasels and hedgehogs in recent years. *J. Zool.*, **156**, 513-549.

Jennings, D.M., Bunyan, P.J., Brown, P.M., Stanley, P.I. & Jones, F.J.S. 1975. Organophosphorus poisoning: a comparative study of the toxicity of carbophenothion to the Canada goose, the pigeon and the Japanese quail. *Pestic. Sci.*, **6**, 245-257.

Ministry of Agriculture, Fisheries and Food. 1973a. *Wheat bulb fly.* (Advisory Leaflet 177). Pinner: MAFF.

Ministry of Agriculture, Fisheries and Food. 1973b. *Pest Infestation Control Laboratory Report 1968-70.* London: HMSO.

Ministry of Agriculture, Fisheries and Food. 1975. *Pest Infestation Control Laboratory Report 1971-73.* London: HMSO.

Ministry of Agriculture, Fisheries and Food. 1978. *Pest Infestation Control Laboratory Report 1974-76.* London: HMSO.

Ministry of Agriculture, Fisheries and Food. 1979. *Pesticides Safety Precautions Scheme.* London: Pesticides Branch, MAFF.

Ministry of Agriculture, Fisheries and Food. 1981a. *Pest Infestation Control Laboratory Report 1977-79.* London: HMSO.

Ministry of Agriculture, Fisheries and Food. 1981b. *Agricultural Science Service: Pesticide science 1979.* (Reference Book 252). London: HMSO.

Ministry of Agriculture, Fisheries and Food. 1981c. *Agricultural Science Service: Pesticide science 1980.* (Reference Book 252 (80)). London: HMSO.

Ministry of Agriculture, Fisheries and Food. 1982. *Agricultural Science Service: Pesticide science 1981.* (Reference Book 252 (81)). London: HMSO.

Ministry of Agriculture, Fisheries and Food. 1983a. *Agricultural Science Service: Pesticide science 1982.* (Reference Book 252 (82)). London: HMSO.

Ministry of Agriculture, Fisheries and Food. 1983b. *June 1983 agricultural returns for the United Kingdom.* (Press notice no. 235). Pinner: MAFF.

Morrison, B.R.S. & Wells, D.E. 1981. The fate of fenitrothion in a stream environment and its effect on the fauna, following aerial spraying of a Scottish forest. *Sci. Total Environ.,* **19,** 233-252.

Needham, P.H., Solly, S.R.B. & Stevenson, J.H. 1966. Damage to honey bee colonies, *Apis mellifera,* by insecticides in Great Britain, 1956-65. *J. Sci. Fd Agric.,* **17,** 133-137.

Newton, I. 1979. *Population ecology of raptors.* Berkhamsted: Poyser.

Newton, I. 1984. Uses and effects on bird populations of organochlorine pesticides. In: *Agriculture and the environment,* edited by D. Jenkins, 80-88. (ITE symposium no. 13). Cambridge: Institute of Terrestrial Ecology.

Ratcliffe, D.A. 1967. Decrease in eggshell weight in certain birds of prey. *Nature, Lond.,* **215,** 208-210.

Sanders, H.G. 1961. *The report of the Sanders Research Study Group: toxic chemicals in agriculture and food storage.* London: HMSO.

Sly, J.M.A. 1981. *Review of usage of pesticides in agriculture, horticulture and forestry in England and Wales 1975-1979.* (Pesticide Usage Survey Report no. 23). Pinner: Ministry of Agriculture, Fisheries and Food.

Stanley, P.I. & Bunyan, P.J. 1979. Hazards to wintering geese and other wildlife from the use of dieldrin, chlorfenvinphos and carbophenothion as wheat seed treatments. *Proc. R. Soc. Lond. B,* **205,** 31-45.

Stanley, P.I. & Hardy, A.R. 1983. Methods of prediction of environmental effects of pesticides. Field trials to assess the hazard presented by pesticides to terrestrial wildlife. In: *Proc. int. Congr. Plant Protection, 10th, Brighton, 1983,* **2,** 692-701. Croydon: British Crop Protection Council.

Stanley, P.I. & Hardy, A.R. 1984. The environmental implications of current pesticide usage on cereals. In: *Agriculture and the environment,* edited by D. Jenkins, 66-72. (ITE symposium no. 13). Cambridge: Institute of Terrestrial Ecology.

Stanley, P.I. & St. Joseph, A.K.M. 1979. Poisoning of dark-bellied brent geese in Essex, February 1979. *Wildfowl,* **30,** 154.

Stevenson, J.H., Needham, P.H. & Walker, J. 1978. Poisoning of honeybees by pesticides. Investigations of the changing pattern in Britain over 20 years. *Rep. Rothamsted exp. Stn, 1977,* **2,** 55-72.

Taylor, J.C. & Blackmore, D.K. 1961. A short note on the heavy mortality in foxes during the winter 1959-60. *Vet. Rec.,* **73,** 232-233.

Tomlin, A.D., Tolman, J.H. & Thorn, G.D. 1981. Suppression of earthworm (*Lumbricus terrestris*) populations around an airport by soil application of the fungicide benomyl. *Prot. Ecol.,* **2,** 319-323.

Turtle, E.E., Taylor, A., Wright, E.N., Thearle, R.J.P., Egan, H., Evans, W.H. & Soutar, N.M. 1963. The effects on birds of certain chlorinated insecticides used as seed dressings. *J. Sci. Fd Agric.,* **14,** 567-577.

Westlake, G.E., Blunden, C.A., Brown, P.M., Bunyan, P.J., Martin, A.D., Sayers, P.E., Stanley, P.I. & Tarrant, K.A. 1980. Residues and effects in mice after drilling wheat treated with chlorfenvinphos and an organomercurial fungicide. *Ecotoxicol. environ. Saf.,* **4,** 1-16.

Westlake, G.E., Brown, P.M., Bunyan, P.J., Felton, C.L., Fletcher, W.J. & Stanley, P.I. 1982a. Residues in mice after drilling wheat treated with carbophenothion and an organomercurial fungicide. In: *Environment and quality of life,* 522-527. (Proc. int. Symp. Principles for the Interpretation of the Results of Testing Procedures in Ecotoxicology, 1980). Luxembourg: Commission of the European Communities.

Westlake, G.E., Bunyan, P.J., Johnson, J.A., Martin, A.D. & Stanley, P.I. 1982b. Biochemical effects in mice following exposure to wheat treated with chlorfenvinphos and carbophenothion under laboratory and field conditions. *Pestic. Biochem. Physiol.,* **18,** 49-56.

Uses and effects on bird populations of organochlorine pesticides

I NEWTON

Institute of Terrestrial Ecology, Monks Wood Experimental Station

1 Introduction

This paper reviews the uses of organochlorine pesticides in Britain and their effects on bird populations, and makes proposals for future work. It is 35 years since DDT was introduced into British agriculture, and more than 25 years since the more toxic cyclodiene compounds came in. Although the uses of all these chemicals have been reduced since their peak in the 1960s, their effects on wildlife are still apparent.

Of all pesticides still used widely, the organochlorines have had the most harmful effects on wildlife populations, especially of predatory birds, some of which have been exterminated over wide areas (Newton 1979). Besides being toxic, these chemicals have 3 main properties which contribute to their effects. First,

they are chemically extremely stable, so that they persist more or less unchanged in the environment for many years. Second, they dissolve in fat, which means that they can accumulate in animal bodies and pass from prey to predator, concentrating at successive steps in a food chain. Predatory birds, near the top of food chains, are thus especially liable to accumulate large amounts. Third, at sublethal levels of only a few ppm in tissues, organochlorines can disrupt the breeding of certain birds. They are also dispersed in air and water currents, or in the bodies of migrant birds and insects, and can thus reach regions far removed from areas of application.

All bird species studied have been found to be susceptible in one way or another to organochlorine

Plate 1. Greater structural or habitat diversity in hedgerows containing trees, as in this Hertfordshire 1980 example, supports a greater variety of breeding species than do low, well-trimmed hedges. (Photograph J H Marchant)

Plate 2. Sustained top trimming of a hedge may result in a loss of structural diversity and degeneration into a series of tree stems of little value to birds, as in this Bedfordshire hedge in 1982. (Photograph R J O'Connor)

Plate 3. Despite almost a half century of herbicide use, there is still a bank of weed seeds in the soil. In this case, charlock, pheasant's-eye, sun spurge and fumitory are shown in a strip of winter wheat which was left unsprayed to help partridge chick survival. (Photograph D Hill)

Plate 4. Red deer in the hills interact in the winter with agriculture, forestry and conservation, when they are forced down from their abundant high-level summer range to lower altitude farmland, plantations and remnants of natural woodland. Where agricultural use of this lower ground intensifies, so does the possibility of conflict through reduction of deer wintering ground. This photograph shows red deer concentrated in a winter feeding site near Loch Laggan in the Cairngorms. (Photograph B Mitchell)

pesticides (Newton 1979). The most marked population declines have occurred in bird feeding raptors, especially the peregrine and sparrowhawk (Ratcliffe 1970, 1980). Lesser or more local declines occurred in other raptor species, such as the kestrel, and in certain seed eaters, such as the stock dove (O'Connor & Mead 1984). Among other animals, various predatory mammals proved particularly vulnerable, including otters, as did several bat species, various amphibia and fish.

2 The chemicals and their uses

DDT came into widespread agricultural use about 1947. It has since been freely used throughout the country against many insect pests of various types of crop, mainly on top fruit (against several pests), brassicas (against flea beetles and caterpillars) and cereals (against leatherjackets). In the physical environment, and in the animal body, most DDT rapidly degrades to DDE. Another organochlorine, γ-BHC (HCH or lindane), came into use at about the same time. It is much less persistent than DDE, and, although often present in bird tissues, it is not known to have had adverse effects on populations.

The more toxic cyclodiene organochlorines, including aldrin, dieldrin and heptachlor, came into wide use after 1955. They were used mainly against pests in the soil, as seed dressings on cereals and other crops, on brassicas against cabbage root fly, on potatoes against wire-worms, and on various minor crops against other pests. Their usage has thus been greater in those (mainly eastern) regions with the greatest proportion of arable land. The active ingredient in dieldrin (HEOD) is also produced in the environment or in the animal body from aldrin. So, on finding HEOD in a bird, it is not possible to tell how much is from aldrin and how much from dieldrin. In the years since 1962, successive Government restrictions have progressively curtailed the use of these cyclodienes. In 1962, they were 'banned' from use on spring sown cereals, in 1965 from sheep dips and other minor uses, and in 1975 from autumn sown cereals. After that date, the remaining uses were chiefly on brassicas and root crops. Heptachlor was used hardly at all after 1964.

The restrictions were not legal bans, but 'voluntary' agreements involving manufacturers, distributors and users, and there was no legal comeback on any farmer who chose to ignore them. Most restrictions did not lead to sudden reductions in usage, but rather to steady declines over a period of years. Thus, although dieldrin had been banned in sheep dips for 15 years, analyses of wool samples showed that some farmers were still using this chemical in 1980 (unpublished data). Similarly, DDT was no longer recommended for use on top fruit after 1976, but orchard surveys revealed extensive usage after this date (Sly 1981), and in 1983 it was still advertized for horticultural use.

Because manufacturers do not disclose their sales, information on organochlorine usage in Britain has resulted chiefly from periodic farm surveys by the Ministry of Agriculture for England and Wales and by the Department of Agriculture and Fisheries for Scotland. These surveys were done on a sampling basis, and gave national estimates of the area of each crop treated with different chemicals. From these figures, the quantities applied were calculated (Table 1, based on Strickland 1966; Wilson 1969; Sly 1977, 1981; Cutler 1981). The surveys revealed a decline in DDT usage during the 1960s, and a further slight decline in the early 70s; in some regions, however, DDT usage increased again between 1974 and 1977 (Cutler 1981). The main point, however, was a continued substantial DDT usage in Britain throughout this period. The same statistics revealed a progressive and marked decline in the use of aldrin and dieldrin between the early 1960s and the late 1970s, and particularly after 1975, following the latest restriction on use on cereals.

Such figures probably reflected the broad trends, but their reliability has been questioned. Among other things, they depend on the honesty of farmers, and there may have been somewhat greater use of organochlorines in recent years than these official data suggest. Only 3 out of 81 brassica growers interviewed independently in Lincolnshire in 1978 did not use DDT (Tait 1983).

Table 1. Estimated annual usage of some organochlorine pesticides in British agriculture/horticulture during different periods (Source: Strickland 1966; Wilson 1969; Sly 1977, 1981; Cutler 1981)

| | England & Wales | | | | | | | | Scotland | | | |
| | 1962–64 | | 1966 | | 1971–74 | | 1975–79 | | 1964–66 | | 1975–77 | |
	Tonnes of active ingredient	Spray hectares*	Tonnes of active ingredient	Spray hectares*	Tonnes of active ingredient	Spray hectares*	Tonnes of active ingredient	Spray hectares*	Tonnes of active ingredient	Spray hectares*	Tonnes of active ingredient	Spray hectares*
All organochlorines†	547	1 475 500	—	1 813 400	131	148 000	166	146 000	76	361 000	60	101 900
DDT	266·2	106 000	—	71 700	78·3	63 800	71·5	60 700	57·8	39 300	33·1	29 600
Aldrin	137·2	91 000	—	45 100	12·8	29 300	18·3	10 300	3·4	1 800	4·5	3 000
Dieldrin	28·4	198 300	—	157 200	11·6	229 700	0·5	5 400	3·4	10 200	0·9	1 300
Heptachlor	5·1	46 500	—	160 300	—	—	—	—	—	—	—	—

*Includes each application separately, so 10 ha sprayed twice would appear as 20 ha.
†Besides those listed below, includes mainly HCH and a few others with minor uses, such as endrin and heptachlor.

A further set of restrictions came into effect in 1981, applicable to all EEC countries, and aimed to phase out completely the use of organochlorines in agriculture, except for very limited purposes for which no reasonably priced alternative was available. In Britain, DDT was still recommended against leatherjackets in cereals and against chafer grubs and cut-worms, while aldrin also had a few small-scale uses. Since then, the recommended use for DDT has been limited to cut-worms. These restrictions are again voluntary, so it remains to be seen how effective they will be on chemicals that can be bought and stockpiled. There are already disconcerting reports of increased DDT use in various parts of Scotland in the last few years. Meanwhile, dieldrin continues to be used in moth-proofing and wood preservation.

3 Effects on birds

DDT and its main metabolites are not particularly toxic to birds. However, the main metabolite, DDE, causes thinning of eggshells (Cooke 1973; Newton 1979). Such shells often break during incubation, so that the reproductive rate is lowered. Metabolites of DDT also cause embryo deaths in intact eggs, thus further lowering the breeding rate. Adverse effects on reproduction can be so great as to lead to population extinction. Different taxonomic groups of birds vary in their sensitivity to DDE residues. With 4-5 ppm DDE in their fresh eggs, raptors show more than 15% shell-thinning, whereas herons show about 10% and gamebirds and songbirds less than 1% (Newton 1979). Evidently the latter families are relatively tolerant to DDE. Birds of prey are thus particularly vulnerable, partly because they are more sensitive than some other birds to a given level of DDE (ie they show more shell-thinning), and also because, being predators, they accumulate larger amounts than most other birds. Of course, it is not the DDE in the egg which causes the thinning, but the DDE in the bird, which the egg level reflects.

The more toxic cyclodiene compounds, including aldrin and dieldrin, cause much more direct mortality of adult birds, in some cases leading to population decline. Some of the deaths from these compounds are immediate, others are delayed. As the organochlorine is stored in body fat, a bird may die when its fat is metabolized, and the chemical is released to other, more sensitive, tissues. Birds may die during periods of food shortage or migration, from residues accumulated in the body during previous months. At lower concentration, aldrin, dieldrin and other organochlorines also cause embryo mortality, thus lowering the breeding rate in the same way as DDE, but without the shell-thinning. Many deaths occur around the time of hatch, when remaining yolk is metabolized, and the organochlorine is released into the chick's body.

4 Population trends

The main decline in bird of prey populations occurred in the late 1950s, following the introduction of aldrin,

dieldrin and heptachlor as seed treatments. The raptors became contaminated primarily through taking seed eating birds, which had themselves consumed treated grain. Large numbers of finches, pigeons and other seed eaters were found dead and dying around newly sown fields, and many bird of prey carcases were also recovered. Other routes of contamination occurred, however, for all species of birds that were analysed in the 1960s were found to contain organochlorine residues (Prestt & Ratcliffe 1972). Fish were also contaminated, providing a source of residues for herons and other fish eaters.

The bird feeding raptors were most affected, particularly the peregrine and sparrowhawk. The extent of their population decline varied between regions, according to the proportion of land that was tilled, and hence the amount of pesticide applied. In both species, the decline was least marked in the north and west, and most marked in the south-east, the region with most arable land.

In parts of the north and west, some resurgence of the populations of both peregrine and sparrowhawk was evident within 3-4 years after the first restrictions were imposed on the use of aldrin and dieldrin in 1962, and, as the years passed, a recovery became increasingly apparent further south and east. In the peregrine, traditional nest sites throughout the country were well known, and the species has been subject to regular surveys (Ratcliffe 1963, 1965, 1972, 1984). The population probably reached its lowest point in 1963. In that year, survey revealed a population only 44% as great as that present during the standard pre-pesticide period of 1930-39, largely concentrated in Scotland. Only 13% of territorial pairs produced young that year. By 1971, a substantial recovery was apparent, with the population at 54% of its former level and 25% of pairs producing young. By 1981, the recovery was much more marked, with the population at 88% of its former level and 49% of pairs producing young. In most inland areas of the north and west, the recovery was complete, and in some districts numbers were even greater than in the pre-DDT period. However, pairs were still largely absent from eastern coastal districts, and completely absent from the south coast of England, east of Devon. These were areas adjacent to rich arable farmland, where pesticide use was particularly heavy.

The sparrowhawk, too, has largely recovered its numbers, spreading eastward in a wave-like manner from western districts (Newton & Haas 1984). At the time of writing, the species is still absent from that part of the country with the greatest proportion of arable land, embracing Lincolnshire, Huntingdonshire, Cambridgeshire and much of Essex, Norfolk, Suffolk and Kent. To my knowledge, breeding has only recently started again in the first 3 of these counties. Hence, the recovery in both the peregrine and sparrowhawk has so far closely reflected the decline, occurring soonest in the north-west where decline was least severe. It followed the reduced use of aldrin and dieldrin, which would presumably have led to improved survival in the adults. Throughout, however, both species have continued to lay thin-shelled eggs, under continuing DDT contamination. Some of these eggs have broken, so breeding success has been less than normal. Evidently, this has not been sufficient to prevent the populations from producing enough surplus young to fuel the recovery.

In the kestrel, decline was evident only in the most arable districts of south-east England, and here recovery soon followed the 1975 ban on aldrin/dieldrin for use on spring sown cereals. The birds were present in numbers again by 1980. In the heron, no decline in population was apparent that could be attributed to pesticides. Nonetheless, the birds were heavily contaminated, and showed marked shell-thinning and egg breakage. Unlike the raptors, however, they could produce up to several repeat clutches per year if previous ones broke, thus greatly reducing the impact of DDE on productivity.

Almost certainly, several seed eating species also declined in the years around 1960, but the only species for which trends have been well documented is the stock dove, which has also recovered in recent years (O'Connor & Mead 1984).

5 Pesticide residues in bird tissues

Since 1963, carcases of predatory birds have been analysed chemically, at Monks Wood Experimental Station, in an attempt to monitor changes in organochlorine residues, and thus provide a check on the effectiveness of Government regulations. Initially, all species were analysed, but eventually the scheme was reduced to fewer, concentrating on kestrel and sparrowhawk for the terrestrial environment, and heron for fresh water. Birds were received from most parts of the country, in response to advertisements placed periodically in bird journals. All carcases were requested, irrespective of form of death. In practice, most such birds died from accidental causes, and few seemed to have died from pesticide poisoning (Cooke *et al.* 1982; Newton *et al.* 1981). The birds obtained in particular years, or in particular regions, showed enormous variation in the organochlorine residues in their livers. The year-to-year changes in residues were therefore not significant, only some of the longer term trends. Note that the scheme began only after the peak period of organochlorine usage when the main decline in sparrowhawk populations occurred. One consequence was that relatively few birds of this species were obtained from eastern districts where the decline was most marked.

The findings confirmed widespread contamination of all 3 species with organochlorine residues. All birds are included in Figures 1-3, irrespective of year, season or

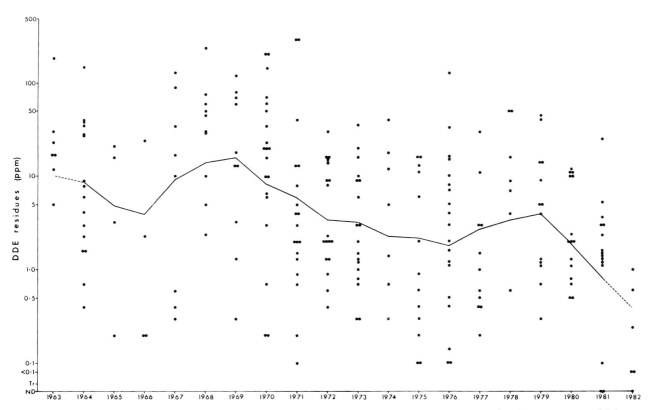

Figure 1a. Levels of DDE in livers of herons received at Monks Wood Experimental Station 1963-82. All herons included, irrespective of region, season or cause of death. Lines show 3-year (– – – 2-year) moving geometric means of residue levels

84

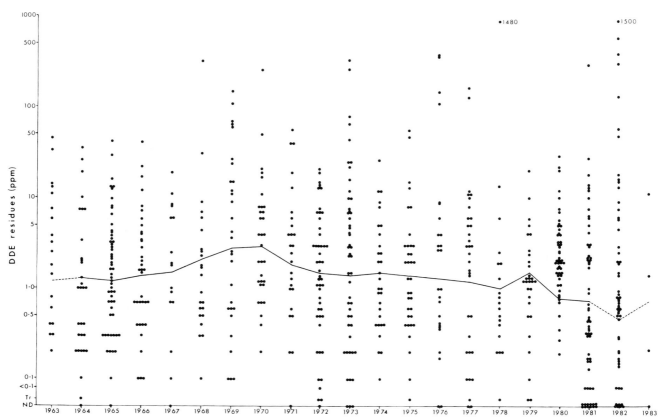

Figure 1b. Levels of DDE in livers of kestrels received at Monks Wood Experimental Station 1963-83. All kestrels included, irrespective of region, season or cause of death. Lines show 3-year (– – – 2-year) moving geometric means of residue levels.

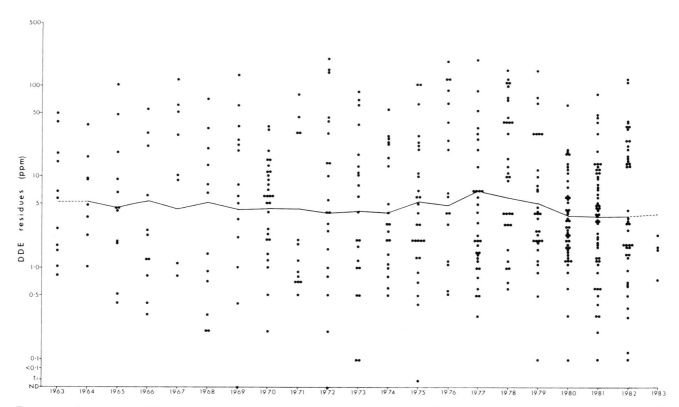

Figure 1c. Levels of DDE in livers of sparrowhawks received at Monks Wood Experimental Station 1963-83. All sparrowhawks included, irrespective of region, season or cause of death. Lines show 3-year (– – – 2-year) moving geometric means of residue levels

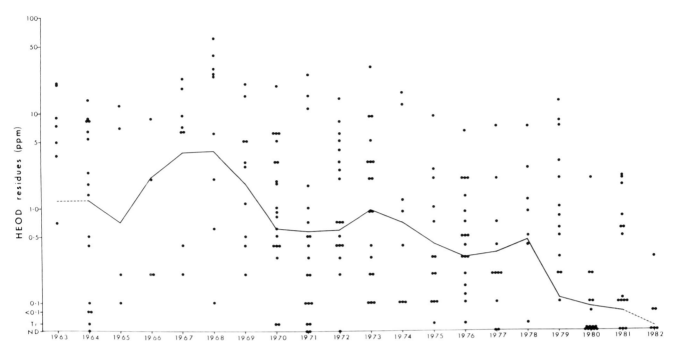

Figure 2a. Levels of HEOD in livers of herons received at Monks Wood Experimental Station 1963-82. All herons included, irrespective of region, season or cause of death. Lines show 3-year (– – – 2-year) moving geometric means of residue levels

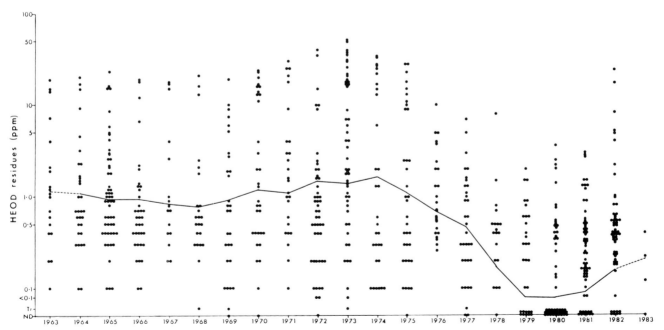

Figure 2b. Levels of HEOD in livers of kestrels received at Monks Wood Experimental Station 1963-83. All kestrels included, irrespective of region, season or cause of death. Lines show 3-year (– – – 2-year) moving geometric means of residue levels

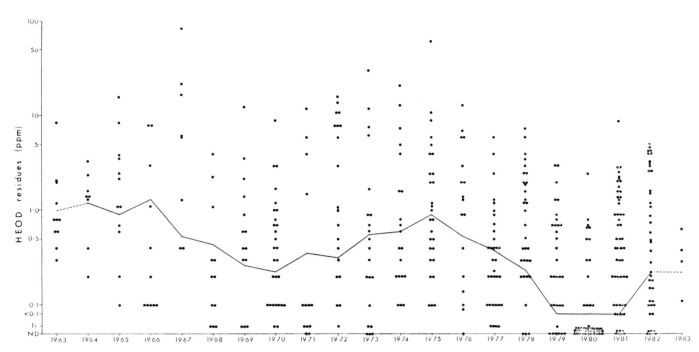

Figure 2c. Levels of HEOD in livers of sparrowhawks received at Monks Wood Experimental Station 1963-83. All sparrowhawks included, irrespective of region, season or cause of death. Lines show 3-year (– – – 2-year) geometric means of residue levels

cause of death. Levels of DDE in livers were generally higher than those of HEOD, not necessarily because of the greater use of DDT than of aldrin/dieldrin (Table 1), but because of the greater persistence and lower toxicity of DDE compared to HEOD, both of which would have led birds to accumulate greater levels of DDE. From most parts of the country, some of the birds contained relatively low levels of these compounds, while other birds had high levels. However, the proportion of individuals with high levels was greater in the east than in the west (Cooke et al. 1982). This fitted the geographical trend in tilled land, and thus presumably also the extent of pesticide usage.

In the long-term trends in residues, the 3 species differed somewhat (Figures 1-2). For DDE, the heron showed a slight, but progressive, decline throughout the 20 years concerned, which became particularly marked after 1981. The kestrel showed a decline only after 1977; before this date, all annual geometric mean levels were greater than 1 ppm, whereas after this year only one annual geometric mean (1980) was greater than 1 ppm. The sparrowhawk, in contrast, showed a consistently high level throughout, with no sign of a decline.

For HEOD, the 3 species revealed a similar order of trend. The heron showed a steady decline in residues from the early 1960s to about 1980, and the kestrel and sparrowhawk showed declines chiefly after 1976 following the last main restriction of aldrin and dieldrin as seed treatments. In all 3 species, however, HEOD levels rose again after 1980, presumably reflecting an increase in usage, but no figures on this are available.

These different patterns probably resulted because the 3 species ate different prey, from different food chains. Much of the organochlorine in water is presumably derived from agriculture, with local inputs of HEOD associated with the mothproofing and wood industries. Levels in herons are therefore likely to reflect recent agricultural usage. As residues of organochlorines persist for years in soils, levels in the 2 terrestrial predators are likely to reflect previous usage, as well as very recent usage. Previous usage is particularly likely to affect the sparrowhawk because several of its prey species feed on worms and other organisms which become contaminated by residues in soil. In other words, because of their feeding habits, the 3 species probably differ in the speed with which they reflect declines in usage, in the order heron, kestrel and sparrowhawk respectively. The possibility that sparrowhawks accumulate their own DDE residues from migrant prey now seems, from analyses of prey species, unlikely to be true (unpublished data). The bulk of DDE found in British predatory birds has almost certainly been applied as DDT in Britain.

The greater contamination of the sparrowhawk than the kestrel agrees with findings in other areas, where bird eaters invariably contain higher organochlorine levels than do mammal eaters (Conrad 1977; Henny 1977). This is partly because the mammal eating raptors are living on herbivorous prey (a food chain with 2 steps), whereas the bird eaters are living largely on carnivorous prey (a food chain with at least 3 steps). In addition, mammals in general are better able to metabolize organochlorines than birds (Walker 1983). So, on the same rate of intake, mammals will generally accumulate less than will birds. There are thus 2 reasons why mammal feeding raptors would be expected to become less contaminated than bird feeding raptors.

For herons, the situation differs. Organochlorines are only slightly soluble in water, but fishes, filtering hundreds of gallons of water per day, can rapidly absorb organochlorines through their gills, as well as from their food. So fish, too, are often a major source of residue, and especially oily fish, such as eels, which are favoured by herons, and particularly by otters.

6 Persistence of DDE in soils
Recent analyses of uncultivated orchard soils showed only a negligible decline in DDT-type residues (especially DDE) during 13 years after DDT was last used, and the expected 'half-life', when concentrations in the soil should have decreased to one half, was estimated at 57 years (Cooke & Stringer 1982). Even if use of DDT was stopped tomorrow, soil dwelling organisms would remain a source of residues to prey species for decades to come. HEOD is much less persistent, with a half-life in soil estimated at 4-7 years (Research Committee on Toxic Chemicals 1964; Edwards 1966). Organochlorines can disappear more rapidly from animal bodies than from the physical environment, but, again, DDE lasts longer than HEOD. For example, in pigeons, the 'half-life' of DDE has been estimated at about 240 days, compared with 47 days for HEOD (Walker 1983). These rates vary between species, and with the condition of the individual.

7 Future work
As the most affected species, sparrowhawk and peregrine, have still not completely reoccupied their former range, continued monitoring of populations is desirable, especially in south-east England, where peregrines are still absent, and where sparrowhawks have only recently started to return. Monitoring until populations have fully recovered is desirable not only for conservation reasons, but also to check whether events are fully consistent with organochlorines being the primary cause of population decline. Also, in view of the continuing high DDE residues in these and other species, continued monitoring of residues and shell thickness is also desirable. There is now only one remaining legitimate use for DDT in Britain, but there are worrying signs of increasing use for other purposes. Substantial use will probably continue whilst the chemical remains freely available, and its removal from all lists of recommended chemicals is highly desirable. If its use could be stopped, it would be instructive to find how long it takes for residues to decline to negligible levels in different species, thus providing data on persistence levels in different parts of the environment. The work of Cooke and Stringer (1982) demonstrating the extreme persistence of DDE in soil might usefully be extended, both with more analyses in future years at the same site, and with further analyses at other sites. This extension would

help to indicate how widely applicable are the results from this one area, and the extent to which persistence varies with soil type. In general, further monitoring of the physical environment, and of selected animal species, will be required for some further years, whether or not DDT remains available commercially.

On the other hand, I can see little value in further research on the mode of action of DDT or on other physiological aspects, not because these aspects are fully understood, but because the chemical is hopefully being phased out, and further basic research could only be regarded as a luxury rather than a priority. The same applies to dieldrin and other organochlorines. However, because of the extent of our existing knowledge of DDT, it will remain a good chemical on which to make general studies of pollutants and their behaviour in the environment. It is also a good chemical for research into the effects on animals of long-term exposure, including the development and mechanisms of resistance. Indeed, the routine screening of a wide range of animals for their sensitivity to DDT, comparing populations from agricultural and non-agricultural areas, might give some idea of the variety of species which have been affected by this chemical (though it would not tell us how many species have been eliminated completely). Such data are not yet available for any chemical, the information on effects being restricted to the pest species themselves and a few other conspicuous or important species, such as birds and bees.

Another major research need concerns not just the organochlorines, but all chemicals used on farmland. The need is for some assessment of the effects of the collective total of chemical use on the farmland flora and fauna, including soil organisms. To some extent, it is too late for this assessment, because much of the change will have occurred already, but, with the continuing increase in numbers of chemicals and applications, further change in flora and fauna seems inevitable. I believe that such a study could reveal effects far greater and wider ranging than previously imagined, some of which might have repercussions on the long-term maintenance of soil fertility. Projects by the Game Conservancy and MAFF go only part way towards fulfilling this need.

8 Summary
8.1   DDT is held responsible for the widespread shell-thinning and lowered breeding success which have occurred in certain predatory birds from the late 1940s, while aldrin and dieldrin are held responsible for the large-scale mortality and population declines which occurred from the late 1950s. The bird eating peregrine and sparrowhawk were the main species affected.

8.2   Since 1962, successive Government restrictions have progressively reduced the amounts of these chemicals used in agriculture. The decline in aldrin/dieldrin use was especially marked after 1975, but DDT continued to be used in substantial amounts until beyond 1980.

8.3 Coincident with reductions in aldrin/dieldrin use, peregrines and sparrowhawks have largely recovered in numbers and recolonized areas from which they were eliminated. However, both are still absent from those (intensely arable) parts of their range with heaviest pesticide use. The peregrine is still absent from sea cliffs (near arable land) in southern and eastern England, and the sparrowhawk is largely absent from a region embracing much of Lincolnshire, Cambridgeshire, and parts of Norfolk, Suffolk, Essex and Kent.

8.4 These population recoveries, associated with reductions in aldrin/dieldrin use, have occurred despite continued shell-thinning and reduced breeding success.

8.5 Sparrowhawk, kestrel and heron specimens, analysed chemically, have all shown declines in HEOD residues in their livers, especially after 1975. Kestrel and heron showed declines in DDE levels.

8.6 Recent work implies that DDE is extremely persistent in soils, and therefore likely to remain a problem, at least to sparrowhawks, for years to come, even if its usage is curtailed now.

8.7 The main priorities for future work include (i) continued monitoring of population trends in affected species, and of residue levels in selected species and in soils; (ii) some assessment of the changes in flora and fauna of farmland due to total chemical use.

In addition, DDT would be a good chemical for more general studies of the behaviour of persistent pesticides, and for studies of the development, and mechanisms, of resistance.

9 References

Conrad, B. 1977. *Die Giftbelastung der Vogelwelt Deutschlands.* (Vogelkundliche Bibliothek 5). Greven: Kilda.

Cooke, A.S. 1973. Shell thinning in avian eggs by environmental pollutants. *Environ. Pollut.*, **4**, 85-152.

Cooke, B.K. & Stringer, A. 1982. Distribution and breakdown of DDT in orchard soil. *Pestic. Sc.*, **13**, 545-551.

Cooke, A.S., Bell, A.A. & Haas, M.B. 1982. *Predatory birds, pesticides and pollution.* Cambridge: Institute of Terrestrial Ecology.

Cutler, J.R. 1981. *Review of pesticide usage in agriculture, horticulture and animal husbandry 1975-1979.* (Pesticide Usage Survey report no. 27). Edinburgh: Department of Agriculture and Fisheries for Scotland.

Edwards, C.A. 1966. Insecticide residues in soils. *Residue Rev.*, **13**, 83-132.

Henny, C.J. 1977. Birds of prey, DDT, and tussock moths in Pacific Northwest. *Trans. N. Am. Wildl. nat. Resourc. Conf.*, **42**, 397-411.

Newton, I. 1979. *Population ecology of raptors.* Berkhamsted: Poyser.

Newton, I. & Haas, M.B. 1984. The return of the sparrowhawk. *Br. Birds*, **77**, 47-70.

Newton, I., Bell, A.A. & Wyllie, I. 1981. Mortality of sparrowhawks and kestrels. *Br. Birds*, **75**, 195-204.

O'Connor, R.J. & Mead, C.J. 1984. The stock dove in Britain 1930-80. *Br. Birds*, **77**, 181-201.

Prestt, I. & Ratcliffe, D.A. 1972. Effects of organochlorine insecticides on European birdlife. *Proc. int. orn. Congr., 15th*, 486-513.

Ratcliffe, D.A. 1963. The status of the peregrine in Great Britain. *Bird Study*, **10**, 56-90.

Ratcliffe, D.A. 1965. The peregrine situation in Great Britain 1963-64. *Bird Study*, **12**, 66-82.

Ratcliffe, D.A. 1967. The peregrine situation in Great Britain 1965-66. *Bird Study*, **14**, 238-246.

Ratcliffe, D.A. 1970. Changes attributable to pesticides in egg breakage frequency and eggshell thickness in some British birds. *J. appl. Ecol.*, **7**, 67-107.

Ratcliffe, D.A. 1972. The peregrine population of Great Britain in 1971. *Bird Study*, **19**, 117-156.

Ratcliffe, D.A. 1980. *The peregrine falcon.* Calton: Poyser.

Ratcliffe, D.A. 1984. Peregrine breeding population of the UK in 1981. *Bird Study*, **31**, 1-18.

Research Committee on Toxic Chemicals. 1964. *Report.* London: Agricultural Research Council.

Sly, J.M.A. 1977. *Review of usage of pesticides in agriculture and horticulture in England and Wales, 1965-1974.* (Pesticide Usage Survey report no. 23). Pinner: Ministry of Agriculture, Fisheries and Food.

Sly, J.M.A. 1981. *Review of usage of pesticides in agriculture, horticulture and forestry in England and Wales, 1975-1979.* (Pesticide Usage Survey report no. 23). Pinner: Ministry of Agriculture, Fisheries and Food.

Strickland, A.H. 1966. Some estimates of insecticide and fungicide usage in agriculture and horticulture in England and Wales, 1960-64. *J. appl. Ecol.*, **3** suppl., 3-13.

Tait, J. 1983. Pest control decision making on brassica crops. *Adv. appl. Biol.*, **8**, 121-188.

Walker, C.H. 1983. Pesticides and birds — mechanisms of selective toxicity. *Agric. Ecosyst. Environ.*, **9**, 211-226.

Wilson, A. 1969. *Further review of certain persistent organochlorine pesticides used in Great Britain.* London: HMSO.

The effects of agricultural practices on weeds in arable land

R J CHANCELLOR, J D FRYER & G W CUSSANS
Weed Research Organization, Yarnton

1 Introduction

Weeds are always present in arable fields and every cultural practice carried out to grow crops will influence, directly or indirectly, the composition of the weed populations occurring there. Many of the cultural practices originate from the need to control weeds and some, especially herbicides, are so effective that they have allowed a revolution in changes in cropping methods. This paper reviews the influence of some individual practices, the research currently in progress, and those aspects of arable weed ecology that need further investigation.

2 The influence of individual practices

2.1 Straw burning

Weed control starts with the harvest of the previous crop, and with one of the most controversial farming activities of recent times. This is straw burning, which is a valuable means of weed control. Many weed seeds are killed, the proportion depending on the temperatures achieved and the position of the seeds. Seeds with only a very light cover of soil survive when those on or above the surface are often killed.

Very high temperatures can be achieved. In an experiment in which 3 different quantities of straw were spread and burnt over wheat stubble on which black-grass seed had previously been spread, the temperatures recorded (Table 1) and the amount of seed killed (Figure 1) were directly related to the quantity of straw burnt. On farm sites naturally infested with black-grass, burning killed between 40-80% of the seed shed (Moss 1981).

Table 1. Temperatures at the soil surface beneath burning straw

Amount of spread straw tonnes/ha	Temperatures at soil surface Peak temperature °C	Duration (sec) of temperature above 200°C
2·1	143	0
4·2	225	10
6·3	270	35

In similar experiments with wild-oats, in which combine harvester swathes were burnt, seed kill averaged 32%. The percentage was higher directly beneath the straw swathes but, of course, lower between them. The average peak temperature recorded in this work was around 500°C and temperatures exceeded 200°C for between 1-2 minutes at the soil surface beneath the swathes (Wilson & Cussans 1975).

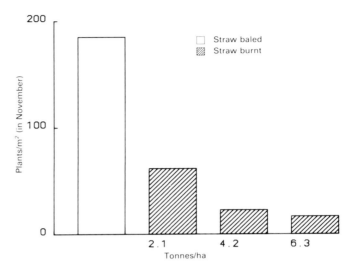

Figure 1. Straw burning kills a high proportion of black-grass seeds shed on to the stubble, the number killed being directly related to the amount of straw burnt

An impressive number of black-grass and wild-oat seeds are killed by burning. Often, however, the most immediately visible consequence is a much earlier flush of autumn germinating seedlings than would otherwise occur, because burning reduces the dormancy of the surviving wild-oat seeds and also creates ideal conditions for the surviving black-grass seeds to germinate. If the seedlings emerge before the crop is sown or emerges, a contact herbicide will kill them. On the other hand, the trend to earlier sowing now puts crops at risk from these autumn germinating weeds, which can be more competitive, and more difficult to kill, than those germinating in spring.

2.2 Cultivations

The primary cultivation implement has traditionally been the mould board plough, which has evolved in Europe over the past 2000 years. Its purpose is to bury the rubbish remaining of the last crop, to help prepare a seed bed for the next, and to control weeds. Weed control is effected by burial of weeds, by cutting them in pieces, by stimulation of dormant seeds and buds to make them more vulnerable, and by drying out roots and rhizomes brought to the surface (Roberts 1982a).

Since 1960, ploughing has declined in Britain and has been replaced by several shallow passes with tine or disk cultivators in order to save time and money. The efficiency of herbicides has made this change possible. Indeed, some crops are planted now without any soil tillage and with a complete reliance on herbicides for weed control, an example of how weed control and husbandry practice interact. This change in cultivation practice can already be seen to have influenced the weed flora.

As with any other practice, ploughing does not eliminate weeds, but selects for or against the success of individual species. Some weeds with dormant and longer lived seeds are favoured by having their seeds buried deep soon after harvest. These tend to be annual dicotyledonous species, the traditional arable weeds, such as scarlet pimpernel, *Polygonum* spp., poppy, field pansy and Cruciferae (Pollard & Cussans 1976; Cussans *et al.* 1979; Froud-Williams *et al.* 1983).

In contrast, a few species, mainly grass weeds, have relatively short-lived seed. Minimum tillage techniques allow the seeds shed from the parent plant to remain on or near the soil surface, increasing their chance of successful germination. If herbicides were 100% effective, the seed reserves in the upper layers of soil could be exhausted in a few seasons, but, unfortunately, herbicides seldom achieve this level of control.

Practically all the annual grass weeds are thus favoured by minimum tillage. Barren brome is the most spectacular example, being almost completely controlled by ploughing. Other species, which survive ploughing well, still show much faster rates of population increase under minimum tillage. In practice, however, it is not just the cultivation method but the interaction between cultivation and control system which determines weed populations. Straw burning is so effective at reducing the rate of increase of black-grass populations that otherwise marked differences due to tillage are minimized (Table 2). A similar but less marked interaction occurs with wild-oats.

Table 2. Changes in density of black-grass seedlings due to the interaction of methods of cultivation and straw disposal (Source: Moss 1981)

Cultivation method	Straw disposal	1975–76	1976–77	1977–78	1978–79
Ploughed	Baled	8	3	7	49
	Burnt	—	5	12	27
Tine cultivated	Baled	88	63	546	1654
	Burnt	—	15	56	97
Direct drilled	Baled	91	102	815	1275
	Burnt	—	9	48	48

All plots were seeded to give a population of 10 seedlings/m^2 in 1974–75

Confirmatory data from many similar experiments have been used to construct a series of simple mathematical models of weed populations. Such models take account of both the beneficial and the harmful effects of factors like straw burning. Assuming consistently typical behaviour by the weed, the models can be used to calculate the proportion of

weed kill required from a herbicide to maintain a weed population at a static level. Table 3 gives typical values for black-grass, and it can be seen that very high efficiency is demanded from black-grass herbicides in minimum tillage systems.

Table 3. A population model for black-grass showing the percentage kill required of a herbicide to maintain a static population in continuous winter cereals (Source: Cussans & Moss 1982)

Cultivation method	Straw burnt	Straw not burnt
Ploughed	50	65
Direct drilled	88	92

Wild-oats do not have such a high rate of reproduction, and so a lower degree of kill is required from herbicides. The seeds are also more dormant when shed than those of black-grass, and so the effect of tillage is less marked. While wild-oat remains a serious problem and a substantial financial burden, in intensive autumn cereal cropping black-grass has become dominant.

2.3 Date of crop planting

Each weed has its own individual periodicity of germination. Consequently, the date of planting the crop is another important factor determining the composition of the weed flora in that crop. Many weed species germinate in both spring and autumn, but some germinate mainly in one or the other so that, for example, continued planting of winter cereals results in an increase of autumn germinating weeds. A survey in 1982 showed that the most frequent broad-leaved weeds recorded just prior to harvest in central southern England included field pansy, cleavers and common chickweed, which have been favoured by the current preponderance of autumn sown cereals (Chancellor & Froud-Williams 1984). The dominance of black-grass, another autumn germinating species, has already been discussed. Thus, even with greatly improved weed control measures, the value of crop rotation is still evident. A few species are exceptionally dependent on specific cropping regimes. The best examples are plants with a very short period of germination, such as marsh cudweed which germinates for only a week or 2 in spring (Chancellor 1964) and can be controlled completely for a year by a single cultivation after the seedlings have emerged in spring.

2.4 Purity of crop seed

Another important factor is the purity of the crop seed that is planted. Seed cleaning was one of the first techniques of weed control and was responsible for the disappearance of some species, formerly of importance. The most notable examples are the darnel and corncockle. Seed cleaning is now a considerable industry, but still a large number of weed seeds is planted each year with the crop. A survey in 1970 by the Weed Research Organization, in which 378 samples of 3.28 kg were taken from seed drills being used in fields, showed that 89% of cereal seed saved by the farmers were contaminated by weed seeds. Of these, 74% contained more than 10 weed seeds and 18% contained more than 1000. Seeds sold by merchants were, however, much cleaner. Of these samples, 36% were contaminated and only 4% contained more than 10 weed seeds. In all, 90 weed species were recorded (Tonkin & Phillipson 1973).

Although the seed industry works to high standards, only very small numbers of seeds are needed to introduce new species, such as *Phalaris paradoxa*, which has only recently been recorded as a weed in cereals in Britain, or to transfer an indigenous weed to clean areas.

2.5 Type, density and spacing of the crop

It has always been said that one of the best weed killers is a vigorous competitive crop. Crops vary greatly in their competitive ability as demonstrated by work with spring wild-oat. Fewer seeds were produced by this weed when growing in spring barley as compared with spring wheat, and very much less than when growing in field beans (Chancellor & Peters 1970). The spacing and density of the crop may also influence the competitive interaction. A study of spring wild-oat and common couch in spring barley showed that crop density had a much greater influence on competition than crop row width (Cussans & Wilson 1975). More recent unpublished work (S R Moss, pers. comm.) suggests that some modern dwarf wheat varieties may be much less competitive and allow more development of black-grass than long strawed varieties.

2.6 Herbicides

The use of herbicides has rightly been regarded as one of the most important advances in agriculture since the introduction of the plough. Although some chemical weedkillers have been available since the end of the last century, it was not until the marketing of the so-called hormone herbicides, MCPA and 2,4-D, in 1946 that they really became a major factor in arable agriculture. Cheap, non-toxic to cereals and other grasses, simple and safe to use and effective against most dicotyledonous arable weeds, these and succeeding chemicals have provided a revolution in crop production methods. Today, about 200 synthetic compounds are available to control a vast range of weeds in crop situations, and in Britain the main arable and vegetable crops are now virtually all sprayed, in many instances more than once in a season (Fryer 1981).

As would be expected, herbicides have had a considerable effect on arable weed populations. Although these changes were not well recorded, there is much circumstantial evidence which has been reviewed by Fryer and Chancellor (1970a, b), and by Way and Chancellor (1976). In addition, there have been studies

of weed changes in horticultural holdings (Roberts 1982b) and in individual fields (Thurston 1969; Chancellor 1976a, b). The evidence, in general, suggests that the overall density of weed populations is declining, but species diversity has been maintained, albeit with major shifts in composition. It has been predicted that the intense pressures of efficient monocropping of cereals will lead eventually to an impoverished weed flora, through disappearance first of very rare species and then of indicators of extreme conditions (Holzner 1978). The survivors will, however, increase in density as more space becomes available.

2.7 Herbicide resistant genotypes

Changes in weed populations have generally been in favour of previously minor species which were *ab initio* tolerant to important groups of herbicides. More recently, however, there has been increasing evidence world-wide of genetic selection within species, excellently summarized in a recent book by LeBaron and Gressel (1982). The problem has been worst with chemicals having a single site of action, notably the triazines, and where crop monocultures have been treated continuously with one herbicide for a number of years.

Although still a minor problem, it has become economically very serious in some countries. Weed populations resistant to triazine have been reported in 37 species of 24 genera that were previously controlled, and resistance to other herbicides is also developing. In Britain, the best known example is groundsel.

2.8 Time of harvesting

When a crop is harvested, the time of harvesting relative to the shedding of weed seeds of individual species can be of great importance in regulating population composition. In cereals, the combine harvester has done much to spread weeds more widely within a field and throughout a farm and, when a combine is shared or hired, between farms. As mentioned above, weed seeds in cereal grain not only constitute a constant threat of renewed infestations, but also act as a vehicle for completely new introductions. This has happened over the last 4 or 5 years with *Phalaris paradoxa* (Anon 1982). When straw is baled and sold for use elsewhere, it, too, can be an important vehicle for weed dissemination. Studies of wild-oat seeds as contaminants of straw showed that, when large numbers of seeds of the weed were unshed at harvest, many thousands were incorporated into each bale. When 99% of the seed was shed, only about 100 seeds were found in each bale (Wilson 1970). In general, it appears that over 80% of spring wild-oat seeds are shed before harvest and only a minority of unshed ones, around 5%, are actually moved out of the field. These may still be a source of infestation in previously clean fields.

2.9 Conclusions

These examples of the complex effects of agricultural practices on weeds demonstrate the continuing need to integrate research on weed biology, herbicide action and practical agronomy. They also illustrate the importance of retaining an element of rotational husbandry in an ever increasingly specialized modern agriculture. Rotation of herbicide use, for example, may be all that is necessary to avoid the development of herbicide resistant weed populations. It has also been suggested (Cussans & Moss 1982) that rotational ploughing in predominantly minimum tillage systems should be retained, especially where black-grass is a problem. Farmers who can resort to the plough even once in 5 years would not only prevent the build-up of adverse soil conditions, but also bury large quantities of black-grass seeds; relatively little old seed would be returned to the surface, because of the mortality during 4-5 years' burial. Indeed, change of any kind is beneficial, for it prevents the build-up of dense weed populations which are poor in species, and are the bane of farmer and ecologist alike.

3 Work currently in progress

3.1 Surveys

Occasional surveys of individual weeds or of all weeds in particular areas have been carried out over the years (Thurston 1954; Phillipson 1974; Elliott et al. 1979; etc), but none has been comprehensive or repeated in subsequent seasons. However, 2 recent surveys by the Weed Research Organization have recorded just prior to harvest species that have survived herbicides in cereal fields in 9 areas in central southern England (Froud-Williams & Chancellor 1982; Chancellor & Froud-Williams 1984). In the first survey, in 1981, grass weeds were recorded in 2626 fields. Nineteen species were recorded altogether, but only Avena spp. (mostly spring wild-oat), common couch, rough meadow-grass and black-grass were frequent and widespread. In the second survey in 1982, the same areas were assessed to see whether similar results were obtained in a second year. They were very similar, although the same fields were not necessarily assessed in both years because leys would have been ploughed up for cereals and cereal fields put down to grass. In 1982, dicotyledonous weeds were also recorded, but as these took much longer to assess, for many are smaller than the crop, only 1021 fields were examined. Autumn germinators, such as field pansy and cleavers, were among the most frequent, having been favoured by the recent trend to autumn sown cereals. A total of 62 species of dicotyledons was recorded. However, the 4 main grass weeds were 2-3 times more frequent than these dicotyledonous species, indicating perhaps that the latter are more frequently or more effectively sprayed with herbicides.

3.2 Non-target species in field margins

The Weed Research Organization has a research grant from a charitable trust, the Perry Foundation, to determine the relative susceptibility of a range of common wild plants to widely used herbicides. This work is in its infancy, but we intend to test 8 chemicals against 50 common species each year. This information will be useful in framing advice and avoiding undesirable side effects, both when field crops are sprayed and when semi-natural vegetation has to be managed by herbicides.

3.3 Weed species in headlands and field margins

Relatively few plants are both serious weeds of arable land and also successful in semi-natural habitats. Unfortunately, some of these are very serious weeds in modern intensive cereal growing. The most notable are common couch, brome, and cleavers, all of which can occur throughout fields but are frequently worse in the headland areas, suggesting progressive invasion or re-invasion from field margins. This is unfortunate in view of recent findings by the Game Conservancy that leaving a 6 m wide unsprayed headland can double partridge chick survival, and presumably also the survival of other bird species, because of the increase in insect populations. We are hoping to initiate some collaborative work on this aspect so that the requirements for floral diversity can be reconciled as far as possible with the requirements for crop growth.

There is also a modest programme of work, which we would like to expand, on selective control of these important weeds with minimum effect on the other plants of field margins. This work is important because a few farmers have used powerful and inappropriate herbicides on field margins, thereby causing considerable damage to the vegetation, and yet frequently failing to achieve the agricultural objective.

3.4 Effects of straw burning

Work continues on the effects of straw burning, extending the work on spring wild-oat, black-grass, and barren brome to other problem species such as cleavers, although straw burning may ultimately be banned. Longer term field work is, in fact, in progress to study the implications of a change from straw burning. Although the farming community is generally anxious to retain this useful and convenient method of straw disposal, there is increasing interest in alternative methods. At current prices, this change implies incorporation of the straw into the soil, which may have implications for weed control systems.

3.5 Effects of other farm practices

The Weed Research Organization work on population dynamics of weeds as influenced by major cultural practices has resulted in a series of simple population models (Cussans & Moss 1982). This work continues and some long-term experiments are in progress to test some aspects of the models.

Weed populations are also being monitored on experiments conducted by other organizations. The most notable example is the Ministry of Agriculture's Boxworth project, where different levels of agrochemical input are being compared. We are also monitoring grass weeds on a private farm where, for commercial reasons, different crop rotations are used on 2 separate areas (Wilson & Scott 1982). If the Common Agricultural Policy of the EEC is revised, with subsequent reduction in gross farm income, there will be an increasing need for research into reduced input systems of farming for economic reasons, as well as studying any possible wider implications.

4 What needs to be done

If one designates weeds of arable land as wild life, then there must inevitably be a conflict of interests between the farmer and the conservationist. However, the main conflict is probably limited to a relatively small number of rare species. Arable land is one of the most ephemeral and artificial of habitats and there is a constant recycling of the early stages of plant succession. Over the centuries, the pressures of the habitat have selected only those species which are well adapted for survival under the constantly changing factors. Of plants largely restricted to arable land, dicotyledonous species are numerically the greatest, but grasses are the most frequent individually. In a survey (Chancellor & Froud-Williams 1984), 62 dicotyledonous and 26 graminaceous weed species, including volunteer crops, were recorded on 1021 cereal fields in central southern England. The most frequent dicotyledonous species, such as field pansy, cleavers and common chickweed, occurred in 7-10% of the fields, while the most frequent grass weeds, such as common couch, spring wild-oat, black-grass and rough meadow-grass, occurred in 24-35% of the fields.

It is these most frequent weeds of both groups which the farmer wishes to control, and no nature conservationist will object, but it is the rare weeds, such as thorow-wax and some species of fumitory, etc, which are at risk and which the conservationist wishes to preserve. What then needs to be done to control and also, selectively, to protect?

4.1 Weed population monitoring

One of the most important requirements is for accurate and detailed information. Three types of survey are needed. First, repeated surveys should be made of weeds in arable crops, the fields being selected to represent different cropping and rotation systems. Second, detailed surveys should be made of individual fields to determine the influence of particular agricultural practices upon the composition of weed populations. Third, rare arable weeds and those requiring extreme conditions for survival should be monitored in their known localities as a conservation measure. These 3 types of survey would both warn farmers and their advisors of increasing weed problems and alert conservationists to declining species.

4.2 Weed biology studies

Additional to the need to make accurate and detailed surveys of weeds is the need to obtain knowledge of their biology and ecology. Two aspects of particular importance both for farmers and conservationists are the length of time seeds are capable of surviving in cultivated soil and the periodicity of their germination. In addition, are the seeds dormant when shed, or do they rely upon burial by ploughing for persistence? Also, what factors break dormancy in their seeds? These facts are unknown for many of the less common arable weeds and would be of immense use in predicting the future behaviour of individual species.

Biological studies of wild plants occurring frequently in hedgerows and field margins would also be useful, for they would help to predict 'new' weed problems that are likely to arise as a result of changes in management. In recent years, species such as barren brome, hogweed and dock have spread into arable land from hedgerows as a result of changed farming practices. Such studies would also reveal which species are likely to be at risk from farming operations, as are possibly yellow rattle, marsh cudweed, etc, through short seed life-spans or because of their special ecological requirements.

4.3 Effects of reduced management

Although pressures on arable weeds have been intensifying over recent years, it seems possible that a reversal may well occur through reduced profitability of cereal production and increased political demand for less chemicals in the environment. It is therefore necessary to investigate systems of management which reduce the inputs for growing arable crops, such as minimum cultivations, reduced or intermittent herbicide and fertilizer usage, etc. These studies, allied with more basic biological studies and population modelling, would be important in predicting which species are likely to increase and, concomitantly, those which are likely to decline.

4.4 Assessment of the importance of field margins

Field margins are important both to the farmer and to wildlife, and their management must be regulated to suit both interests. To wildlife, they constitute home and survival corridors, but to the farmer they may be a source of weed infestation. Hedge bottoms are liable to be sprayed to keep weeds in check, and indiscriminate fertilizer distribution often reaches well beyond the cultivated area. These practices can substantially alter the plants occurring in field margins, and consequently affect wildlife. The methods of management of these areas, including field headlands, should be assessed, as is already being done by the Game Conservancy. Conversely, it would be useful from the farmer's point of view to know how rapidly weed species can spread from unsprayed margins and hedgerows into fields.

4.5 Methodology of ecological weed studies

Many arable weeds are short-lived as plants, although often they persist for many years as seeds in the soil. It is therefore essential to standardize methods of assessing their occurrence in ecological studies. Assessing numbers of seedlings or plants is the easiest method, but it must be remembered that the composition of the population will be largely determined by the season when the soil was last cultivated and that the seedlings occurring represent only a small fraction of the total number of seeds remaining dormant in the soil.

The most accurate method of assessing weed populations is, then, to determine the number of seeds lying dormant in the soil. However, although there are various methods of doing this, none is either quick or necessarily very accurate, for seed identification is usually difficult and viability determination is slow. It is necessary to establish guidelines for the assessment of weed populations in ecological studies.

5 Summary

All agricultural practices in arable land can influence the occurrence and composition of weed populations, and the effects of some are reviewed. Many of these practices originate from the need to control weeds and some, particularly herbicides, are so efficient that they have changed cropping methods. It has been predicted that the intense pressures of monocropping of cereals will lead eventually to an impoverished weed flora, with rare species and those requiring unusual conditions disappearing first. The main problem of arable weeds is seen as a dichotomy of interests. While it is essential to control important weed species, it is also desirable to conserve rare ones. In remedy, it is suggested that research priorities include accurate monitoring of weed species, biological studies of less frequent species, and investigations of the effects of less intensive agricultural practices. The importance of field margins both to farmers and wildlife should also be assessed, and the methodology of ecological weed studies standardized.

6 References

Anon. 1982. New weed threat to Anglian cereals. *Fmrs Wkly*, **97**, 47.

Chancellor, R.J. 1964. Emergence of weed seedlings in the field and the effects of different frequencies of cultivation. *Proc. Br. Weed Control Conf., 7th*, 599-607.

Chancellor, R.J. 1976a. Weed changes over 11 years in Wrenches, an arable field. *Proc. Br. Crop Prot. Conf. Weeds, 1976*, 681-686.

Chancellor, R.J. 1976b. Changes in the weeds of upper Begbroke Field (1961-1976). *Proc. int. Coll. Weed Biology and Ecology, 5th, 1976, Dijon*, 227-234.

Chancellor, R.J. & Froud-Williams, R.J. 1984. A second survey of cereal weeds in central southern England. *Weed Res.*, **24**, 29-36.

Chancellor, R.J. & Peters, N.C.B. 1970. Seed production by *Avena fatua* populations in various crops. *Proc. Br. Weed Control Conf., 10th*, 7-11.

Cussans, G.W. & Moss, S.R. 1982. Population dynamics of annual grass weeds. *Proc. Symp. Decision Making in the Practice of Crop Protection, Brighton, 1982, 91-98*.

Cussans, G.W. & Wilson, B.J. 1975. Some effects of crop row width and seedrate on competition between spring barley and wild oat *Avena fatua* L. or common couch *Agropyron repens* (L.) Beauv. *Proc. Eur. Weed Res. Soc. Symp., Paris, 1975*, 77-86.

Cussans, G.W., Moss, S.R., Pollard, F. & Wilson, B.J. 1979. Studies of the effects of tillage on annual weed populations. *Proc. Eur. Weed Res. Soc. Symp., Mainz, 1979*, 115-122.

Elliott, J.G., Church, B.M., Harvey, J.J., Holroyd, J., Hulls, R.H. & Waterson, H.A. 1979. Survey of the presence and methods of control of wild oat, blackgrass and couchgrass in cereal crops in the United Kingdom during 1977. *J. agric. Sci., Camb.*, **92**, 617-634.

Froud-Williams, R.J. & Chancellor, R.J. 1982. A survey of grass weeds in cereals in central southern England. *Weed Res.*, **22**, 163-171.

Froud-Williams, R.J., Drennan, D.S.H. & Chancellor, R.J. 1983. Influence of cultivation regime on weed floras of arable cropping systems. *J. appl. Ecol.*, **20**, 187-197.

Fryer, J.D. 1981. Weed control practices and changing weed problems. In: *Pests, pathogens and vegetation: the role of weeds and wild plants in the ecology of crop pests and diseases*, edited by J.M. Thresh, 403-413. London: Pitman.

Fryer, J.D. & Chancellor, R.J. 1970a. Herbicides and our changing weeds. In: *The flora of a changing Britain*, edited by F.H. Perring, 105-118. Hampton: Classey.

Fryer, J.D. & Chancellor, R.J. 1970b. Evidence of changing weed populations in arable land. *Proc. Br. Weed Control Conf., 10th*, 958-964.

Holzner, W. 1978. Weed species and weed communities. *Vegetatio*, **38**, 13-20.

LeBaron, H.M. & Gressel, J. 1982. *Herbicide resistance in plants*. Chichester: Wiley.

Moss, S.R. 1981. The response of *Alopecurus myosuroides* during a four year period to different cultivation and straw disposal systems. *Proc. Conf. Grassweeds in Cereals in the United Kingdom, Reading*, 15-21.

Phillipson, A. 1974. Survey of the presence of wild oat and blackgrass in parts of the United Kingdom. *Weed Res.*, **14**, 123-135.

Pollard, F. & Cussans, G.W. 1976. The influence of tillage on the weed flora of four sites sown to successive crops of spring barley. *Proc. Br. Crop Prot. Conf. Weeds, 1976*, 1019-1028.

Roberts, H.A. 1982a. *Weed control handbook: principles*. Oxford: Blackwell Scientific.

Roberts, H.A. 1982b. Seed banks of soils under vegetable cropping in England. *Weed Res.*, **22**, 13-16.

Thurston, J.M. 1954. A survey of wild oats (*Avena fatua* and *A. ludoviciana*) in England and Wales in 1951. *Ann. appl. Biol.*, **41**, 619-636.

Thurston, J.M. 1969. Weed studies on Broadbalk. *Rep. Rothamsted exp. Stn, 1968*, 186-209.

Tonkin, J.H.B. & Phillipson, A. 1973. The presence of weed seeds in cereal seed drills in England and Wales during spring 1970. *J. natn. Inst. agric. Bot.*, **13**, 1-8.

Way, J.M. & Chancellor, R.J. 1976. Herbicides and higher plant ecology. In: *Herbicides: physiology, biochemistry and ecology*, edited by L.J. Audus, vol. 2, 345-372. London: Academic Press.

Wilson, B.J. 1970. Studies of the shedding of seed of *Avena fatua* in various cereal crops and the presence of this seed in the harvested material. *Proc. Br. Weed Control Conf., 10th*, 831-836.

Wilson, B.J. & Cussans, G.W. 1975. A study of the population dynamics of *Avena fatua* L. as influenced by strawburning, seed shedding and cultivations. *Weed Res.*, **15**, 249-258.

Wilson, B.J. & Scott, J.L. 1982. Population trends of *Avena fatua* and *Alopecurus myosuroides* on a commercial arable and dairy farm. *Proc. Br. Crop Prot. Conf. Weeds, 1982*, 619-628.

Impacts of agriculture on southern grasslands

M G MORRIS

Institute of Terrestrial Ecology, Furzebrook Research Station

1 Introduction

This paper aims to outline the changes which intensification of agriculture has produced in lowland grasslands, and particularly on their invertebrate faunas. It also, and more importantly, identifies 4 main areas of research which are judged to be vital for an understanding, and possible reconciliation, of modern agriculture and wildlife conservation.

2 Agricultural impacts

The primary aim of agriculture is, and always has been, to channel photosynthetic solar energy directly or indirectly into a form which can be assimilated by man as food. The primary aim may be associated with a number of different subsidiary aims, which at different times have had a varying effect on the primary aim because of economic, social and other factors.

Until, say, the decade 1940-50, agriculture was sufficiently inefficient overall to allow some photosynthetic energy to be channelled into pathways which did not produce food. This inefficiency was not intentional, but occurred because agriculture lacked the technology and means to be efficient (in terms of energy transfer). The conservationist, inasfar as he existed before 1940, and wildlife were the beneficiaries of inefficient agriculture. There is no means of knowing how far inefficient agriculture in historic terms reduced or altered the wildlife interest, except in the very broadest terms, for instance in the change in the proportion of woodland compared with grassland on agricultural holdings, or in the past records of species which are now locally or nationally extinct.

This analysis, although, of course, simplistic, helps explain and emphasize why modern intensive agriculture and wildlife conservation are fundamentally incompatible. When lowland grasslands, specifically, are considered, it is evident that the picture is one of straightforward destruction of all the kinds of grasslands which are richest for wildlife. This destruction has been of 2 distinct kinds, though ultimately the results have usually been the same.

First, much grassland has been converted into arable land, because of the profitable advantages of specializing in cereals rather than sheep or cattle. Areas which have 'traditionally' been regarded as grasslands, such as the South Downs, have been ploughed up and sown to barley and other cereals over what is perceived to be a very short period. Changes of this sort, though perhaps not on the same scale, have occurred in the past, largely in response to economic factors such as the rise (or fall) in the price of wool, or the ability (or inability) to import grain more cheaply than it could be grown.

The second type of change has occurred in the areas of grassland themselves. Traditional technology, often complex and highly evolved, eg the management of water meadows, has given way to systems which concentrate on the production of single-species crops of particularly high yielding strains of grasses, such as rye-grass, deliberately 'improved' by breeding. Emphasis is on leys, or very short-term 'permanent' grasslands. Species-rich swards have been changed by the application of 'artificial' fertilizers, particularly nitrogen, which greatly affect the competitive advantage enjoyed by a few vigorous grasses over herbaceous species. Sod-seeding, and 'single pass' machines which combine herbicide application to existing swards, sowing of more 'productive' grass species, and fertilizer treatment in one operation, though in less general use, have contributed to changes in the type and species composition of agricultural grasslands. More generally, draining of the lower lying and wetter grasslands and 'improvement' of poor, acid grasslands on sandy soils have also taken place, with the original swards being either destroyed or greatly changed.

Generally speaking, farmers find it profitable to convert only relatively large areas of comparatively flat or gently sloping land to arable or ley. With very few exceptions, however, lowland grasslands are examples of plagioclimax vegetation, in which ecological succession (to woodland or forest) is in dynamic equilibrium with management in the form of grazing or mowing for silage or hay, or a mixture of grazing and cutting. The loss of management from these areas which have escaped destruction, usually small and steep, itself leads to very considerable changes in the sward, though to some extent these are reduced or retarded because soils on such steep areas tend to be thin and physically unstable. Although such changes are profound, they are less catastrophic than those produced by ploughing or re-seeding, and in some cases may even be beneficial, at least temporarily, to some species of wildlife (Morris 1971; Thomas 1983).

3 Effects on wildlife

The effects of changes in lowland grasslands on their plant species composition are obvious enough. Large numbers of herb species do not grow in rye-grass leys, and orchids do not flower in barley fields on the chalk.

The effects on phytophagous insects which are restricted to particular species of plants are almost equally apparent. Familiar examples are the Adonis and chalkhill blue butterflies, which feed only on horseshoe vetch. The foodplant grows only in unimproved, traditionally grazed, calcareous grasslands, and where it is absent the butterflies will not be found.

However, little information exists on how other, more general, feeders have been affected by these changes. The Game Conservancy has studied intensively 'whole faunas' on farmland, including the biomass of invertebrates available as food for gamebirds such as partridges. The faunas of the grasses themselves, and the extent to which rye-grass or other agricultural species supports diverse associations have been investigated in much less detail. Preliminary work by Morris and Rispin (unpublished) shows that rye-grass leys support fewer generalist Hemiptera, particularly grass feeding leafhoppers, and Coleoptera than unimproved grassland on the same farm. Grass feeding butterflies, such as species of Satyridae and Hesperidae, do not apparently utilize species of rye-grass as foodplants.

Though agricultural land is, or was, an important habitat for vertebrates, these animals, because of their size and mobility, tend to be less restricted to 'grasslands', 'woodlands' or other physiognomically defined biotopes. Although they are in a sense less restricted and more flexible in their ecological requirements, their conservation in fragmented and isolated habitats poses special problems which are less pressing for plants and invertebrates.

4 Current research

Research on the conservation of the invertebrate animals of lowland grasslands has tended to concentrate on the management of existing nature reserves and other protected sites. There has been a *de facto* recognition, or at least assumption, that their conservation on agricultural grasslands is inappropriate. Survey and, to a lesser degree, site selection play a far greater part in the conservation of invertebrates than they do for plants (where past survey has been more thorough) or vertebrates, particularly birds (where, despite the many RSPB reserves, the animals tend to be less site-dependent). Research on grassland management has included investigation of traditional practices (grazing, mowing), as well as of more radical ones (burning, re-seeding with 'conservation' mixtures) and the timing and duration of management. It has proved difficult to persuade reserve managers to depart from relatively simple management systems, such as 'annual light grazing', for a number of reasons.

4.1 Structure of grasslands

Management research has readily identified structure and its dynamics as important factors in the conservation of grassland invertebrates. Different species require very different conditions in the sward, with some, such as the Adonis blue butterfly or the leafhopper *Macrosteles laevis*, present only on very short, recently managed swards. Other species require much taller, less recently disturbed grasslands and, in general, there are more of these species. Management of small grassland nature reserves, therefore, has to be well organized, with an emphasis on maintaining both 'short' and 'tall' grasslands con-

tinuously in time (though not in space) by the practice of rotational management. Though grassland structure is clearly important in determining the presence and abundance of invertebrate animals, recent research has identified other factors. In particular, the availability of nitrogen has been identified as crucial for many insect populations, perhaps most. Pressing needs for further research in this field are identified in the next section.

4.2 Effects of area and isolation

Of more recent relevance has been research on the general topic of the effects of area and isolation on invertebrate populations, with emphasis on practical ways of dealing with local extinctions on nature reserves through 'artificial' re-establishment of populations, once their detailed requirements have been thoroughly understood. The actual effects of fragmentation and isolation of grassland habitats have been little studied, although valuable insights into the probable nature and magnitude of the problems have been acquired from studies on other biotopes, particularly lowland heaths.

5 The needs for future research

5.1 Modern agricultural land as a habitat for wildlife

Despite clear perceptions by both agriculturalists and conservationists, and much useful work, there is still a need to assess the value of lowland agricultural grasslands, particularly leys, as a wildlife habitat and resource in the context of wildlife on farmlands. In many farms, there are still patches of unimproved grassland and these, too, need to be assessed as reservoirs of wildlife. Although there should be no pre-judging of the issue, most conservationists, and some agriculturalists, would expect that modern agricultural grasslands are a poor habitat for wildlife. If this is the case, the next main area of research is particularly relevant.

5.2 The nature of the 'background matrix' for wildlife, ie the countryside—has it been eroded by modern intensive agriculture?

To some extent, this is an approach to the value of agricultural grasslands from the other side. In particular, the question needs to be asked whether 'background conservation' has drifted away from agricultural grasslands to other areas, such as roadside verges, urban grasslands (including gardens), amenity grasslands, military ranges, and the lower echelons of 'protected sites', ie those not managed primarily for wildlife conservation, such as much National Trust land.

5.3 Ecological processes and agricultural impacts

Whilst the first 2 areas of research contain a large element of survey work, the third topic requires detailed ecological investigation. The processes which need to be understood to assess the past, present and future impact of intensive agriculture concern the capture and transfer of energy, and involve a subject which has lost some of the 'fresh bloom of youth' just

Plate 5. *The concentration of sheep on the edge of moorland has resulted in the loss of heather dominant vegetation. There is a need to investigate the consequences of certain husbandry practices for future land management and wildlife. (Photograph P J Hudson)*

Plate 6. *Immature red grouse suffering from louping ill, a virus infection transmitted by the sheep tick* Ixodes ricinus. *Although the diseases transmitted by ticks cause serious economic loss to hill farmers and grouse moor owners, the population dynamics of this parasite are poorly understood. (Photograph P J Hudson)*

Plate 7. Agricultural improvement alters the landscape mosaic which, with a high proportion of semi-natural vegetation, has been generally characteristic of marginal upland areas. This trend is seen in a view in mid-Wales. In the foreground, rough pasture is being improved in stages to more uniform boundaries. In the mid-distance, moorland reclamation is dissecting the former heather and bracken hills, with scattered scrub on slopes, into a pattern of ley grassland and small conifer plantations. (Photograph P G Ainsworth)

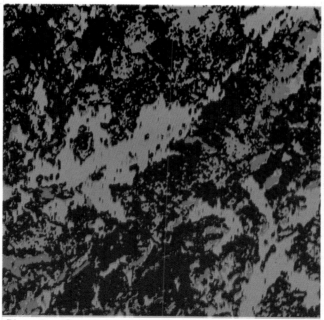

Plate 8a. Supervised classification of a 20 km x 20 km area in mid-Wales
Key: Dark green — woodland   Yellow — pasture
      Light green — wetland   Blue — lakes
      Brown — moorland   Mauve — scree/rock

Plate 8b. Change in mature forest cover, 1975-82
Key: Green — increase in forest cover between 1975 and 1982
     Blue — reduction in forest cover between 1975 and 1982

(Photographs: R J Parsell)

recently—ecological energetics. The ecology of crop production in energy terms is the key issue. Almost equally important are studies of the processes in which fertilizer use affects wildlife, though probably the importance of other farm chemicals lies with herbicides rather than insecticides, insofar as grasslands, in particular, are concerned.

5.4 The prospects of alternative conservation scenarios in the late 1980s and beyond

In the view of most wildlife conservationists, the intensification of agriculture, and the changes it has produced have reached a point when the traditional view of farmers as the 'guardians of our wildlife heritage' can no longer be substantiated, despite the influence of Farming and Wildlife Advisory Groups generally, and the influence of individual farmers in specific cases. The most popular proposals are ones which have received considerable exposure recently: in effect, agriculture must change radically to conserve not just wildlife but landscape and the wider countryside, in the interests of the public at large. The proposals differ in their details. Some aim to bring agriculture within the framework of planning controls. Others have the objective of developing social and fiscal structures which, at least to some extent, take away the need for farms to respond to market forces, on the one hand, and to partly artificial stimuli (such as the CAP) on the other. Whatever the detail, many conservationists are saying publicly that agriculture 'must' change, though the public and political will to do so has not been demonstrated. A particular concern is the fate of SSSIs under the 1981 Wildlife and Countryside Act. Already there are signs that the Act is not operating effectively, and that, in some respects, it may be having some reverse effects from those intended, eg in pushing up the prices of SSSI land.

A minority considers a very different scenario. It is clear that, if agriculture does not change radically, then some very different attitudes towards wildlife conservation may have to be adopted. In particular, nature reserves and other 'protected areas' will have an enhanced status, and their management and manipulation (for instance in establishing plants and animals on them) will become much more important. The management of grassland reserves has already attracted some research, but more is needed.

Another exciting field is the re-creation and reconstruction of ecologically diverse and interesting biotopes on devastated land. This is an area which has been neglected in conservation texts on grassland (eg Duffey et al. 1974), but given prominence by others (Bradshaw 1977). Although the difficulties in approaching 2 antagonistic areas of prediction for the future of agriculture and conservation are immense, the problems will have to be faced in the context of research. In many ways, a prediction that agriculture will change radically seems unrealistic. Studies of the functions of nature reserves and their manipulation will never be entirely wasted, but their practical value will be reduced if such radical changes do occur. It is clear that these problems involve not just ecologists and agricultural scientists, but economists, social scientists and many others.

6 Summary

Agricultural grasslands are efficient machines for producing food; 'waste', as wildlife, is becoming scarcer. Traditional grasslands have been destroyed, some by conversion to arable land, others to leys. Current invertebrate research is on management of protected sites and their fragmentation and isolation, vegetation structure, and nitrogen availability. Four broad themes for future work are: the degree to which agricultural grasslands conserve wildlife, the nature of 'background conservation' and its relation to protected sites, ecological processes, and realistic conservation scenarios for the late 20th century.

7 References

Bradshaw, A.D. 1977. Conservation problems in the future. *Proc. R. Soc. Lond. B*, **197**, 77-96.

Duffey, E., Morris, M.G., Sheail, J., Ward, L.K., Wells, D.A. & Wells, T.C.E. 1974. *Grassland ecology and wildlife management*. London: Chapman & Hall.

Morris, M.G. 1971. The management of grassland for the conservation of invertebrate animals. In: *The scientific management of animal and plant communities for conservation*, edited by E. Duffey & A.S. Watt, 527-552. (Symposium of the British Ecological Society no. 11). Oxford: Blackwell Scientific.

Thomas, J.A. 1983. The ecological status of *Thymelicus acteon* (Lepidoptera: Hesperiidae) in Britain. *Ecol. Entomol.*, **8**, 427-435.

Effects of drainage on natural vegetation

J O MOUNTFORD & J SHEAIL
Institute of Terrestrial Ecology, Monks Wood Experimental Station

1 Introduction

This paper discusses the extent to which wildlife communities may be affected by changes in land drainage. It identifies the main areas where research is required for conservation purposes. Several references are made to work that has already been commissioned by the Nature Conservancy Council (NCC) from the Institute of Terrestrial Ecology (ITE).

2 What is the problem?

Trafford (1982) summarized the ways in which changes in the soil water regime can upgrade the quality of farmland and, therefore, lead to higher food production. Government policy is to encourage this type of improvement both where it is cost-effective and causes no unacceptable harm to the environment and conservation interests. Encouragement takes the form of capital grant-aid. If agreement cannot be reached locally between the farmer and conservation bodies, cases may be referred to ministers for resolution.

Because most drainage schemes take place on existing farmland, rather than on areas newly reclaimed for farming, the agricultural industry has tended to under-rate the impact of its work on wildlife (Trafford 1978). Spokesmen for the industry have often overlooked the fact that the schemes are intended to destroy the very artefacts of the agricultural landscape which act today as refugia for wildlife, namely the drainage ditches, rhynes and dykes. Over the last 40 years, important changes have taken place in the management of both the watercourses and the adjacent land. In order to raise the agricultural productivity of the wetlands, drainage schemes have been installed to change the extent and periodicity of surface water, and to reduce the levels of water in the ground and watercourses. The less direct effects of drainage improvements include modifications to the management of the bank vegetation and neighbouring wetland pastures, and the ploughing up of that pasture for cultivation.

The precise extent and character of these changes vary both within and between wetland areas. They are, for example, more marked in the Romney Marsh (proper) than in the area to the south-west, the Walland Marsh, which is on the Kent-Sussex border. The example of the Romney Marsh suggests that the scope for transforming the surface and under-drainage of a wetland is now so considerable, and the impact of more intensive forms of grassland management and of cultivation is now so extensive, that few, if any, refugia for pasture and pasture-dyke species will survive, unless explicit steps are taken for nature conservation purposes.

Agricultural land drainage has become 'one of the sharpest points of conflict with conservation' (Trafford 1982). Surveys and research investigations are needed to establish which watercourses in the traditionally wetland areas support a *relic* flora and fauna, and to assess the likely effects of the replacement of one man-induced ecosystem by another. What types of plant and animal are likely to appear and disappear?

3 What is being done?

In recording what is happening in the farming environment, 4 priorities may be identified. These are:

  i. to record the chronology and extent of changes in drainage regime;
  ii. to record changes in the pattern of agricultural land use and management;
  iii. to record changes in the wetland communities, and selected plant and animal species within these communities;
  iv. to identify the reasons for change in biological interest, where observed.

3.1 Changes in drainage regime

There remains a general lack of quantitative data on the areas where drainage schemes are being carried out in Britain. On the assumption that nearly all field drainage between 1940 and 1979-80 was grant-aided, and using data available from the Ministry of Agriculture, Green (1979) plotted the areas which benefited on a divisional, county and, from 1973, parish scale. These studies provided a national and regional perspective, but they were of little use in elucidating what was happening on specific tracts of land. For a catchment area in Huntingdonshire, Green (1979) was able to plot the incidence of field drainage and ditching schemes at a scale of 1:10 560, using the manuscript master drainage maps of the Ministry of Agriculture. Because of the way the maps had been annotated, the approximate date of the scheme could be given.

ITE has now demonstrated the value of this data source for studying the incidence and chronology of drainage schemes over much more extensive areas, including the Romney Marsh, Pevensey Levels, Somerset Moors and Levels, and the Misson Levels of the Humberside/Nottinghamshire/South Yorkshire border. About 60% of the Romney Marsh, 30% of the Misson Levels, and 10% of the Somerset Levels have experienced the direct effects of tile drainage schemes. The value of the data source should not, however, be exaggerated. Some extensive drainage schemes are now being carried out without grant-aid, and there is no certain and comprehensive way of monitoring them. Second, no information related to the payment of grant-aid can be published where this would enable activity on individual holdings to be identified.

3.2 Changes in land use and management

Drainage is intended to increase the productivity of existing grass and ploughed land, or, in an increasing number of cases, to prepare the way for the conversion of long-established grassland to arable production. The precise relationship between drainage activity and land use varies both in time and place. In parts of the Romney Marsh, tile drainage was installed in the late 1960s as a means of ensuring that the potato crop could be lifted in a wet autumn. It encouraged improvements to arterial drainage which, in turn, made possible the ploughing up of land that had previously been suitable only for grass production.

Some impression of the pattern of land use in the past, and the chronology of change, may be gained by using a combination of sources. An Annual Census of Agriculture (the June returns) has been made each year since 1866. The manuscript returns on a parish basis can be consulted in the Public Record Office and appropriate offices of the Ministry of Agriculture. However, because of the variable size of parishes and the frequently wide variety of land forms within each parish, these returns are of limited value in large-scale studies of land use change. The Land Use Surveys carried out in the 1930s, and in the early 1960s, suffer from the limitations common to all *ad hoc* surveys: they vary in the amount of detail shown and are available for very few points in time.

Vertical air photographs taken by the RAF in the mid- to late 1940s provide an important base-line for land use studies, but it has often been difficult to obtain prints. Recently, satellite imagery has developed to a point where it will be of considerable value in documenting environmental change. Details of field boundaries and watercourses, as derived from large-scale Ordnance Survey maps, can be superimposed on the images. If there is adequate ground-truth for the present time, these images may provide insights into land use changes over the previous decade.

3.3 Changes in biological interest

Generally, it is easier to find archival data on plants than on animals, with the possible exception of birds, and the amount of detail varies widely between localities. Among the more relevant sources for the plant life of Romney Marsh are the published flora of Kent (Hanbury & Marshall 1899) and of Sussex (Wolley-Dod 1937), and the field notes of local naturalists (made since the War).

To assess the present situation, ITE has used a stratified random sampling approach. The length of ditch is measured in representative areas of each soil type, with sites allocated in proportion to the calculated total length of ditches in the entire area of each

soil series. Sites to be examined are located using random grid co-ordinates, and 100 m samples are recorded, examining both bank and water. Other sites are chosen where earlier site-specific data are available. In the Romney Marsh, those sites recorded in the 1940s and 1950s were revisited in order to assess how far the grazing marshes might have altered in the succeeding 30 years. The composition of each list will be influenced by the season of the year, the ability of the recorder to identify species, the management phase at the time of visit, and the purpose of the data collection. When the coarse distribution of species (at the 10 km square, tetrad or parish level) was the primary objective of the survey, many recorders did not bother to record common species in any detail. These omissions can give a misleading impression of the overall vegetation, within which rarer plants may occur.

A proportion of sites must be visited more than once in order to ensure that the conclusions reached are not based entirely on a 'single frame' in the dynamic 'moving picture' of individual ditches. Watercourses in drained or undrained land, and those in pastoral or arable systems, each have their own characteristic species complement. However, the proportions of each plant may differ from year to year, reflecting both natural and man-induced factors.

3.4 Reasons for change

A growing body of literature focuses attention on the close relationship between drainage activity and land use change, and on the implications for nature conservation (Lukehurst 1977; Wade & Edwards 1980; Driscoll 1983; Swales 1982a, b). For its study areas, ITE has established (i) where and when under-drainage and ditch improvement schemes have taken place; (ii) the period of land use change, and the prevailing pattern of agriculture over the last 100 years; and (iii) the distribution of vascular plants in the late 19th century, *c.* 1950, and the early 1980s.

The next stage in the ITE study will examine more rigorously the apparent correlations between (i) and (ii), and the changes identified under (iii). The examination currently falls into 3 parts.

i. Trials of 4 wetland species (lesser water-parsnip, greater water-parsnip, flowering rush and branched bur-reed) have begun at Monks Wood to ascertain how depth of water, or height above water, can affect production and growth. These trials should demonstrate the demands of the individual species, and how the conversion of a gently sloping bank to a steep, trapezoidal channel section may limit available habitat.

ii. A trial has been set up in the Romney Marsh, whereby a ditch has been cleared of its dominant common reed, and specimens of 4 species typical of shallow pasture ditches have been

100

introduced (fool's water-cress, tubular water-dropwort, frogbit and tufted forget-me-not). Because the ditch lies in arable land, the experiment should provide the opportunity to separate the effects due to shade created by tall emergents (eg the reed) from other factors brought about by the conversion from pasture. The reed will continue to be suppressed and the input of nutrients monitored. The trial should help in answering the question "how far is the decline in 'pasture species' a result of conversion to arable land as opposed to the establishment of tall dense emergent vegetation?"

iii. ITE is collaborating in an experiment which has been set up by the Grassland Research Institute in Devon, which uses what are essentially 1 ha field lysimeters to observe the effects of drainage and varying nitrogen applications on the production of bullocks in terms of live weight gain. ITE is monitoring the changes in the composition of the turf under the different forms of management and drainage regimes.

These trials represent only a very small proportion of those required to investigate the inter-relationships between drainage activity, land use and management, and the species composition of grazing marsh vegetation (Figure 1).

4 What needs to be done?

The paper has cited some research being done by ITE to provide a basis for prescribing what aspects of the drainage/wildlife interface need to be investigated over the next few years. ITE has adopted an archival and field survey approach, complemented more recently by field trials. So far, the study has been confined to vascular plants. Four further lines of enquiry are as follows.

i. To assess conclusions reached with respect to plant species and communities in relation to changes in bird, mammal and invertebrate groups.

ii. To collaborate with soil scientists, hydrologists, drainage engineers, agronomists and land econ-

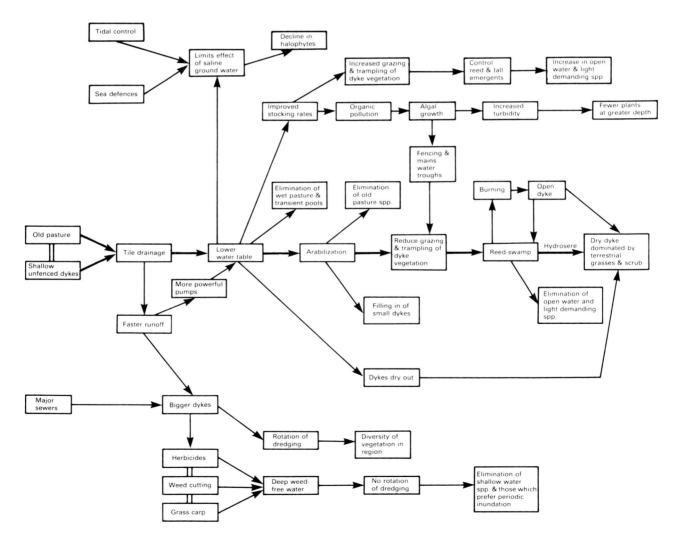

Figure 1. The inter-relationship of drainage, land use and management, and botanical status

omists in order to describe precisely the result of drainage operations. Without a greater appreciation of the findings, methods and techniques of these other disciplines and professions, there can be little precision in answering the question 'how does a specific form of drainage, applied at a specific point in time, in a specific place, on a certain soil type, affect a particular kind of plant or animal life?'

iii. To acquire and compare a greater range of base-line data, derived from the past and present, from a wide range of wetland systems in order to monitor future trends more rigorously. We need to demonstrate the considerable variety of conditions prevailing within each wetland area, and the bearing this variety has on such questions as 'are the effects of contemporary agricultural change unprecedented in that area?' and 'how far do the drainage techniques being applied in one area have a similar impact on wildlife to those in another?'

iv. To obtain more detailed knowledge of the autecology of the species affected by drainage and land use change, and, especially, of the ecological processes that can affect the rate and character of species displacement and colonization.

5 Summary
In order to assess the extent to which wildlife communities may be affected by land drainage, a greater knowledge is required of the chronology and extent of drainage in the past, changes in land use and management, and changes in wildlife. The methodology used by ITE in a study of grazing marsh vegetation is described. Priorities for research in monitoring and predicting trends include obtaining comparable knowledge of changes in birds, mammals and invertebrates, collaboration with agricultural scientists, collection of more base-line data from a wider range of habitats, and autecological studies of species liable to displacement or to become colonizers.

6 References
Driscoll, R.J. 1983. *Land use surveys in Broadland: an inventory of surveys.* Unpublished.

Green, F.H.W. 1979. *Field drainage in Europe: a quantitative survey.* (Report no. 57). Wallingford: Institute of Hydrology.

Hanbury, F.J. & Marshall, E.S. 1899. *Flora of Kent.* London: Hanbury.

Lukehurst, C.T. 1977. *The Stour Marshes: a study of agricultural changes, 1840-1966.* PhD thesis, University of London, Birkbeck College.

Royal Society for the Protection of Birds. 1983. *Land drainage in England and Wales: an interim report.* Sandy: RSPB.

Swales, S. 1982a. A 'before and after' study of the effects of land drainage works on fish stocks in the upper reaches of a lowland river. *Fish. Manage.,* **13,** 105-114.

Swales, S. 1982b. Environmental effects of river channel works used in land drainage improvement. *J. environ. Manage.,* **14,** 103-126.

Trafford, B.D. 1978. Recent progress in field drainage: part II. *Jl R. agric. Soc.,* **139,** 40.

Trafford, B.D. 1982. *The background to land drainage policies and practices in England and Wales.* Paris: Seminaire L'Ecole Polytechnique, Assainissement agricole, Economie et Environnement. Unpublished.

Wade, P.M. & Edwards, R.W. 1980. The effect of channel maintenance on the aquatic macrophytes of the drainage channels of the Monmouthshire Levels, South Wales, 1840-1976. *Aquat. Bot.,* **8,** 307-322.

Williams, M. 1970. *The draining of the Somerset Levels.* Cambridge: Cambridge University Press.

Wolley-Dod, A.H. 1937. *The flora of Sussex.* Hastings: Saville.

The effects of eutrophication on aquatic wildlife

P S MAITLAND
Institute of Terrestrial Ecology, Edinburgh

1 Introduction
This paper reviews the eutrophication process, and in particular the effect of so-called 'cultural' eutrophication on lakes. Appropriate case histories relevant to agriculture are presented, and current and potential research is reviewed in relation to ameliorating the worst ecological effects of excessive nutrient input.

Biological productivity in fresh waters throughout the world has been the focus of many recent research projects, especially those initiated during the International Biological Programme. Over the last 2 decades, there has been an increasing awareness of problems associated with excessive growth of algae and higher aquatic plants, particularly in lakes, and to a lesser extent in rivers and estuaries.

Normally, as lakes age they undergo change, and a natural process of maturation takes place. Precipitation and natural catchment drainage contribute nutrients which support and enhance the growth of algae and macrophytic vegetation. However, the activities of man in agriculture, urbanization, and the discharge of sewage and industrial wastes increase the amounts of organic and inorganic sediments and the nutrient input to lakes. In these ways, the natural processes of enrichment and sedimentation are accelerated, and the quality of the water changes materially, often at a relatively rapid rate.

There is no simple relationship between the process of eutrophication and the actual amounts of nutrients present or entering the waters concerned. Rawson

(1955) emphasized the complex interrelationships of climatic, physical, chemical and biological factors affecting the productivity of lakes. The basin morphology, catchment geology, temperature, nutrients and other variables all influence the trophic nature of a water body.

2 Eutrophication

2.1 Eutrophication process

The view that all lakes originate as oligotrophic systems, gradually become more eutrophic, and then fill in completely is actually too simplistic. Many lakes lose nutrients from the watershed as they increase in age, and change from eutrophic to oligotrophic systems. However, most lakes do gradually become richer; in particular, lakes in areas affected by man's activities may receive unnaturally large amounts of nutrients which increase lake productivity. The nutrients are mainly from agricultural fertilizers, industrial wastes and sewage effluents. Their impact on the lake is to make it change rapidly from oligotrophic to eutrophic, and this acceleration is sometimes referred to simply as eutrophication or often as cultural eutrophication. Detailed accounts of this process have been given by Hasler (1947), Beeton (1965), Sawyer (1966), and others. The nutrients specifically involved in the eutrophication process are nitrates and phosphates, which in nature are frequently present in small (and therefore limiting) amounts. Other less important nutrients include magnesium, potassium, sulphates, trace elements and organic growth factors (Vollenweider 1968).

One of the major effects of eutrophication is the excessive growth of algae. In waters used for domestic and industrial purposes, for example, the excessive growth may result in massive and expensive filtration problems. Algal blooms are frequently aesthetically unpleasant, resulting in slimy floating green masses of objectional odour. Many algae impart unpleasant tastes and odours to water, and some release toxic substances. Extensive growths of phytoplankton may also result in turbid waters through which light cannot penetrate and which have high oxygen demand. In many eutrophic waters, there are extensive growths of macrophytes which interfere with swimming, boating, fishing and other recreation. Macrophytes also play an important role in the eventual extinction of lake basins. Linked with these changes in the plant communities, there are changes in fauna. Usually the invertebrate community becomes much less diverse, although the species which remain may become very abundant. A significant change usually takes place in the composition of the fish fauna, with salmonid species being replaced by coarse fish. In extreme eutrophication, primary production is so high that subsequent decomposition of organic matter and respiration at night completely deoxygenate the water, and fish may be eliminated altogether.

With increasing land use and the significant movement of particulate and dissolved material from catchments to their water courses, numerous water bodies have undergone serious ecological deterioration over the last few decades. Considerable attention was given in the past to domestic and industrial sewage outflows, but many other land use activities such as agriculture, tourism and recreation also contribute significantly to a reduction of water quality in lakes and rivers. In particular, high rates of fertilization and increased stocking density of grazing animals have added significantly to the amounts of major nutrients (especially phosphorus and nitrogen) passing into fresh waters. Unfortunately, the diffuse character of these sources makes their study much more difficult than that of point sources (eg a domestic sewage outfall), especially as the chemical make-up of agricultural fertilizers may also change in time.

Nitrogen, which is much more abundant than phosphorus in most fresh waters, rarely limits primary production, whilst increased amounts of phosphorus can lead to excessive algal growth, depletion of oxygen, and subsequent fish deaths. Phosphorus is frequently designated as the most important limiting nutrient. One of the most important sources of phosphorus is domestic sewage, but significant amounts of phosphorus are also carried into fresh waters from agricultural land during heavy rainfall. Most nitrogen passing into watercourses appears to come from adjacent soils, and intensively fertilized farmland represents the main source of nitrogen to fresh waters draining from agricultural areas. Several studies have indicated that some 10-25% of nitrogen applied as fertilizers runs off into adjacent running waters. Apart from eutrophication problems, high levels of nitrate become a health hazard when they reach concentrations greater than 11 mg per litre.

Within the water bodies themselves, various biological indicators can be used to quantify the changes which take place during cultural eutrophication. In general, plant and animal communities become much less diverse, and many sensitive species are lost. In the phytoplankton, blue-green algae often become predominant, and form the basis of periodic massive blooms. Some species of macrophytes grow extremely well initially, though they may die back later. Zooplankton and zoobenthos communities always become much simpler with the loss of many sensitive species. A number of indices has been developed based on community structure and species diversity which indicate the direction of change. Studies of lake sediments can also provide extremely useful information on the trophic history of a lake.

2.2 Origin of nutrients

2.2.1 Natural sources

The main contribution of natural nutrients to surface waters is through the normal runoff from soil. Soluble chemicals in the soil are removed through erosion and solution and pass into adjacent watercourses. The ratios of nutrients coming from surface runoff compared to those from groundwater vary in each catchment according to local soils and geology. The levels of nutrients in runoff water depend likewise on the type of soil involved. Massey *et al.* (1950) found that the enrichment ratio (concentration in eroded material divided by concentration in soil) for phosphorus, nitrogen, organic matter and exchangeable potassium was always more than one. The enrichment ratio usually increases as erosion decreases. Loss of organic matter from the soil is considered a serious aspect of soil erosion and usually necessitates large amounts of artificial fertilizer to replace the loss.

Sylvester (1961) showed that, although relatively clean streams draining afforested ground contain low concentrations of nutrients (similar to the concentrations in a eutrophic lake), very small increases in soluble phosphate are all that are necessary to increase production significantly. The inputs of various nutrients from atmospheric precipitation have been studied less than most other sources. However, in some cases they can be an important additional source and should always be taken into account when preparing nutrient budgets. In some areas, contributions from dust or rainfall can be significant.

Many of the nutrients in standing waters are derived from sediments. This is especially true in shallow waters where sediments are more easily disturbed by wind action. Several studies have shown that significant fractions of nutrients from the sediments enter the water column under reducing conditions (Mortimer 1942).

2.2.2 Artificial sources

Most of the nutrients derived from artificial sources originate in agricultural drainage, industrial waste and domestic sewage. The importance of these sources varies in different catchments, and relevant data are available from numerous studies. Rohlich and Lea (1949) examined the sources of nutrients entering Lake Mendota. In one year, 7936 kg of soluble phosphorus entered the lake. The greatest single contributor was Six Mile Creek, which supplied about 40% of the nutrients although it made up only 20% of the flow. The total amount of inorganic nitrogen entering the lake was 111 000 kg, mostly in the form of nitrates. Allochthonous contributions of soluble phosphorus and inorganic nitrogen were thought to be low.

Engelbrecht and Morgan (1961) stated that the amount of phosphate varied according to the nature and amount of phosphates in the soil, mode of drainage, topography, intensity and distribution of rainfall, rates of infiltration and percolation, and other features. Sylvester (1961) found nitrates to be twice as high in sub-surface drainage and the ratio of nitrogen to phosphorus to be 2.5 times that in surface drainage water. The greatest concentrations of total phosphorus were found in surface irrigation drains, of soluble phosphorus and nitrogen in sub-surface drains, and of total nitrogen in urban street drains.

In characterizing the Chickamauga Reservoir in Tennessee, Stream Sanitation Staff (1964) noted that there were many local point sources of pollution. Fortunately, the relatively rapid flushing of such reservoirs prevented their rapid eutrophication. Ohle (1955) found that nutrients in north German lakes were derived mainly from the increased activities of man. Organic sewage and kitchen wastes were major contributors and brought about significant changes in Plon Lake from 1926-29. The rapid eutrophication of such lakes is distinguished from normal eutrophication by the enormous production of plankton, as well as the speed of enrichment. The contribution of nutrients from artificial sources was greater than that from natural drainage waters. Moreover, the increased flow of nutrients into oligotrophic lakes was felt by Ambuhl (1962) to be much more important than the input to eutrophic lakes (see Maitland 1981).

2.3 Case histories relevant to agriculture

Much of the important evidence concerning the eutrophication of fresh waters has come from a study of case histories, from which it has been possible to determine the onset and gradual eutrophication of many bodies of water. Insight may also be gained into the problems of eutrophication. However, extremely detailed and long-term studies are rare, even from some of the most important lakes in the world. Usually, though these lakes have been the subject of extensive research, it has not been directed to the study of eutrophication. Many of the case histories do not concern nutrients directly, but other indices used to interpret the changes taking place.

2.3.1 North America

Whiteside (1965) described the eutrophication of Potato Lake, Arizona, on the basis of palaeoecological evidence from sediment cores. The loss on ignition (equivalent to the organic matter) at different levels in the sediments was also studied. An interesting feature of the cores from this lake was the sudden variation in organic matter near the mud-water interface. Whiteside attributed this variation to recent changes brought about by man's activities within the catchment, especially agriculture and logging.

The Great Lakes of North America are among the largest bodies of fresh waters in the world. Following the collapse of a major fishery in 1925, Wright and Tidd (1933) investigated Lake Erie. After an analysis of its water chemistry, they concluded that pollution from human sources had increased plankton to such an extent that there had been a significant reduction of oxygen in the water. Beeton (1963) described changes in Lake Erie and in some of the other Great Lakes. He pointed out significant changes in the zoobenthos of Lake Erie after the summer of 1953, when oxygen depletion caused a massive mortality of mayfly larvae. The number of caddis fly larvae also decreased, but there were increases in midge larvae and worms. In subsequent surveys, Beeton (1965) verified that large areas of Lake Erie still had low oxygen values. He classified Lakes Huron, Michigan and Superior as oligotrophic, Lake Ontario as morphometrically oligotrophic or mesotrophic, and Lake Erie as eutrophic. All of the Great Lakes were considered to show progressive increases in various ions and total dissolved solids, with the exception of Lake Superior.

2.3.2 Europe

The Bodensee is one of the clearest examples of lake eutrophication. Kliffmuller (1962) showed that, in 1935, when the first recorded measurements were made, no measurable phosphate was present. In 1950, 2-3 mg/m^3 were found, and in 1954, 2-4 mg/m^3. By 1959, the amount of phosphate had increased to 7-9.5 mg/m^3. Based on the phosphate content only, the lake probably changed from oligotrophic to eutrophic between 1935 and 1962. Numann (1964) reported that, as a consequence of enrichment, the growth of whitefish had increased so much that they were being caught prior to maturity by gill nets, resulting in a decrease in the fishery. In addition to the accelerated growth, various other changes in the lake caused changes in the breeding areas of fish present, which meant that 4 previously isolated whitefish were able to inter-breed. Isolation mechanisms present before enrichment had been minimized.

Loch Leven in Scotland has shown numerous changes in its flora and fauna over the last century which have been attributed to eutrophication. Species associated with oligotrophic conditions such as charr and desmids have declined or disappeared, and prolonged algal blooms have been a feature of recent years. Much of the macrophytic vegetation has disappeared, and there have been major changes in the composition of zooplankton and zoobenthos. These changes have been associated with, and are probably due to, artificial enrichment of the lake by fertilizers draining from farm land and sewage from the townships of Kinross and Milnathort. Holden and Caines (1974) recorded large quantities of nitrate nitrogen carried into the loch, equivalent to 250 tonnes of nitrogen in 1969. The use of nitrogenous fertilizers in the catchment increased about 3 times from 1952-68.

2.3.3 Australasia

Lake Haruna in Japan is the site of one of the earliest studies of eutrophication in Asia. Yoshimura (1933) showed that there were gradual changes in the water transparency over a period of 24 years, decreasing from 9.5 m in 1906 to 2.3 m in 1932. Nutrients were assumed to have entered the lake from the areas of grassland in its catchment, and the decreasing values of transparency along with the more recent appearances of blue-green algae were regarded as a definite indication of enrichment.

As part of a review of the eutrophication of 3 lakes in New Zealand (Lake Okataina, Lake Ngapouri and Lake Okaro), Fish (1963) examined the performance (especially the growth rates) of trout. The fish in Lake Okataina grew significantly faster and seemed healthier in other ways than those in the other 2 lakes, both of which had higher primary production and lower dissolved oxygen levels than Lake Okataina, largely because of eutrophication. The main cause was believed to be the development of agriculture in the catchments of Lakes Ngapouri and Okaro, which resulted in poorer conditions for trout in the lakes.

2.4 Rehabilitation

The causes of the degradation of lake ecosystems by eutrophication are now fairly clear, and appear to be associated largely with the increased inflow of material from the catchment. Methods for rehabilitating such lakes have been reviewed by Bjork (1980) and include sediment removal, manipulation of bottom sediment, aeration of the hypolimnion, manipulation of biological components in the ecosystem, and, of course, the control of nutrient input. Though the treatment of industrial discharges varies considerably for each industry, standard methods are now available for the efficient treatment of domestic sewage. Over the last few years, there has been a considerable decrease in the discharge of organic matter and phosphorus.

2.4.1 Sediment removal

Lake Trummen in Sweden is one of the classical cases of lake restoration by sediment removal. The history of its development, degradation and restoration has been described by Bjork (1972), Andersson et al. (1975) and others. This shallow lake received sewage and industrial discharges for about 30 years, and changed rapidly from an oligotrophic to a eutrophic system. The extensive layers of rich sediment which were deposited during eutrophication were so great that, although the sewage was eventually diverted, the lake showed no recovery during the following decade. Because of this, the sediments which had accumulated during the period of sewage discharge were suction dredged during the summers of 1970 and 1971, and altogether about 300 000 m^3 of sediment was pumped out. Following this action, the concentration of nutrients decreased considerably and the oxygen conditions improved. Blooms of blue-green algae disappeared and transparency increased in summer. The sediment which was removed has been used to improve the nutrient-poor soils of the area, and the lake is now used for sport fishing and swimming.

2.4.2 Sediment manipulation

Because of the difficulties in some districts of finding suitable areas on which to deposit lake sediment, the manipulation of sediments in situ was considered desirable. The first feasibility trial was carried out on Lake Lillesjon (Ripl 1978) into which sewage had been discharged for many years. When sewage was finally diverted in 1971, the lake was in a very poor state with total oxygen deficiency and luxuriant growth of duckweed, sometimes covering most of the water surface. The upper layers of sediment were black and extremely rich in phosphorus.

The method involves oxidizing the top sediment layer by adding nitrate and precipitating the phosphorus by adding an iron salt. Because of the rapid denitrification, the nitrogen leaves the ecosystem as a gas. In Lake Lillesjon, iron chloride was added resulting in a decrease of pH to 3. Under these conditions, hydrogen sulphide evolved, but 2 weeks after the first treatment the transparency increased from 2.3 m to more than 4.2 m. The water of the lake is fully oxygenated all the year round, and the superficial layers of sediment now act as a trap for phosphorus. Phytoplankton crops are not extensive, and the lake is used for swimming and sport fishing.

2.4.3 Hypolimnion aeration
The use of compressed air has been developed by Hasler (1957) and others to increase the circulation in lakes. The objective was to prevent the deoxygenation of the hypolimnion during summer, and the killing of fish during winter. Ambuhl (1962) experimented with the artificial mixing of water in Lake Pfaffiker in Switzerland. Compressed air was pumped into the centre of the lake for extensive periods. Both the total heat content of the lake and the amount of oxygen increased.

2.4.4 Biological manipulation
Apart from chemical treatment such as the use of copper sulphate to reduce algal blooms, other attempts have been made to manipulate the biology of eutrophic systems. The regular removal of large amounts of macrophytes by cutting and dredging has been attempted in some lakes, but is generally considered to be an expensive process. In other lakes, the removal of large numbers of fish has been considered as a way of depleting the total nutrients. However, although probably effective in very nutrient-poor arctic systems, it has been relatively unsuccessful in eutrophic waters.

2.4.5 Nutrient reduction
In many lakes, phosphorus appears to be the main factor limiting primary production. The addition of phosphorus is often mainly via the discharge of sewage effluents, and if these can be diverted around the lake then significant improvements can be expected. The eutrophication of Lake Washington from 1933-55 has been described by Edmondson (1966). Typically, blue-green algae started to dominate the phytoplankton and oxygen deficits occurred in the hypolimnion. Eventually, plans were developed to divert all of the sewage from the city of Seattle from Lake Washington to Puget Sound. Following this diversion, there was a rapid parallel drop in the levels of phosphorus and phytoplankton, while nitrate dropped less rapidly. This reversal of eutrophication is regarded as being one of the classical examples of artificial oligotrophication.

3 Current research
Current research on eutrophication has changed considerably over the last few years. Much less effort is now directed towards describing the eutrophication process, and rather more to the ways of diverting it or reducing its harmful effects. The zoning of land use is of major importance, if natural aquatic systems are to be protected from the worst effects of eutrophication. Good farming practices are being developed which provide benefits not only for the farmer, but also for other inhabitants of the catchment. Proper planning of sewage schemes in urban areas can help to alleviate the overloading of sewage systems. Methods for the prevention of eutrophication of drinking water reservoirs have been developed. These include the exclusion of animals and man from reservoir catchments, the development of adequate sewage systems where exclusion is impracticable, strip cropping and contour farming.

The intensive research on biological production and eutrophication which was carried out during the International Biological Programme has been replaced by a new series of projects under the aegis of the UNESCO Man and the Biosphere (MAB) programme. Many of the research activities in this programme relate to land use impacts on inland waters, and there is active participation in this field by Austria, Bulgaria, Czechoslovakia, Federal Republic of Germany, German Democratic Republic, The Netherlands, Poland, Spain, Sweden, Switzerland, and the United States of America. There are no MAB research projects in the United Kingdom or special MAB funding within this particular field.

However, recent work in the UK parallels that being carried out elsewhere in Europe. It includes the typology, trophic state and hydrobiological regime of important lakes, and the results provide a basis for recommendations to the Government about future exploitation and management. Rivers are being classified in terms of water quality in relation to their biology, and attention has been given to improving the position of biological methods of analysis. The possibility of managing lakes by controlling their nutrient cycling is also being investigated. The main aim here is to find out just how the nutrient loading of these systems can be reduced in order to control algal growth under given nutrient loadings. Much of this type of research involves monitoring the release of nutrients from watersheds and following their impact as loads on the aquatic biota.

4 Future research
The literature concerning eutrophication shows that systematic measurements of variables over a reasonable time period are rare. It is often difficult to prove

that changes have actually taken place in the lake. Unless background data on nutrients, transparency, algae, production, zooplankton, zoobenthos and sediments are available, then statements concerning the eutrophication of a water body may be doubtful. It is important, therefore, that, as well as new, stimulating projects in this field, a reasonable amount of effort should be devoted to systematic surveys of important waters, to establish base-line data and obtain information from which trends can be noted.

The variables to be measured and the frequency of recording are often difficult to identify where resources are limited. Temperature, oxygen and transparency are certainly valuable parameters to record. To be of maximum value, such studies should extend over several years because of the influence of climate. Modern techniques of remote sensing are being developed rapidly at the moment, but their value in surveillance programmes is not yet clear.

Basing their conclusions on the results of recent symposia, Duncan and Rzoska (1980) have specified a minimum monitoring programme for quantifying the effects of land use in a watershed on its waters. The prerequisites for such a programme are as follows.

   i. An inter-calibration centre for ensuring compatibility of results by testing analytical methods.

   ii. A workshop on methods of raw data analysis for purposes of comparison. This should establish a common terminology and computational procedures for deriving quantities such as nutrient loadings from raw monitoring data.

   iii. Criteria for the selection of research catchments should include area, representativeness of regional characteristics and land use. Land use should be defined in some detail and intensity of usage should be quantified.

   iv. A detailed description of the main characteristics of the watershed and its main water bodies: regional relief and geology; soils; available water resources; natural soil drainage and erosion hazard; hydrographical network, including permanent/temporary discharge; natural terrestrial vegetation and its level of biological productivity; characteristics of the major rivers and lakes, including their trophic status and previous lake history from sediment core analysis.

It is also noted that the following considerations relate to the parameters to be monitored.

   i. Frequency of measurement will depend on the main growing season, timing of hydrological events and nature of measurement, but both a time sequence throughout the year and mean annual or seasonal quantities are required.

   ii. Ideally, parameters should be measured in absolute concentrations of weight per unit volume.

   iii. Overall watershed parameters required for possible correlation with quantities measured within the watershed include the levels and seasonal patterns of precipitation and evaporation, discharge and inputs of airborne materials. Local measurements should include precipitation, surface and sub-surface runoff and percolation to the groundwater, together with their chemical content.

   iv. Water quality parameters of watercourses and recipient water bodies should include nitrogen, phosphorus and carbon; other elements, eg calcium, magnesium, etc; biocytes; suspended matter; physico-chemical parameters (eg dissolved oxygen, pH, conductivity and temperature); and biological parameters. The latter could include a wide variety of measurements, including BOD, chlorophyll, phytoplankton, zooplankton and zoobenthos, and fish.

   v. Collation, presentation, interpretation and publication of results.

   vi. Development of a model of the land use impact on lakes and reservoirs in the watershed.

In addition to the above recommendations, the following specific studies have been suggested for MAB projects on the mechanisms of land use impacts on inland waters. These include, first, whole watershed studies of different types.

   i. Long-term monitoring of small watersheds subjected to various levels of fertilization.

   ii. Long-term monitoring of water bodies in small watersheds before and after changed land use. The measurements should include all the recipient waters in the catchment.

   iii. Long-term development of models encompassing the whole watershed and its terrestrial and aquatic components and including the submodels, the hydrodynamic, physico-chemical and biological aspects.

Second, there are a number of particular topics.

   iv. Detoxification processes in aquatic sediments and the role of bacteria.

   v. Transfer mechanisms of the elements and fertilizers and pollutants from soil to underground water, and consequent biological changes.

   vi. Inputs of airborne material into watersheds.

   vii. The role of littoral macrophytes as biological filters for nutrients.

viii. The contamination of groundwater and its biological consequences.

Several projects encompassing some of the above topics are already in progress in the United Kingdom and elsewhere. However, there is still considerable scope for progress in many areas, particularly in quantifying the transfer of nutrients from one part of the system to another. The present controversy over the effects of acid precipitation on freshwater ecosystems in Great Britain has effectively demonstrated our ignorance about many of the processes that take place between materials landing on the soil and their transfer to neighbouring watercourses.

5 Discussion
Fernald (1980) has emphasized that proper land use planning is the key to the mitigation of negative impacts on water quality. Land use planners and other public decision-makers often do not understand the data available from the scientific community. At the operational level, the public decision-maker must play a major role in the control of eutrophication and many other harmful processes affecting our environment. Fernald assumes that the land use decision-making process is a sequence of rational steps which can be applied at any level of planning. The elements in his process include formulation of land use objectives; the identification of future land use needs; the gathering and analysis of the upland data; the evaluation of land use laws, policies and regulations; the identification and evaluation of policy influences; the evaluation of land use change methodology; and implementation of land use decisions.

Although, as outlined above, there are still a number of relevant areas for current and future research concerning the effects of eutrophication on aquatic wildlife, sufficient is already known about the impact of eutrophication to mean that the control of the problem lies mainly in the hands of planners and decision-makers, rather than with the scientific community. Excessive quantities of nutrients from various sources lead to a destabilizing of natural aquatic systems, with consequent loss of sensitive species, and massive increases of tolerant ones. Periodic massive deaths of algae and macrophytes lead to de-oxygenation and fish kills. In theory, the remedies are often simple; in practice, they may be rarely carried out. Until sensible long-term planning of land use overtakes the short-term gains of various forms of land mis-management, eutrophication will continue to be a problem.

6 Summary
6.1 Eutrophication is a natural process whereby freshwater ecosystems age and enrich with time. Most lakes are eventually doomed to extinction.

6.2 The process is accelerated because of cultural eutrophication, in which several of man's activ- ities (notably agriculture, industry and urbanization) add significantly to the load of nutrients and other materials entering lakes and rivers. The phenomenon is world-wide.

6.3 The most obvious effects of such eutrophication are the production of unstable plant and animal communities in fresh waters, with periodic massive algal blooms and fish kills. Contamination of water supplies and objectionable odours are usually associated with such changes.

6.4 The subject has been extensively researched and control measures are now feasible in many situations. Point sources of eutrophication are easier to deal with than diffuse ones. In addition, many rehabilitation methods have now been developed to reverse the process.

6.5 The major controls now lie in the hands of land use planners and politicians. Nonetheless, we are still ignorant about many of the processes that take place between materials landing on the soil and their transfer to neighbouring watercourses.

7 References
Ambuhl, H. 1962. Die kunstliche Beluftung des Pfaffikersees. *Verbandsbericht VSA*, **77**, 1-9.

Andersson, G., Berggren, H. & Hamrin, S. 1975. Lake Trummen restoration project. *Verh. int. Verein. theor. angew. Limnol.*, **19**, 1097-1106.

Beeton, A.M. 1963. Limnological survey of Lake Erie: 1959 and 1960. *Tech. Rep. Gt Lakes Fish. Commn*, **6**, 1-32.

Beeton, A.M. 1965. Eutrophication of the St Lawrence Great Lakes. *Limnol. Oceanogr.*, **10**, 240-254.

Bjork, S. 1972. Swedish lake restoration programme gets results. *Ambio*, **1**, 154-165.

Bjork, S. 1980. Restoration of degraded lake ecosystems. *Proc. Man and the Biosphere (MAB) Workshop 1978*, 196-219.

Duncan, N. & Rzoska, J. 1980. Land use impacts on lake and reservoir ecosystems. *Proc. Man and the Biosphere (MAB) Workshop 1978*, 1-34.

Edmondson, W.T. 1966. Changes in the oxygen deficit of Lake Washington. *Verh. int. Verein. theor. angew. Limnol.*, **16**, 153-158.

Engelbrecht, R.S. & Morgan, J.J. 1961. Land drainage as a source of phosphorus in Illinois surface waters. *Trans. Semin. Algae & Metro. Wastes, 1960*, 74-79.

Fernald, E.A. 1980. The land use decision-making process. *Proc. Man and the Biosphere (MAB) Workshop 1978*, 220-255.

Fish, G.R. 1963. Limnological conditions and growth of trout in three lakes near Rotorua. *Proc. N.Z. ecol. Soc.*, **10**, 1-7.

Hasler, A.D. 1947. Eutrophication of lakes by domestic drainage. *Ecology*, **28**, 383-395.

Hasler, A.D. 1957. Natural and artificially (air-ploughing) induced movement of radioactive phosphorus from the muds of lakes. *Proc. int. Conf. Radioisotopes Scient. Res., 1st, Paris, 1957*, **4**, 568-675.

Holden, A.V. & Caines, L.A. 1974. Nutrient chemistry of Loch Leven, Kinross. *Proc. R. Soc. Edinb.*, **74**, 101-121.

Kliffmuller, R. 1962. Der Anstieg des Phosphat-Phosphors als Ausdruck fortschreitender Eutrophierung im Bodensee (Obersee). *Int. Rev. ges. Hydrobiol. Hydrogr.*, **47**, 118-122.

Massey, H.F., Jackson, M.L. & Bay, C. 1950. Runoff analysis as a measure of erosion losses and potential discharge of mineral and organic matter into lakes and streams. *Rep. Univ. Wis. Lake Invest. Comm. 1950*, 1-28.

Maitland, P.S. 1981. Introduction and catchment analysis. In: *The ecology of Scotland's largest lochs: Lomond, Awe, Ness, Morar and Shiel*, edited by P.S. Maitland, 1-27. (Monographiae biologicae no. 44). The Hague: Junk.

Mortimer, C.H. 1942. The exchange of dissolved substances between mud and water in lakes. *J. Ecol.*, **30**, 147-201.

Numann, W. 1964. Die Veranderungen in Blaufelchenbestand (*Coregonus wartmanni*) und in der Blaufelchenfischerei als Folge der kunstlichen Eutrophierung des Bodensees. *Verh. int. Verein. theor. angew. Limnol.*, **15**, 514-523.

Ohle, W. 1955. Die Ursachen der rasanten Seeneutrophierung. *Verh. int. Verein. theor. angew. Limnol.*, **12**, 373-382.

Rawson, D.S. 1955. Morphometry as a dominant factor in the productivity of large lakes. *Verh. int. Verein. theor. angew. Limnol.*, **12**, 164-165.

Ripl, W. 1978. Oxidation of lake sediments with nitrate. *Univ. Lund Inst. Limnol. Publ.*, 1-151.

Rohlich, G.A. & Lea, W.L. 1949. The origin and quantities of plant nutrients in Lake Mendota. *Rep. Univ. Wis. Lake Invest. Comm. 1949*, 1-8.

Sawyer, C.N. 1966. Basic concepts of eutrophication. *J. Wat. Pollut. Control Fed.*, **38**, 737-744.

Stream Sanitation Staff. 1964. *Quality of water in Chickamauga Reservoir*. Chattanooga: Tennessee Valley Authority.

Sylvester, R.O. 1961. Nutrient content of drainage water from forested, urgan and agricultural areas. *Trans. Semin. Algae & Metro. Wastes, 1960*, 80-87.

Vollenweider, R. A. 1968. *Scientific fundamentals of the eutrophication of lakes and flowing waters with particular reference to nitrogen and phosphorus as factors in eutrophication*. (DAS/CSI/68.27). Paris: Organization for Economic Cooperation and Development.

Whiteside, M.C. 1965. Palaeoecological studies of Potato Lake and its environs. *Ecology*, **46**, 807-816.

Wright, S. & Tidd, W.M. 1933. Summary of limnological investigations in western Lake Erie in 1929 and 1930. *Trans. Am. Fish. Soc.*, **63**, 271-285.

Yoshimura, S. 1933. Rapid eutrophication within recent years of Lake Haruna, Gunman, Japan. *Jap. J. Geol. Geogr.*, **11**, 31-41.

The effects of flood alleviation and land drainage on birds of wet grasslands

C J CADBURY
Royal Society for the Protection of Birds, Sandy

1 The habitat

This paper largely concerns lowland neutral grasslands below 600 ft (183 m) which are subject to freshwater flooding or waterlogging. It therefore includes flood plain grasslands, washlands, coastal grazing marshes, and more open areas of flood plain mire which grade into base-rich marshes and fens with beds of common reed in the absence of grazing (Ratcliffe 1977). It excludes salt marshes and the uplands. Embanked washlands (or ings) are a feature of the low-lying regions of eastern England. They tend to be flooded more frequently in winter than most other flood plain grasslands and, because of their flood relief function, water is allowed to lie on the fields for longer in the spring. The traditional use of washland in summer is grazing by cattle, though in more accessible areas a hay crop is taken first (Thomas *et al.* 1981).

2 Loss of habitat

Until the mid-17th century, there were about 3380 km^2 of wetland in the fens of Cambridgeshire (including Huntingdonshire) and adjacent Lincolnshire and Norfolk; 98% was drained before 1939, and a further 4000 ha during or just after the Second World War. Only 1% now remains as a fragmented relict and much of this area is in a drier state than formerly. Of the 6094 ha of washland, 49% is now arable (Thomas *et al.* 1981). Even in Cambridgeshire, little over 4000 ha of damp or wet grassland still exist, and 62% is represented by the Ouse Washes (1860 ha) and Nene Washes (604 ha); most of the other 30 damp grassland sites are less than 50 ha in size.

The Survey of Breeding Waders of Wet Meadows, carried out in 1982 by the British Trust for Ornithology (BTO), the Royal Society for the Protection of Birds (RSPB) and the Nature Conservancy Council (NCC), covered a substantial proportion of the damp grassland sites in England and Wales and showed how restricted the habitat had become (Smith 1983a). In many counties, there is little land left to drain except by refinements to existing drainage. Few extensive areas remain. The largest is the Somerset Moors (c.12 000 ha) but, since 1958, a series of pump drainage schemes has reduced the frequency, duration and depth of winter flooding over much of the area.

The RSPB's survey of reed beds in 1979 and 1980 located only 109 in excess of 2 ha in England and Wales; 70% were less than 20 ha, and half of the total area of reed (2169 ha) was restricted to 15 sites. Over one third of the reed beds were largely dry and the majority showed signs of degeneration as a result of a lowering of the water table. With an abandonment of reed cutting and grazing, hydroseral development is no longer arrested and carr had developed at 70 sites (Bibby & Lunn 1982).

3 The ornithological importance of wet grasslands in England and Wales and the status of birds characteristic of the habitat

Reservoirs, flooded gravel pits and depressions caused by mining subsidence support substantial populations of waterfowl, particularly in winter, but are no habitat substitute for many of the species that are characteristic of wet grasslands. These include breeding waterfowl such as shoveler, snipe and black-tailed godwit, and wintering wildfowl such as Bewick's swan, white-fronted goose and wigeon.

The 1982-83 survey much improved the knowledge of the status of breeding waders in the lowlands inland and provided a basis for evaluating the ornithological importance of individual sites in a national context (Smith 1983a, b). Of the 1366 sites examined, 22%, mostly the drier ones, were unoccupied by breeding waders. Though breeding lapwings occurred on two-thirds of the sites, snipe and redshank were present on only 32% and 35% respectively. Almost one third of the breeding waders on grassland were recorded in 5 outstanding areas: the Ouse Washes (Cambs and Norfolk), Nene Washes (Cambs), Derwent Ings (North Yorks), North Kent Marshes and Somerset Moors (Table 1, Figure 1). A total of only 2143 drumming snipe was recorded on lowland grasslands (Smith 1983a), possibly representing a total population of about 4000 pairs (R E Green pers. comm.); 50% were in Cambridgeshire and Norfolk and 34% were at the Ouse and Nene Washes. This small number is likely to represent a substantial proportion of the breeding snipe in England and Wales. The British breeding population of black-tailed godwits is only about 70 pairs, virtually all of which occur on wet grasslands.

The relatively mild winters enable Britain and Ireland to support large populations of waterfowl when wetlands at a similar latitude inland on the Continent tend to be frozen. In Britain, grasslands subject to shallow flooding are, however, now restricted to a few areas which hold a substantial proportion of the national, if not north-west European, populations of certain species (Prater 1981; Salmon & Moser 1983). There are 11

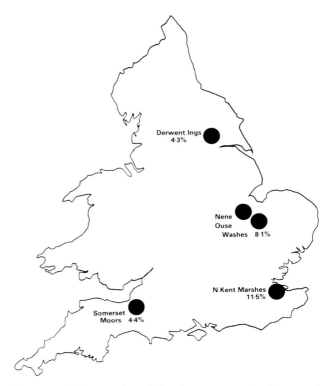

Figure 1. The 5 prime inland wet grassland areas for breeding waders in England and Wales with the proportion of the total number of breeding pairs counted in the lowlands in 1982-83 (Source: amended data from Smith 1983a,b)

wet grasslands, including 4 close to estuaries, which rank as being of international importance for wintering wildfowl. As with breeding waterfowl, the Ouse and Nene Washes, the Derwent Ings and certain sites on the North Kent Marshes are outstanding (Table 2).

Damp permanent pasture, particularly in coastal areas, supports large numbers of lapwings, golden plovers and other waders in winter and spring. Though the largest numbers of golden plovers tend to be in northern England, notable winter concentrations occur on the Derwent Ings, on grazing marshes in Kent and Sussex, and in south-west England, including the Somerset Moors (Fuller & Lloyd 1981). These moors

Table 1. Breeding wader populations of 5 major wet grassland areas in England (Source: modified from Smith 1983a)

	Area surveyed (ha) (incl. some arable land)	Snipe (drumming) (% total England & Wales)	Redshank (pairs)	Total pairs of waders (% total England & Wales)
Ouse Washes (1982)	1 914	501 (23·4)	203	1 089 (8·2)
Nene Washes (1982)	1 040	237 (11·1)	55	503 (3·8)
Derwent Ings (1982-83)	1 092	181 (8·5)	88	576 (4·3)
North Kent Marshes (1982-83)	8 177	16 (0·8)	610	1 543 (11·5)
Somerset Moors (1983)	11 891	154 (7·2)	62	586 (4·4)
Total for the 5 areas	24 114	1 089 (50·1)	1 018 (40·0)	4 297 (32·0)
Total for lowland wet grasslands surveyed in England & Wales 1982-83		2 143	2 482	13 369

110

Table 2. Wet grassland areas in England and Wales of international and national importance for wintering wildfowl, 1978–83. The importance of 4 sites is influenced by the proximity of an estuary

	The number of species for which the sites attained qualifying levels for international/national importance		
	International	National	Total
Ouse Washes, Cambs/Norfolk	5*	5	10
Derwent Ings, North Yorks	2*	4	6
Nene Washes, Cambs	2*	3	5
Swale inc. Elmley, Kent (estuary)	3	1	4
Martin Mere, Lancs (near estuary)	2	2†	4
Lower Avon, Hants	1*	2	3
Somerset Moors	1*	2	3
Yare Marshes, Norfolk	1*	2	3
Medway, Kent (estuary)	1	2†	3
Thames, Kent (estuary)	—	3	3

Single species only:
International: Walmore Common (Gloucs)* and Walland Marsh (Kent)*
National: Amberley (Sussex)†, R. Idle (Notts/S Yorks)†, Dryslwyn (Dyfed)

(Sites of international* or national importance† for the Bewick's swan)

and the Gwent Levels are a staging post for about 2 000 whimbrel returning northwards to their sub-arctic breeding grounds (Ferns *et al.* 1979).

4 Effects of drainage on populations of wintering wildfowl

Grey geese provide examples of the detrimental effects of drainage on wildfowl. At the Nene Washes, the average winter maximum number of pink-footed geese during the 1950s was 4400. Following flood control operations in 1961-62 and an increase in arable farming, which resulted in the loss of a roost site and more disturbance, the number of geese using the Washes in late winter rapidly decreased to almost nil (Figure 2). Throughout the 1960s, the low-lying pastures flanking the Rivers Severn and Camlad (Shropshire and Montgomeryshire) were regularly frequented by 700 to over 1000 European white-fronted geese (Rutter *et al.* 1964). A flood alleviation scheme led to the eventual desertion of the site which was one of very few used by large numbers of this race in Britain. Similarly, on the Somerset Moors, the reduced winter flooding has led to a marked decline in usage by most species of duck in the last 20 years.

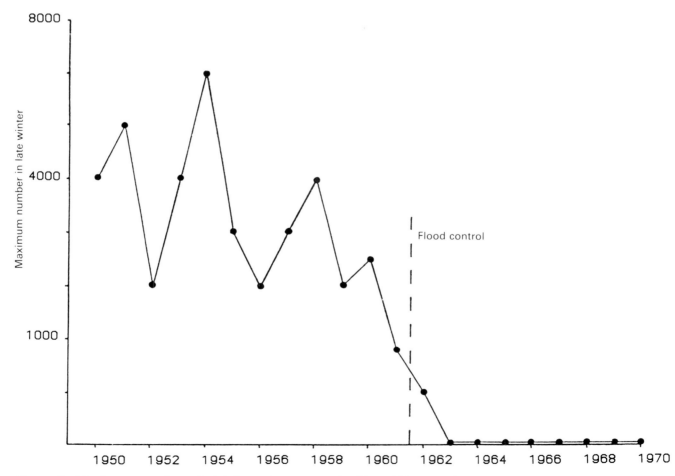

Figure 2. Maximum number of pink-footed geese at the Nene Washes, Cambs, 1950-70

5 Effects of drainage on the populations, distribution and variety of breeding waterfowl

There is little detailed information on the populations of waterfowl that frequented the East Anglian wetlands before the massive loss of habitat in the 19th century. Drainage, however, was probably a major factor responsible for the population declines and temporary extinction as breeding birds of 8 species, including bittern and black-tailed godwit. Though small populations of most of these species have become re-established, habitat loss has severely restricted their potential to spread.

Over the years 1968-72 in which data were collected for the BTO's *Atlas of breeding birds*, snipe were recorded as probably breeding in 724 lowland 10 km squares in England and Wales (Sharrock 1976). In the 1982-83 Breeding Wader Survey, they were found in only 260 squares. Although fewer records would be expected in such a survey, most of which was accomplished in one year, than in the 5 years of the *Atlas* period, a marked contraction in range is indicated. It is probable that snipe have disappeared from many sites which formerly held small numbers (Smith 1983a). In Sussex, there was apparently a major decline in both the snipe and inland redshank populations between 1938 and 1965-67 (Shrubb 1968). A survey in 1980-81 showed that a number of smaller sites had been drained, and these species had become concentrated in a few areas (Mitchell 1983). In Oxfordshire, there were 112 pairs of redshank breeding mainly on grassland in 1939 (Wood 1940) but only 15 pairs in 1982 (Smith 1983a).

The breeding birds of 4 areas in Cambridgeshire and Lincolnshire Fens were surveyed in 1982. The plots were selected to provide a graded series from wet grassland to arable land which had been drained for over 100 years. Seven species of wildfowl and 5 waders bred on the wet washland, but on the drier sites only the ubiquitous mallard was present and the waders were reduced to one species or were absent. Dry grassland and arable land supported a markedly lower density of waders than the undrained area (Table 3) (Clack 1982).

The high water table and regularity of early spring flooding have a major influence on the exceptionally rich variety of waterfowl, 11 or 12 species of wildfowl and 8 species of waders, which breed most years at the Ouse Washes. Even there, the annual fluctuations in numbers reflect flood conditions. Extensive shallow flooding in spring tends to retain a higher proportion of wintering birds and arrests those on passage. In the absence of flooding, potential breeding populations may disperse to breed elsewhere. The fluctuations are most marked in wildfowl and snipe which are more dependent on wet conditions than the lapwing. The wet spring of 1975 was a marked contrast to the spring of 1976 when dry conditions prevailed (Table 4). In the absence of spring flooding, garganey and pintail, both ducks with breeding populations of less than 50 pairs in Britain, tend not to remain on the Washes (Thomas 1980; RSPB unpublished data).

6 Ecological effects of drainage and intensive agriculture on breeding waders

Recent ecological studies of breeding meadowland waders in the Netherlands (Beintema in press) and England have revealed some of the more subtle influences of drainage and more intensive farming on these birds. Snipe chicks have a more restricted home range than those of many other waders and remain with their parents for 6 weeks within 300 m of the nest site. All their food requirements are obtained from this area. Earthworms, leatherjackets, and other soil invertebrates are important in the diet of both adult and young snipe during the breeding season (R E Green pers. comm.) and, because these are obtained by probing, the substrate has to be penetrable by a snipe's bill. This explains why the highest densities of breeding snipe occur in areas where the water table is high and on peaty soils which retain moisture. Of the 154 drumming snipe recorded on the Somerset Moors in 1983, 75% were in areas that were wet in May and the remainder were in damp locations. Furthermore, three-quarters of the birds were in fields in which the substrate was peat rather than clay (Weaver & Chown 1983). The prevalence of clay soils which become relatively impenetrable in drying out may explain why only 16 drumming snipe were recorded on 8177 ha of

Table 3. Variety and densities of breeding wildfowl and waders on a series of farmland plots ranging from wet grassland to arable on long drained land in the fens of Cambridgeshire and Lincolnshire, 1982 (Source: Clack 1982)

	Area (ha)	Wildfowl		Waders	
		Species	Density/ 100 ha	Species	Density/ 100 ha
Wet grassland (washland)	173	7	10·6	5	63·8
Largely dry grassland (drained for >100 yrs)	102	1	7·8	1	3·9
Arable for 20 years (drained washland but close to undrained land)	129	2	4·7	3	11·2
Arable for 30–40 years (drained washland)	125	1	4·0	1	1·6
Arable for >100 years (drained fenland)	99	1	3·0	0	—

Table 4. Breeding wildfowl and wader populations (mid-May) at the Ouse Washes, Cambridgeshire and Norfolk, in a wet and dry spring
(Source: unpublished RSPB data)

Spring flooding	Wildfowl			Waders		
	Total (prs)	Mallard (males)	Shoveler (males)	Total (prs)	Lapwing (prs)	Snipe (drumming)
1975 Extensive	1 865	1 324	306	1 027	300	513
1976 None	980	735	110	808	312	330
Ratio 1975/76	1·9	1·8	2·8	1·3	1·0	1·6

The total area of the Ouse Washes is 1 935 ha, 1 860 ha of which are permanent grass

the North Kent Marshes in 1982-83 (Smith 1983a, pers. comm.). At the Ouse Washes, snipe nest at densities of 60-90 pairs/100 ha in the wetter areas, compared with 15-20 pairs/100 ha in the dry fields. Surface water is probably not essential for breeding snipe. Provided that the ground remains moist, the duration of the nesting period, including replacement clutches, may extend over 12 weeks, compared with 6 weeks under dry conditions. Later clutches tend to avoid predation but are more susceptible to trampling by cattle and food may be less available for the young (R E Green pers. comm.).

Adult black-tailed godwits on their breeding grounds feed by probing and thus, like snipe, require a high water table which keeps the top 15-20 cm of the soil moist. Their chicks, on the other hand, feed by picking flies and beetles off the vegetation (Beintema 1982) and they are therefore less dependent on wet conditions than young snipe or the mobile broods of redshank which concentrate around shallow pools and ditches. Lapwings will also move their chicks from the nest site to areas more suitable for feeding; this may mean a shift from arable land to adjacent grasslands (Redfern 1982). The diet of lapwing chicks consists mainly of surface dwelling invertebrates such as beetles, but larger young consume earthworms and tipulid larvae and dig insects out of dung pats (Beintema 1982). Lapwing broods, therefore, favour closely cropped pasture or sites where the vegetation is suppressed by waterlogging or trampling.

In the earlier phases of draining, increased cattle stocking levels and more intensive grazing tend to result in higher densities of breeding waders. These birds benefit from the tussocky structure of the swards for nesting and, in the case of lapwings and snipe, possibly from the invertebrates associated with dung. More intensive farming, with drainage improvements and the use of fertilizers and slurry to enhance the quality of pasture, may result in an increased biomass of earthworms and an advance in the breeding season of waders, particularly lapwing and black-tailed godwit. On the other hand, by bringing forward the growing period of the grass, cattle can be put out to pasture earlier and at high densities, increasing the vulnerability of nests and young to trampling. Weather induced mortality of chicks may also increase with earlier breeding. The use of herbi-

cides reduces the variety of dicotyledonous plants and this may affect populations of insects on which young godwits feed.

In the Netherlands, drainage and the intensive farming that has followed have probably had a major influence on the decline in breeding population of ruff (from 6000 to 1000-1500 'pairs') and snipe over the last 30 years. Following a marked increase up to 1960, the breeding population of black-tailed godwits has fallen from 116 000 pairs in 1967 to 70 000 in 1979 (Cramp & Simmons 1983). The threshold level at which intensive agricultural management detrimentally affects breeding meadowland waders differs between species. The ruff is lowest in the sequence, followed by redshank, godwit and lapwing, with oystercatcher the highest (Beintema in press). Snipe might be expected to have a low 'tolerance' level.

Lapwings breed in a wide variety of open habitats, including damp pastures, but prefer to nest on cultivated ground (Klomp 1954; Galbraith & Furness 1983). The oystercatcher has recently spread inland in East Anglia and has taken to nesting on arable fields (Murfitt & Weaver 1983), a favoured habitat in parts of lowland Scotland. In the Yare Basin, oystercatcher, lapwing and yellow wagtail all showed positive selection of arable land for nesting, though most of these birds fed on pasture. Lapwings, however, only nested on arable land which was bare in spring and did not use areas with autumn sown cereals. Redshank favoured pasture for nesting, though, unlike snipe, they will also nest in crops if there are suitable wet feeding areas nearby (Round 1979; Murfitt & Weaver 1983).

A regional analysis of the BTO's Common Birds Census results has indicated that, though lapwing populations are increasing in the north and west, they have been declining on farmland in the east and south of the country (Mead & Smith 1982) where an increasing proportion of the cereal crops is sown in autumn. The lapwings breeding on grasslands will therefore assume a greater importance (Smith 1983a). In a lowland valley in Switzerland, lapwings breeding on intensively farmed arable land only reared a mean of 0.35 young, compared with 0.8 young per laying female on wet grasslands, though hatching success was similar in the 2 habitats. Dry conditions in the arable fields resulted in a decline in the availability of invertebrate prey, in contrast to the pastures and main meadows to which the chicks from the marshy areas moved. The populations on the arable areas were apparently being sustained by immigration (Matter 1982).

7 Conservation and restoration of the wet grassland habitat

Of 1366 wet meadow sites (about 133 140 ha) covered in the Breeding Wader Survey, 23 (8533 ha or 6.4% of the total area surveyed) qualified as being of national importance for one or more species of waders. A further 188 were of regional importance (Smith 1983b). Most of the nationally important sites and many of the regionally important ones are already SSSIs. There is a strong case for scheduling the remaining areas.

With so few large damp or wet grassland sites remaining in lowland England and Wales, further loss of this habitat has become critical. It would be unwise, however, to restrict the conservation of wet grass-lands to the 5 prime areas and further concentrate populations of birds. When they are excluded from favoured sites by freezing, lack of flooding or deep floods, it is important that the birds can move to alternative sites. It is also undesirable to have a large proportion of a population at risk from disease or poisoning. Moreover, productivity may be reduced at high breeding densities as a result of predator concentrations and intraspecific competition. It is also essential that the grassland is grazed, ideally by cattle, if its ornithological and botanical interests are to be maintained.

A high proportion of the lowland grasslands has been partially drained and is far from realizing its ornithological potential. There are considerable opportunities to restore and create wetlands for birds. Elmley, the RSPB's reserve on the North Kent Marshes, provides one example (Cadbury 1981). Until the RSPB started to manage the 1117 ha area, it was largely well drained grazing marsh. Since 1976, 23% has been subject to seasonal flooding and the remain-ing 3% largely set aside for permanent flooding. In response to management, particularly more flooding, there has been a pronounced increase in the variety and total numbers of breeding wildfowl and, since 1979, a sharp increase in the numbers of breeding waders (Table 5). The density of redshank on the unflooded area has not exceeded 20 pairs/100 ha, except in an exceptionally wet spring. By contrast, on the flooded areas, the density increased from 27 to 73 pairs/100 ha between 1976 and 1979, though there has been a decrease subsequently (Table 6, Figure 3). The January counts of wildfowl on the reserve increased from an average maximum of 3900 (4 years, 1976-79) to 17 600 (4 years, 1980-83) (Table 5). Both the increased flooding and the establishment of an extensive refuge free of wildfowling activity have probably contributed to the greater usage of Elmley by wintering wildfowl.

Some of the best reed beds for birds in Britain, such as Leighton Moss (Lancashire), Minsmere and West-wood Marshes (Suffolk), and Oxwich (Glamorgan), have developed recently following the abandonment of grazing on poorly drained coastal land (Bibby & Lunn 1982). Given an adequate supply of unpolluted water, there must be further opportunities to improve the ornithological quality of existing reed beds by making them wetter and to create new ones on low ground.

8 Future research

8.1 Surveys in upland valleys

Land drainage has progressed so far in the lowlands that its future impact on birds is likely to be greatest in northern Britain. In the dales of northern England and straths of the Scottish Highlands, drainage and grass 're-seeding' have already made inroads into the areas of damp pasture and rough grazing. These habitats have been identified as important for breeding snipe, curlew and redshank in the recent Scottish Ornithologists' Club survey (Galbraith & Furness 1983). An EEC-funded Highlands and Islands Agricultural Development Programme could accelerate the rate of land use change in the unintensively farmed areas of the Highlands. There is an urgent need for further

Table 5. Populations and variety of breeding wildfowl and waders and numbers of wildfowl in January in relation to flooding at the RSPB's Elmley reserve, north Kent
(Source: P Makepeace & L Street in Cadbury 1981 and from unpublished reports)

	1975	1976	1977	1978	1979	1980	1981	1982	1983
Permanent flooding (ha)	—	2	3	5	33	33	33	33	33 Much temp. flooding
Breeding wildfowl (prs)	73	201	201	273	195	345	395	362	409
Species	5	6	7	9	10	9	11	9	10
Breeding waders (prs)	873	368	472	486	401	622	928	628	743
Species	4	5	4	4	4	4	5	5	5
Maximum January wildfowl numbers ('000)	0·6	1·8	8·0	1·1	4·8	14·4	15·2	22·8	17·8
January conditions	Very wet disturbance	Dry	Wet	Wet & mild	Frozen	Dry & cold	Wet & mild	Very cold	Mild

Shelduck excluded

Table 6. Nesting densities of redshank in flooded and unflooded areas of coastal grazing marsh at Elmley, north Kent (Source: P Makepeace & L Street in Cadbury 1981 and unpublished reports)

| | Redshank pairs/100 ha | | | | | | | |
	1976	1977	1978	1979	1980	1981	1982	1983
Unflooded (822 ha)	28	12	11	12	18	20	12	15
Flooded (295 ha)	27	39	58	73	68	63	46	44
Area of permanent water (ha)	2	3	5	33	33	33	33	33 (Much temp. flooding)

surveys of breeding waders in the upland valleys for which there was incomplete cover in Scotland, and which were omitted from the 1982-83 survey in England and Wales. Information is also required for Orkney and Shetland where marginal land which supports substantial but unquantified breeding wader populations is similarly threatened by drainage and more intensive farming.

8.2 Ecological studies on waders using upland farms
As a complement to the surveys, there should be more detailed studies to examine the effects on waders of land use changes on upland farms, to expand on the findings of Galbraith and Furness (1983). Information is required on the effects of fragmentation of moorland and the use made by such birds as lapwing, curlew and golden plover of under-drained and re-seeded pasture. Densities may increase but productivity of these birds may decline.

8.3 Ecology of breeding waders on Hebridean machair
The exceptionally high densities of breeding waders on the machair and in the adjacent marshes in the Outer Hebrides have long been recognized but have

only recently been quantified in detail (Fuller 1978, 1981; Wilson 1978). An EEC-funded Integrated Development Programme (IDP) poses a serious threat to breeding habitat of such species as dunlin, snipe, redshank and red-necked phalarope. The phalarope, with less than 30 pairs in Scotland and Ireland, has been the subject of some (unpublished) recent research by the RSPB, but ecological studies are needed to identify the requirements of the other 3 species in this type of habitat.

8.4 Ecology of the corncrake
The IDP in the Outer Hebrides also threatens one of the last strongholds of this rapidly decreasing species in western Europe. Surveys of calling corncrakes have indicated that poorly drained fields with yellow iris and other marshy habitats are important to the species, particularly early in the breeding season (Cadbury 1980; Henderson 1983). Such is the elusive nature of the corncrake that, apart from calling birds, virtually nothing is known about its use of the different habitats available on crofting land (Figure 4). In this respect, telemetry offers scope for tracking birds which spend most of their time hidden in vegetation.

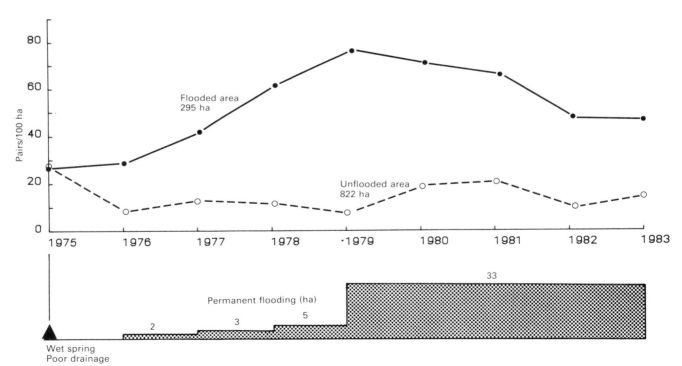

Figure 3. Densities of breeding redshank in relation to managed flooding on coastal grazing marsh at Elmley, north Kent, 1975-83

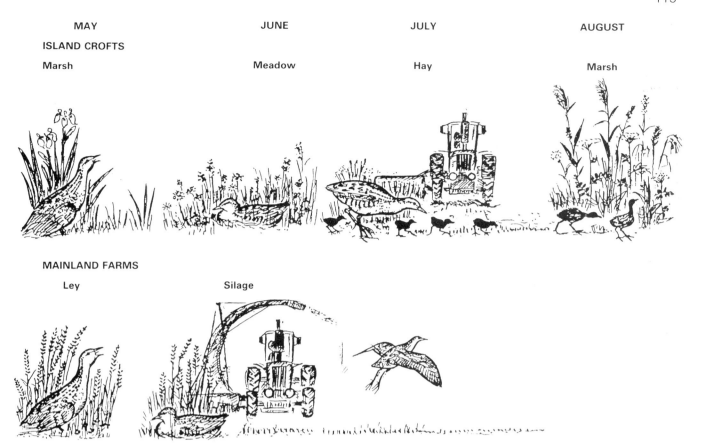

MAY	JUNE	JULY	AUGUST

ISLAND CROFTS

| Marsh | Meadow | Hay | Marsh |

MAINLAND FARMS

Ley   Silage

Figure 4. The use of different habitats on Hebridean crofts by breeding corncrakes and a reason for the decline of the species in mainland Britain

In such instances, where potentially damaging agricultural schemes receive considerable grant-aid from the EEC and Government, there is a strong case for a share of the funding to be apportioned to research and survey work on the threatened habitat and wildlife.

8.5 The implications of intensive farming on birds

Drainage tends to precede more intensive farming, involving the use of fertilizers, higher stocking levels, and eventually the conversion to arable land. The effects on breeding waders have been examined in the Netherlands (Beintema in press) but are only beginning to receive attention in Britain. Intensive agriculture also affects wintering wildfowl which are increasingly exploiting farmland and, in some instances, are in conflict with human interests (Owen 1977; Thomas 1981; Round 1982). It should, however, be recognized that some of the birds which cause damage to crops have been displaced from their more natural feeding habitats by land drainage and agricultural operations. Where refuges are managed to provide alternative feeding areas, their bird use and that of adjacent farmland should be carefully monitored (see 8.6).

8.6 Experimental work to measure the effects of management

Sufficient progress has been made in fundamental ecological studies to identify some of the more important requirements of certain wetland birds. It is now time to carry out some experimental management in which such aspects as water levels, grazing intensity, mowing, and possibly manure or fertilizer applications are carefully manipulated and the effects monitored. In many instances, it will be more practical to quantify the effects on vegetation and invertebrates rather than on birds which tend to range over large areas. Some of this surveillance will demand a long-term commitment. The findings will been needed as the emphasis in bird conservation moves from land acquisition to habitat management.

9 Summary

Flood alleviation and land drainage have resulted in a massive reduction in the areas of damp and wet grassland in the lowlands of England and Wales. Though the main phase was in the 18th and 19th centuries, loss of the habitat continues. Half the washland in the East Anglian Fens and recently over one third of the North Kent Marshes have been converted to arable land. The majority of the remaining wet grassland sites are threatened. Many of the species which are characteristic of lowland wet grasslands and therefore vulnerable to drainage have been unable to benefit from the relatively new man-made wetlands such as reservoirs and flooded gravel pits.

Land drainage in the lowlands over the last 40 years has led to a contraction in the breeding range of both snipe and inland populations of redshank. Each was only present in one third of 1366 grassland sites in England and Wales surveyed in 1982-83. One third of all the breeding waders and half the drumming snipe recorded were concentrated in 5 areas.

Drainage and conversion of grassland to arable land lead to a marked reduction in the variety and densities of breeding waterfowl. Shallow flooding in spring tends to retain birds that have wintered and arrests those on passage. In the absence of water, the birds disperse.

The earlier phases of grass management following drainage may initially lead to higher densities of breeding waders, but above a certain threshold of intensive farming, which varies with different species, there are detrimental effects which result in reduced reproduction and eventually a population decline.

Future priorities for research include studies to assess the impact of land use changes on breeding waders in upland valleys; to identify the habitat requirements of certain breeding waders and the corncrake associated with damp machair and poorly drained crofting land in the Outer Hebrides; to investigate the implications of intensive farming on birds; and to measure the effects of various management practices under experimental conditions.

10 References

Beintema, A.J. 1982. Meadowbirds in the Netherlands. *Annu. Rep. Res. Inst. Nat. Manage. 1981*, 86-94.

Beintema, A.J. In press. The decline of meadowbirds in the agricultural land in Holland. *Proc. int. Orn. Congr., 18th, Moscow, 1982.*

Bibby, C.J. & Lunn, J. 1982. Conservation of reed beds and their avifauna in England and Wales. *Biol. Conserv.*, **23**, 167-186.

Cadbury, C.J. 1980. The status and habitats of the corncrake in Britain 1978-79. *Bird Study*, **27**, 203-218.

Cadbury, C.J. 1981. Habitat restoration for birds. In: *Habitat restoration and reconstruction*, edited by E. Duffey, 30-40. (RERG report no. 7). Cirencester: Recreation Ecology Research Group.

Clack, J.S. 1982. *Breeding bird survey of three arable and two grassland areas in Cambs./Lincs., 1982.* RSPB report, unpublished.

Cramp, S. & Simmons, K.E.L. 1983. *Handbook of the birds of Europe, the Middle East and North Africa*, vol. 3. Oxford: Oxford University Press.

Ferns, P.N., Green, G.H. & Round, P.D. 1979. Significance of the Somerset and Gwent Levels in Britain as feeding areas for migrant whimbrels *Numenius phaeopus. Biol. Conserv.*, **16**, 7-22.

Fuller, R.J. 1978. Breeding populations of ringed plovers and dunlins in the Uists and Benbecula, Outer Hebrides. *Bird Study*, **25**, 97-102.

Fuller, R.J. 1981. The breeding habitats of waders on North Uist machair. *Scott. Birds*, **11**, 142-152.

Fuller, R.J. & Lloyd, D. 1981. The distribution and habitats of wintering golden plovers in Britain 1977-78. *Bird Study*, **28**, 169-185.

Galbraith, H. & Furness, R.W. 1983. Breeding waders on agricultural land. *Scott. Birds*, **12**, 148-153.

Henderson, F. 1983. *Numbers of corncrakes and habitat use in the Uists, Outer Hebrides, 1983.* RSPB report, unpublished.

Klomp, H. 1954. Die terreinkeus van de kievit *Vanellus vanellus. Ardea*, **41**, 1-139.

Matter, H. 1982. Einfluss intensiver Feldbewirtschaftung auf den Bruterfolg des Kiebitzes *Vanellus vanellus* in Mitteleuropa. *Orn. Beob.*, **79**, 1-24.

Mead, C. & Smith, K. 1982. *The Hertfordshire breeding bird atlas.* Tring: HBBA.

Mitchell, O. 1983. The breeding status and distribution of snipe, redshank and yellow wagtail in Sussex. *Sussex Bird Rep.*, **34**, 65-71.

Murfitt, R.C. & Weaver, D.J. 1983. Survey of the breeding waders of wet meadows in Norfolk. *Norfolk Bird Mammal Rep.*, **26**, 196-201.

Owen, M. 1977. The role of wildfowl refuges on agricultural land in lessening the conflict between farmers and geese in Britain. *Biol. Conserv.*, **11**, 209-222.

Prater, A.J. 1981. *Estuary birds of Britain and Ireland.* Calton: Poyser.

Ratcliffe, D.A. 1977. *A nature conservation review: the selection of biological sites of national importance to nature conservation in Britain.* 2 vols. Cambridge: Cambridge University Press.

Redfern, C. 1982. Lapwing nest sites and chick mortality in relation to habitat. *Bird Study*, **29**, 201-208.

Round, P.D. 1979. *An ornithological survey of the Yare Basin, spring and summer 1979.* RSPB report, unpublished.

Round, P.D. 1982. Inland feeding by brent geese *Branta bernicla* in Sussex, England. *Biol. Conserv.*, **23**, 15-32.

Rutter, E.M., Gribble, F.C., Pemberton, T.W. 1964. *A handlist of the birds of Shropshire.* Wem: Shropshire Ornithological Society.

Salmon, D.G. & Moser, M.E. 1983. *Wildfowl and wader counts 1982-83: the results of the National Wildfowl Counts and Birds of Estuaries Enquiry.* Slimbridge: Wildfowl Trust.

Sharrock, J.T.R. 1976. *The atlas of breeding birds in Britain and Ireland.* Berkhamsted: Poyser.

Shrubb, M. 1968. The status and distribution of snipe, redshank and yellow wagtail as breeding birds in Sussex. *Sussex Bird Rep.*, **20**, 53-60.

Smith, K.W. 1983a. The status and distribution of waders breeding on wet lowland grasslands in England and Wales. *Bird Study*, **30**, 177-192.

Smith, K.W. 1983b. *Breeding waders of lowland grasslands—a site evaluation scheme.* BTO/RSPB report, unpublished.

Thomas, G.J. 1980. The ecology of breeding waterfowl at the Ouse Washes, England. *Wildfowl*, **32**, 73-88.

Thomas, G.J. 1981. Field feeding by dabbling ducks around the Ouse Washes, England. *Wildfowl*, **31**, 69-78.

Thomas, G.J. 1982. Autumn and winter feeding ecology of waterfowl at the Ouse Washes, England. *J. Zool.*, **197**, 131-172.

Thomas, G.J., Allen, D.A. & Grose, M.P.B. 1981. The demography and flora of the Ouse Washes, England. *Biol. Conserv.*, **21**, 197-229.

Weaver, D.J. & Chown, D.J. 1983. *Somerset Moors breeding bird survey 1983.* RSPB report, unpublished.

Wilson, J.R. 1978. Agricultural influences on waders nesting on the South Uist machair. *Bird Study*, **25**, 198-206.

Wood, P.C. 1940. Redshank census 1939. *Rep. Oxf. orn. Soc. 1939*, 38-40.

The importance of hedges to songbirds

R J O'CONNOR
British Trust for Ornithology, Tring

1 Introduction

Any experienced ornithologist assessing the bird interest of agricultural land in Britain will attach considerable importance to the network of hedgerows characteristic of mixed and pastoral farming (eg Williamson 1967, 1971). Yet the quantitative evidence on this view is contradictory. Moore (1970) saw the maintenance of hedges as essential, whilst Pollard *et al.* (1974) considered them inessential within the national picture. Murton and Westwood (1974) viewed the habitat as sub-optimal and the concern over their bird populations mis-placed. The majority of these views, however, are based on individual case studies and lack adequate statistical analysis of the relationships between bird numbers and hedgerow quantity and quality over a wide spectrum of farm types.

The present paper has 3 aims: (i) to re-assert in the light of new evidence the fundamental importance of farmland hedgerow as a bird habitat; (ii) to consider some of the factors that have led previous authors to take a contrary view; and (iii) to indicate areas in which additional research is needed to improve our present knowledge of hedgerow birds. The principal sources of new data used here are the British Trust for Ornithology's Common Birds Census (CBC) and Nest Records Scheme and the recent studies of Osborne (1982a, b) and Arnold (1983). Space does not permit a full documentation of the new information presented below, but Morgan and O'Connor (1980) used essentially similar methods and give some detail about the data sources used here for habitat studies.

Hedges can serve birds in several ways, in addition to providing breeding season requirements for songposts and nest sites, for example as feeding sites, as cover from predators, as roosting sites, and as avian highways for movement and dispersal. In this paper, I am concerned only with the relationship between hedgerows and breeding bird communities.

The number of individual birds breeding on farmland increases steadily with increase in hedgerow abundance (Figure 1). The number of species present, on the other hand, increases non-linearly with hedgerow, rising to a peak at densities of around 13-18 km/ha and declining slowly thereafter (O'Connor & Fuller in press). We interpret this finding as a changing balance between open-field and hedgerow species: at low hedgerow densities, the field species dominate; as hedge density increases, additional species dependent on hedges for some but not all of their ecological needs can breed (eg grey partridge which requires hedges for nest cover); and at very high densities of hedgerow, the needs of most small songbirds are met, but the field species such as skylark now lack the open horizon of their 'prairie' habitat and no longer breed.

For individual species, abundance may respond to hedge density by increasing or decreasing monotonically, or may show a more complex non-linear dependence on the availability of the hedgerow. Hence, any summarization of species dependencies in terms of linear correlation coefficients (the most frequently

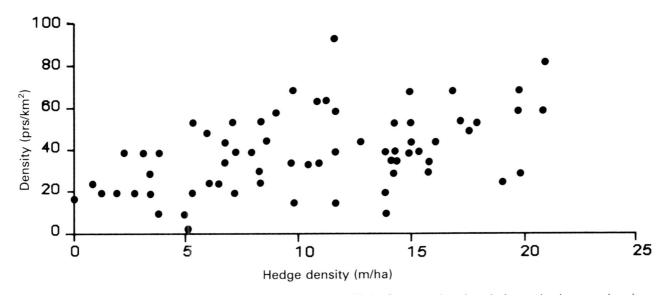

Figure 1. *Density of breeding birds recorded on Common Birds Census plots in relation to hedgerow density on each farm*

used (and abused) measure of dependence) is at best a minimum estimate of the extent to which birds depend on hedges. Even so, analysis of the CBC data for some 57 common farmland species shows that no fewer than 30 of them (52%) are statistically correlated in abundance with the local density of hederow. Table 1 lists the passerine species for which correlation with hedge abundance was greater than for any other landscape element studied. Note the diversity of taxonomic and guild classes that relate to hedgerow: the list includes 2 thrushes, 3 titmice, 4 finches, 2 corvids and 3 migrant warbler species, and these species include both ground and arboreal birds and both seed and insect feeders.

Table 1. Species whose abundance on Common Birds Census farmland plots was most closely correlated with hedgerow densities on the farm (see text for details)

Kestrel	Marsh tit
Cuckoo	Blue tit
Long-eared owl	Great tit
Wren	Magpie*
Dunnock*	Carrion crow
Robin	Chaffinch
Blackbird	Goldfinch
Lesser whitethroat	Linnet*
Whitethroat	Bullfinch
Chiffchaff	

*These species were best correlated with hedgerow of all types. Unstarred species were correlated with the abundance of hedgerows containing trees.

Detailed examination of our data indicates that these correlations are essentially with hedgerow abundance, rather than the result of cross-correlation with some other variable of greater ecological import for birds, eg neighbouring woodland. Arnold (1983) has similarly found that, in predicting the number of species breeding in small quadrat (5 ha) samples of farmland in Cambridgeshire, local habitat features were nearly 3 times as important as were features of the general countryside around each quadrat (32% against 12%). Field species were more influenced by countryside features than were the hedgerow species, but, even when considering only the breeding passerines, the importance of the local habitat features was greater (46% against 32%). Osborne (1982a) also examined the influence of landscape features within a 250 m radius of individual hedges (on a farm in Dorset), and found that the densities of scrub and hedges were the variables most highly correlated with the frequency of birds in the study area.

2 The influence of hedge characteristics

Are all hedges equally valuable to birds? Even quite crude analysis suffices to show that they are not. Table 2 shows that hedges containing trees were some 4-5 times more frequently good predictors of the abundance of individual species than was the abundance of hedges that did not contain trees. This is merely a special case of the general tendency for structurally diverse habitat to hold more species, as in the classic

Table 2. Species dependencies* on hedgerow densities

	Number (%)† of species whose abundances were		
	positively correlated* N (%)	negatively correlated* N (%)	Total N (%)
Hedgerow containing trees	41 (71·9)	2 (3·5)	43 (75·9)
Hedgerow without trees	9 (15·8)	0 (0·0)	9 (15·8)
Hedgerow of any type	29 (50·9)	1 (1·8)	30 (52·6)

*Measured as Spearman rank correlation coefficients between species density (as CBC clusters per unit area) and hedgerow density (length of hedge per unit area of CBC plot), on farms on which the species was present
†Percentage of the 57 species present on at least 10 of the 65 farms examined

BSD-FHD (Bird Species Diversity – Foliage Height Diversity) correlation of MacArthur (1958). Osborne (1982a, 1983) has taken this area of study further. He examined the influence of detailed micro-habitat features of hedgerows on the birds recorded there during the breeding season, using a variety of multivariate techniques to handle the cross-correlations involved. Features with strong influence on the bird community were the number of shrub and tree species in the hedge (Plate 1). The number of bird species present was also correlated with tree species diversity in the hedge, with the number of live trees present, and with the number of herb species reported. The total of individual birds in the hedge, on the other hand, was rather better correlated with the numbers of dead trees present and with the diversity of growth forms displayed by the trees present. Most important of all, though, was the basal area of the hedgerow. Osborne concluded that the most valuable hedges for birds were those with a large basal area and containing many tree species, including at least some dead timber.

Arnold (1983) has similarly considered the influence of landscape characteristics on the breeding bird communities of farmland plots in Cambridgeshire. Within arable farmland, he found that the presence of any structure increasing the 3-dimensional diversity of the plot, whether in the form of ditches, hedgerows or tree-lines, increased the diversity of breeding species in the area. However, the presence of hedges had a greater effect than any other element, with tall hedges being more effective than short hedges.

All 3 studies thus agree on the importance of trees within hedgerows in promoting greater abundance of breeding pairs in an area. However, these studies also indicate that the detailed structure of the hedges is rather important in determining the size and nature of the bird community present in an area. Pollard *et al.* (1974) similarly emphasized the variation in bird community in hedges with different structure along their length, and drew attention to the significance of ground cover in promoting bird numbers, most probably by reducing predation. Parslow (1969) points to the greater value of tall hedges in this respect: those trimmed to below 1.2 m held fewer species and pairs and produced fewer young than did taller hedges less susceptible to predation (Plate 2). Rands (1982) has similarly implicated the risk of predation as determined by hedgerow management (in his study, in relation to the amount of dead grass in the hedge base) as an important parameter determining the density of grey partridges breeding in different areas. On the other hand, the marked preference for hawthorn hedges shown by birds might be as well explained by their rich invertebrate fauna as by the greater cover afforded nests by their early leafing (Pollard *et al.* 1974). Apart from these studies, however, quantitative analyses of the impact of particular hedgerow management regimes on the birds present are almost non-existent and constitute a major gap in our knowledge.

3 Differences between species

Not all species, even amongst hedgerow birds, necessarily respond to those hedgerow characteristics promoting the overall species count (or even overall bird abundance) of the area. Different species depend on different features of the hedges, according to their use of the hedge for feeding, cover, nest sites, and so on (Pollard *et al.* 1974). Thus, on the CBC plots studied here, the abundance of the dunnock is most strongly correlated with the presence of low hedges without standards, unlike the majority of birds considered above (cf Table 1). Similar interspecific differences in habitat correlates have been demonstrated for 6 common farmland species by Osborne (1982a) and for a wider variety of species and species groups by Arnold (1983). In the latter's study, for example, dunnock numbers were correlated positively with ditch cover and negatively with the frequency of dead trees present; titmice numbers were correlated with hedge height and the density of live trees; yellow-hammers were correlated with the richness of herb species present in ditches and hedges, and negatively with the extent of short hedgerow in the area; and tree sparrows were more abundant the more trees and tall hedges there were present. Other species showed similar diversity of major habitat correlates. These findings have the extremely important conservation implication that there is no ideal hedge structure which will maximize the numbers of all species and that the preferences of each must be established individually.

4 Are hedges a secondary habitat?

Hedges are now generally regarded as secondary habitat that can readily be replaced, for example by planting up an equivalent area of woodland. This view is based on the woodland origin of most common farmland birds, with these species secondarily adapting to the 'linear woodland' constituted by hedgerows but still preferring to breed in woodland wherever a choice is available (Williamson 1967). By examining the habitats used by wrens as their population recovered from the severe winter of 1962-63, Williamson (1969) showed that woodland was more rapidly re-colonized than other habitats, indicating a prefer-

ence for woodland; riparian vegetation was next most preferred, then gardens, and finally field hedges. Osborne (1982a) has since shown that shrub-rich hedges are colonized in preference to shrub-poor ones, which are used only in years of high population density. Similar results have been obtained for the chiffchaff and great tit by Osborne (1982a) and Krebs (1971) respectively, and other cases have been suggested by Batten and Williamson (1977).

These results seem to suggest unequivocally that some species of birds use hedgerow only as a secondary habitat, but this conclusion has recently been challenged by Osborne (1982a) on 2 grounds. First, the wren populations tracked nationally by the CBC do not, in fact, reveal the greater variability on farmland expected if a buffer effect prevails (Kluijver & Tinbergen 1953; Brown 1969) and, second, some repeat studies of the great tit populations studied by Krebs do not confirm his results but point to other possible explanations (Krebs 1977; Webber 1975). However, in a review of the problems associated with identifying hierarchical habitat preferences, O'Connor and Fuller (in press) show that a strong density-dependence within wren populations is an important limitation to population fluctuations, even in less preferred habitats. O'Connor (1980a) addresses the same problems for the great tit.

Rather less evidence is available to demonstrate the alternative situation, that particular species might use hedges in preference to other habitats. Yellow-hammers, however, have been demonstrated to use woodland as an overflow habitat from farmland, with the pattern of population distribution determined largely by the balance of reproductive advantage between the 2 habitats. At low densities, clutch size is high on farmland (principally in hedgerow sites and in scrub), but decreases sharply as the local densities of breeding birds build up. In woodland, clutch size is initially lower than on farmland but, because it does not decrease as sharply with density as in farmland, it eventually equals that of farmland nests, with consequent shifts in favour of woodland breeding (O'Connor 1980b).

Removal experiments form an important class of evidence on the importance or otherwise of particular habitats for birds, but there have been very few such experiments for hedgerow. Edwards (1977) removed a variety of species from field hedges at a site in southern England, with varied results. Several of the commoner hedge species (blackbird, song thrush, dunnock, and chaffinch) were rather slow to re-invade and did not do so completely, whilst for other species, eg great tit, the vacancies were not taken up. However, as the birds involved were unmarked, their origin was unknown.

Another channel of evidence for the value of hedge-row as breeding habitat lies in the examination of breeding success therein. Snow and Mayer-Gross (1967) found that, for 4 common species (blackbird, song thrush, dunnock and chaffinch), the proportion of nests fledging at least one young was higher on farmland than in woodland. However, their measure of success is really satisfactory only where predation is the main cause of nest loss. If food supplies were to limit chick rearing, the number of young fledged needs to be taken into account. Table 3 presents preliminary estimates of nest success calculated on this basis, using the bias-free computational method of Mayfield (1961, 1975). Three of the species studied here were also studied by Snow and Mayer-Gross, but the dunnock is replaced by the greenfinch. The results suggest that farmland is a marginally better habitat for egg production and survival than woodland, as found in the earlier study, but all 4 species had poorer rearing success on farmland than on woodland. Though not conclusive because thus far so few species have yet been analysed, the data suggest that farmland is not an ideal habitat in which to rear young. Krebs (1971) found that great tits nesting in hedgerows laid fewer eggs and suffered higher mortality than did pairs in woodland.

Table 3. Clutch size, egg loss and chick loss in farmland and woodland

	Ratio of farmland to woodland value		
	Clutch size	Egg loss	Chick loss
Blackbird	1·01	1·10	0·93
Song thrush	1·02	1·00	0·97
Greenfinch	1·00	0·95	0·82
Chaffinch	1·02	1·08	0·84

Beyond the studies just reviewed, there is little evidence from which to assess the relative merits of hedgerow and woodland as nesting habitat, and the question must therefore continue as one in need of research. Its resolution is especially important for understanding the role of farmland populations in the dynamics of bird populations in Britain, for if farmland is merely a secondary habitat contributing few individuals to future breeding populations, then conservation concern about agricultural practices in relation to hedgerow is mis-placed (Murton & Westwood 1974). If, on the other hand, population recruitment from hedgerows is high, then the enormous acreage of farmland in Britain makes the loss of hedgerow a major conservation matter (Moore 1970; Osborne 1982a).

5 Consequences of hedgerow removal

The conservation issue in relation to hedgerows turns both on their value to wildlife and on the rate of their removal under the impact of modern farming methods. Pollard *et al.* (1974) estimated that some 193 000 km of hedgerow were removed in England and Wales between 1946 and 1974, though the amounts of hedgerow removed differed substantially between regions. Data from the first 4 years of the

CBC (1963-66) indicated an average loss rate of about 2.48 m/ha on the CBC study plots. Pollard *et al.* revised this figure, as a measure of the national loss rate, downwards, to about 1.22 m/ha to take account of the concentration of CBC plots in the south and east of England, the areas of most intensive removal. Analysis of subsequent CBC data indicates a decline since that date to about 0.5 m/ha in 1980.

Population loss amongst hedgerow birds is unlikely to be directly proportional to the extent of hedge removed, as it is rare for all the hedgerow in an area to be removed. Hence, the displaced birds may be able to crowd into the remaining hedges (Hooper 1970, 1984). Figure 2 illustrates this possibility for a case of temporary hedge loss on a Hertfordshire farm. Here, the cutting back of the majority of the internal hedgerows on the study farm was associated with only temporary changes in robin and dunnock numbers. The pairs continuing to breed on the farm, in fact, redistributed themselves into the boundary hedgerows and into adjacent gardens, holding smaller territories under these crowded conditions until they could spread back into the regenerating hedgerow. On the other hand, Figure 2 also shows that the number of birds on this farm, which has greatly intensified its cereal production, has declined relative to the general run of farms in the farmland CBC as a whole, suggesting that factors other than hedgerow density may be important to the maintenance of bird populations on arable land (see below).

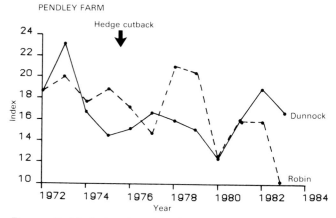

Figure 2. Variation in robin (dotted line) and dunnock (solid line) densities on Pendley Farm, Hertfordshire, in relation to the cutting back of most internal hedgerows in winter 1975-76. Densities are presented as an index (= ratio of CBC clusters to 'national' CBC index) to correct for weather-induced changes in population level

Previous attempts to evaluate the consequences of hedgerow removal have given varied results and led authors to divergent conclusions about its importance. Bull *et al.* (1976) found little effect on the total number of birds breeding on a Norfolk farm subjected to a 30% removal of its hedges over a 4-year period, though the structure of the bird community changed in favour of field species (up 34%) at the expense of summer visitors and hole-nesting species. Watnough (1974) found very similar changes on a Cambridgeshire farm that lost over 90% of its hedgerow. Murton and Westwood (1974) also found rather small overall changes on their study plot at Carlton (Cambs), and concluded that the issue of hedge removal was greatly over-stated and of peripheral importance to conservation. Against this, Evans (1972) found that the number of breeding birds on his Ely site more than halved as the length of hedge present was reduced from 8300 to 450 m/km. Hooper (1970) suggested that the effects of hedge removal might be non-linear, with a given loss less serious at high densities of hedgerow than at low. Figure 3 presents evidence supporting this explanation, and similar evidence can be presented for other species (unpublished). Actually, the effect in Figure 3 goes beyond that needed to confirm Hooper's suggestion, as for many species dependence on the local density of hedgerow is not merely non-linear but highly unimodal. There is then an optimum density of hedge for each species, and this optimum may additionally vary from species to species. Rands (1982) has demonstrated similar non-linear relationships in habitat correlates in relation to grey partridge numbers. Moreover, the type of hedgerow present may also be relevant (see above, and unpublished).

Given such non-linearities of dependence on hedgerow density, it is easy to appreciate that the initial and final densities of hedges in the individual studies of removal are as crucial as are the absolute and relative extents of hedge removed. The amalgam of these non-linear responses underlies the non-linear dependence of species number on hedge abundance noted above (O'Connor & Fuller in press).

Pollard et al. (1974) have indicated the regional concentration of hedgerow losses. In regions where stock continue to be important, hedgerows serve a function on agricultural land and are maintained, but where farming is essentially arable, hedges are without function and have some disadvantages. As a result, hedge losses have been concentrated in the arable eastern counties of England. This regionality can be expected to have consequences for those bird species dependent on hedges during the breeding season. Thus, in a sample of counties for which MAFF statistics demonstrate a 50% loss of pasture over the 20 years of the CBC, blackbird numbers have fallen by about 30% to date, with no sign of any respite (O'Connor & Shrubb in press). Similarly, analysis of CBC plots in counties with high and with low cattle densities shows that blackbird densities are higher in the cattle intensive areas, in which recorded hedgerow losses are also lower (O'Connor & Shrubb unpublished).

It is perhaps necessary to note here that 2 obvious alternative explanations can be discounted. First, the possibility that the farms chosen by CBC participants are perhaps atypically good for birds has been examined by Fuller et al. (in press). They found that the CBC farms, in fact, closely accord in general characteristics with the national pattern displayed in MAFF statistics and in land use data collected by Bunce et al. (1981). Second, the possibility that the bird/cattle/hedges correlations were an artefact of the regional distribution of cattle rearing was controlled for by matching cattle and non-cattle counties in our samples. The link between bird numbers, stock rearing and hedge retention has so far been established only in the case of blackbirds, but other analyses have indicated

Figure 3. Density of breeding pairs of mistle thrushes on CBC farms in relation to the amount of hedgerow with trees present

that other ground feeders such as song thrush and mistle thrush have declined in arable regions. However, we have not yet established for these cases whether it is the loss of hedgerow in the arable regions that is responsible, or whether it is some associated correlate that is proximately responsible, eg the loss of spring cultivations resulting from the recent switch to winter cereals.

One final point in relation to the regional distribution of hedge removal needs making here. Most or all of those studies attempting to assess the consequences of such loss for bird populations have been located in eastern England where loss has been most severe. However, eastern areas of Britain are richer in species than are western areas, within areas of equivalent habitat (Fuller 1982; and maps in Sharrock 1976), so conclusions as to effects on bird populations cannot be extrapolated to other areas of the country on the basis of present evidence.

6 Future research needs

The outline of current understanding of bird hedge interactions suggests the following conclusions for future research. First, the broad correlation of gross hedgerow habitat and bird numbers is reasonably well established, but the role of micro-habitat features is virtually unknown. Second, it seems clear that each bird species has its own spectrum of preferred habitat features, so that there is no universal hedge management regime available to cater for birds in general. An optimal regime has to be decided in the light of species-oriented objectives, and the necessary information for this decision must be collected species-by-species. Third, geographical factors need to be taken into account when interpreting the results of any research conducted, rather than generalizations across Britain being made. Fourth, the relative importance of hedgerow populations in maintaining numbers in Britain as a whole remains poorly understood. Finally, just how significant hedge removal is in relation to other changes in agricultural practice is completely unknown.

7 Acknowledgements

The BTO's CBC and Nest Records Scheme are conducted as part of a contract for services in ornithology between the Nature Conservancy Council and the British Trust for Ornithology. The present work was conducted within that programme.

8 Summary

Farmland bird densities are statistically well correlated with local hedgerow abundance, with more than one half of all species showing positive correlations. No other landscape element is as well correlated. Hedgerows containing trees are far more significant than those without trees.

The abundance of songbirds in farm hedgerow is not a static parameter but alters with population pressure for many species. In general, hedgerows are a secondary or less preferred habitat into which birds move to breed only when better habitats are saturated. Breeding success is consequently low in hedgerow nests. Results from longitudinal studies and from 'before and after' studies of hedge removal confirm these findings. These studies indicate further that hedge loss is most significant below a threshold value, above which density compensation accommodates the loss in whole or in part.

Rates of hedge removal have decreased since the 1960s, but losses are concentrated regionally. In some areas of arable intensification, birds such as blackbird and song thrush have become less abundant, but it is not yet possible to attribute this decline to loss of breeding habitat rather than to lack of spring cultivations (on which to feed) as spring cereals are replaced by winter crops.

Amongst the major questions needing further research are the following.

i. What micro-habitat features of hedgerow management promote bird densities?

ii. What are the critical thresholds of hedgerow density and spatial patterning before density compensation ceases to be effective?

iii. How significant for equilibrium population sizes are those individuals breeding in hedges?

9 References

Arnold, G.W. 1983. The influence of ditch and hedgerow structure, length of hedgerows, and area of woodland and garden on bird numbers on farmland. *J. appl. Ecol.*, **20**, 731-750.

Batten, L.A. & Williamson, K. 1977. Some ecological implications of the Common Birds Census. *Pol. ecol. Stud.*, **3**, 237-244.

Brown, J.L. 1969. The buffer effect and productivity in tit populations. *Am. Nat.*, **103**, 347-354.

Bull, A.L., Mead, C.J. & Williamson, K. 1976. Bird-life on a Norfolk farm in relation to agricultural changes. *Bird Study*, **23**, 163-182.

Bunce, R.G.H., Barr, C.J. & Whittaker, H.A. 1981. An integrated system of land classification. *Annu. Rep. Inst. terr. Ecol. 1980*, 28-33.

Edwards, P.J. 1977. "Re-invasion" by some farmland bird species following capture and removal. *Pol. ecol. Stud.*, **3**, 53-70.

Evans, P.J. 1972. The Common Birds Census: eight years at Ely. *Rep. Camb. Bird Club 1971*, 36-39.

Fuller, R.J. 1982. *Bird habitats in Britain*. Calton: Poyser.

Fuller, R.J., Marchant, J.H. & Morgan, R.A. In press. How representative of agricultural practice in Britain are Common Birds Census farmland plots? *Bird Study*, **32**.

Hooper, M.D. 1970. Hedges and birds. *Birds*, **3**, 114-117.

Hooper, M.D. 1984. What are the main recent impacts of agriculture on wildlife? Could they have been predicted, and what can be predicted for the future? In: *Agriculture and the environment*, edited by D. Jenkins, 33-36. (ITE symposium no. 13). Cambridge: Institute of Terrestrial Ecology.

Kluijver, H.N. & Tinbergen, L. 1953. Territory and the regulation of density in titmice. *Archs neerl. Zool.*, **10**, 265-289.

Krebs, J.R. 1971. Territory and breeding density in the great tit, *Parus major* L. *Ecology*, **52**, 1-22.

Krebs, J.R. 1977. Song and territory in the great tit, *Parus major*. In: *Evolutionary ecology*, edited by B. Stonehouse & C.M. Perrins, 47-62. London: Macmillan.

MacArthur, R.H. 1958. Population ecology of some warblers of north-eastern coniferous forests. *Ecology*, **39**, 599-619.

Mayfield, H.F. 1961. Nesting success calculated from exposure. *Wilson Bull.*, **73**, 255-261.

Mayfield, H.F. 1975. Suggestions for calculating nest success. *Wilson Bull.*, **87**, 456-466.

Moore, N.W. 1970. The conservation of animals. In: *Hedges and hedgerow trees*, edited by M.D. Hooper & M.W. Holdgate, 53-57. (Monks Wood symposium no. 4). Abbots Ripton: Nature Conservancy.

Morgan, R.A. & O'Connor, R.J. 1980. Farmland habitat and yellowhammer distribution in Britain. *Bird Study*, **27**, 155-162.

Murton, R.K. & Westwood, N.J. 1974. Some effects of agricultural change on the English avifauna. *Br. Birds*, **67**, 41-69.

O'Connor, R.J. 1980a. Pattern and process in great tit (*Parus major*) populations in Britain. *Ardea*, **68**, 165-183.

O'Connor, R.J. 1980b. Population regulation in the yellowhammer *Emberiza citrinella* in Britain. In: *Bird census work and nature conservation*, edited by H. Oelke, 190-200. Lengede: Dachverband Deutscher Avifaunisten.

O'Connor, R.J. & Fuller, R.J. In press. Bird population response to habitat. *Proc. int. Bird Census Comm.*, no. 8.

O'Connor, R.J. & Shrubb, M. In press. Birds and agricultural development in Britain. In: *Birds and man*, edited by J. Dunning. Johannesburg: Witwatersrand Bird Club.

Osborne, P.E. 1982a. *The effects of Dutch elm disease on farmland bird populations.* DPhil. thesis, University of Oxford.

Osborne, P.E. 1982b. Some effects of Dutch elm disease on nesting farmland birds. *Bird Study*, **29**, 2-16.

Osborne, P.E. 1983. The influence of Dutch elm disease on bird population trends. *Bird Study*, **30**, 27-38.

Parslow, J.L.F. 1969. Breeding birds of hedges. *Rep. Monks Wood Exp. Stn 1966-68*, 21.

Pollard, E., Hooper, M.D. & Moore, N.W. 1974. *Hedges.* (New naturalist no. 58). London: Collins.

Rands, M.R.W. 1982. The importance of nesting cover quality to partridges. *Annu. Rev. Game Conservancy, 1981*, no. 13, 58-64.

Sharrock, J.T.R. 1976. *The atlas of breeding birds in Britain and Ireland.* Berkhamsted: Poyser.

Snow, D.W. & Mayer-Gross, H. 1967. Farmland as a nesting habitat. *Bird Study*, **14**, 43-52.

Watnough, B. 1974. The common birds census at Barton Farm, Coton: 1967-73. *Rep. Camb. Bird Club 1973*, 41-45.

Webber, M.I. 1975. *Some aspects of the non-breeding population dynamics of the great tit* (Parus major). DPhil. thesis, University of Oxford.

Williamson, K. 1967. The bird community of farmland. *Bird Study*, **16**, 210-226.

Williamson, K. 1969. Habitat preferences of the wren on English farmland. *Bird Study*, **16**, 53-59.

Williamson, K. 1971. A bird census study of a Dorset dairy farm. *Bird Study*, **18**, 80-96.

The use of birds as indicators of change in agriculture

ANNE BRENCHLEY
Maidstone (previously at University of Aberdeen, Culterty Field Station)

1 Introduction

From 1939 to the present day, more than 76% of Britain's land mass has been classified as agricultural land (MAFF 1940-82), and little wildlife, with the possible exception of those confined to coastal sites, could have escaped the influences of agricultural development.

Birds have been popular subjects of distribution surveys and research studies for most of this century, and there is more information on their populations than for any other groups of animals. British farmland is currently thought to support up to 130 breeding species of bird, with another 100 species utilizing farmland but breeding elsewhere (Sharrock 1976). Several more visit Britain in winter and feed on farmland, eg geese, whooper swans, fieldfares, redwings, etc.

Farmland constitutes such a large proportion of the total land mass that a vast number of birds inhabit it (Shrubb 1970). Eighty-one species are thought to maintain their British populations at fairly low levels (100 000 pairs or less) and are consequently amongst the species most vulnerable to agricultural development. Other species are more common (100 000-1 000 000 pairs), with a few being abundant (1 000 000 pairs or more; Tables 1 & 2). Some of the most abundant species have been able to exploit the farmland habitat very successfully and at some time have come to achieve pest status. The most notable of these are the starling, skylark, wood pigeon, rook and house sparrow.

As well as studies deliberately aimed at examining the effects of agricultural changes on birds, many ecological studies were undertaken independently and they provided essential information on the status, habitat requirements and behaviour of a wide variety of species. As the impact of agriculture must be felt by most of Britain's birdlife in some respect, it makes sense to capitalize on this store of knowledge already available and use birds as indicators of change.

2 Agriculture and its effect on bird habitats

Agricultural changes are known to have brought about

Table 1. Population sizes of farmland birds in Great Britain
(Source: Moore 1980)

Population category (number of pairs)	Number of species in category	Estimate of number of pairs in category
>1 000 000	17	56 000 000
100 000–1 000 000	32	10 000 000
<100 000	81	2 000 000
Totals	130	68 000 000

2 major effects on the variety of habitats available to birds in Britain (Murton & Westwood 1974; Flegg 1975; Mellanby 1981).

i. The reclamation and drainage of marginal land (ie lowland bogs, fens, heaths, wet meadows and woodland) have inevitably led to the reduction in total area of non-agricultural habitat.

ii. Increased specialization and changing farming practices have resulted in the alteration of niches available within agricultural habitat.

2.1 Loss of non-agricultural habitat
The area of land devoted to agriculture decreased from about 80.4% of the total land area in 1939 to 75.7% in 1982 (MAFF 1940-82), due to intense competition for

Table 2. Bird species typically associated with farmland or recorded on farmland CBCs with an estimate of their population size (Source: Sharrock 1976)

Estimated number of breeding pairs in Great Britain		
<100 000	100 000–1 000 000	>1 000 000
Barn owl	Blackcap	Blackbird
Corn bunting	Bullfinch	Blue tit
Corncrake	Carrion crow	Chaffinch
Cuckoo	Chiffchaff	Dunnock
Little owl	Collared dove	Great tit
	Garden warbler	Greenfinch
	Goldfinch	House sparrow
	Jackdaw	Linnet
	Kestrel	Meadow pipit
	Lapwing	Robin
	Lesser whitethroat	Rook
	Long-tailed tit	Skylark
	Magpie	Song thrush
	Mallard	Starling
	Marsh tit	Willow warbler
	Mistle thrush	Wood pigeon
	Moorhen	Wren
	Partridge	
	Pheasant	
	Pied wagtail	
	Red-legged partridge	
	Reed bunting	
	Sedge warbler	
	Spotted flycatcher	
	Stock dove	
	Swallow	
	Tree sparrow	
	Treecreeper	
	Turtle dove	
	Whitethroat	
	Yellowhammer	

space between urban, industrial, forestry and agricultural development, but nonetheless agricultural improvement is the prime factor involved in the loss of natural and semi-natural habitats in Great Britain today. At most, about 10% of the total land mass is considered as undeveloped, and the reclamation of these areas for farmland is often stimulated by the generous and possibly mis-guided incentives of Government grants and subsidies (Mellanby 1981).

The reduction in habitats simply restricts their capacity to support the birds typically associated with these sites, and the subsequent decline of these species is not difficult to understand. The implications of agricultural changes for birds inhabiting farmland are more complicated and therefore less easy to predict or counteract.

2.2 Changes within farmland
The diversity of farmland birds which a particular area can support depends on the range of niches available. Pond drainage, hedgerow removal, replacement of old farm buildings with modern ones, and scrub clearance all contribute to the reduction in total number and variety of available niches. As the majority of farmland birds, even the more common ones, depend upon the traditional types of field boundary to provide their food, if not their nest sites, the replacement of the hedge and ditch by the amalgamation of fields or by a simple fence may cause some populations to suffer.

The limited number of niches available within the fields supports such birds as the skylark and partridge, which have become adapted to the pattern of seasonal abundance and availability of food. Recent changes in cropping practices, eg regular applications of fertilizers and pesticides, continuous cropping without rotations, increased area of arable crops grown and increased autumn cultivation, have inevitably altered the pattern of food availability and have possibly increased nest disturbance and egg and chick destruction.

3 How birds can indicate change
The statistical evidence that changes within the agricultural habitat itself have occurred is readily obtainable, but the effects of such changes on wildlife are more difficult to define. All too often the effects of habitat changes are suggested by correlations between population levels and factors of the changing agricultural environment; it is very rare for these suggested effects to be demonstrated experimentally. However, birds may be expected to indicate their response in several ways, eg change in behaviour, population decline or increase, or population redistribution. Population changes are the most common type of evidence, albeit circumstantial, that are presented to support the idea that agricultural development influences wildlife.

In the short term, such population changes are not conclusive evidence in themselves, but, with many years of bird population data available, long-term trends can certainly point to agriculture being the main cause. The mechanisms involved vary according to the individual species concerned, but these mechanisms are known for only a few, notably gamebirds (Potts 1970).

3.1 Habitat loss and population decline

The fast constriction and fragmentation of non-agricultural habitats have meant that bird species such as the nightjar, Dartford warbler and many lowland waders are now in serious decline (Bibby & Tubbs 1975; Sharrock 1976; Gribble 1983; Smith 1983). Species with such restricted distributions are often chosen for detailed study and survey. Extreme care should be taken when interpreting the decline of some summer migrants such as the nightingale and redstart, particularly when a restriction in the breeding habitat is not thought to be the cause (Sharrock 1976; Hudson 1979). In nearly all cases where agricultural changes are thought to be involved, however, these studies suggest that the only method of maintaining viable populations is the adequate protection and maintenance of diverse habitat types throughout Great Britain (Fuller 1982).

3.2 Pesticides, wildlife incidents and population declines

Some of the most direct and unfortunate results of the introduction of new techniques in agriculture arose from the widespread use of organic chemicals, especially pesticides, in the 1950s and 1960s. These are discussed elsewhere in this volume.

3.3 General population trends of farmland birds

On initial examination, much of the widespread concern over the welfare of farmland bird species appeared to be unfounded. Few of the 40 or so dominant or common farmland birds have declined significantly since 1962, when the British Trust for Ornithology began the Common Birds Census (CBC) (Williamson & Homes 1964; Batten & Marchant 1976, 1977a, b; Marchant 1978, 1980, 1982, 1983; Marchant & Hyde 1980a, b; Marchant & Taylor 1981). Although this method cannot cover the more poorly represented species, it does show general trends for the predominant ones. It is interesting to note that most species populations have fluctuated about an equilibrium level (approximately index 100 in most cases), and few have either steadily increased or decreased.

Two species with notable increases are the wren and the mallard. The wren is well known to decline after bad weather conditions and its numbers decreased dramatically after the 1978-79 and 1981-82 winters (Marchant 1983). The reason for its overall population increase since 1966 is unknown, although it is possible that the 1966 index value did not truly represent the normal population level, so soon after the effects of the 1962-63 winter. The rise in mallard population may

be due to feeding and stocking by wildfowling interests and in this respect, along with the pheasant, it is an anomalous species to census.

The dramatic decline of the whitethroat was not attributed to changes in the breeding habitat, but was probably due to climatic shifts in the Sahel region of Africa, thus causing mortality on migration (Whinstanley et al. 1974). Reductions in the population of the garden warbler and other summer migrants may be due to similar reasons, although this is less certain.

Other species directly associated with farmland that have declined are the corn bunting and the corncrake. Open, predominantly arable regimes seem to favour the corn bunting, so reasons for its decline are possibly unconnected with agriculture. The corn bunting has been studied more for its polygamous mating system than for its habitat requirements in relation to agriculture, and this species may be worthy of further study. With the impending threat of agricultural improvement reaching the Western Isles of Scotland, through the funds of the EEC Integrated Development Programme, the last remaining populations of the corncrake may suffer depletion. The somewhat out-dated and non-profit making crofting practices of the Western Isles are ideally suited to this species. Increased cultivation and grassland improvement would deprive the corncrake of its favoured leys and damp grasses (Cadbury 1980) found amongst the mosaic of small fields and variety of nearby non-agricultural habitats. In the Outer Hebrides, the late grass cutting and as yet little silage making mean that the corncrake has adequate cover and reduced chances of nest or brood destruction. Almost any 'improvement' of the present agricultural system would threaten the British population of corncrakes.

On the positive side, CBC population trends indicate that the carrion crow and blackcap are increasing, so that on balance, at least on farmland, as many species are increasing as are on the decline. Studies of farmland bird communities show that the species diversity has not changed a great deal in the past 20 years (Williamson 1971; Benson & Williamson 1972; Robson & Williamson 1972; Murton & Westwood 1974; Bull et al. 1976). Two studies monitored population changes before and after drastic changes in farm land use had occurred. Despite major changes having taken place at Carlton, Cambridgeshire, from 1963 to 1971-72, the number of breeding species increased from 52 to 56 (Murton & Westwood 1974). In Norfolk, Bull et al. (1976) found that 30% hedgerow removal, the draining of 4 ponds, 50% loss of pasture, and a change from barley and oats to wheat production did reduce the species diversity slightly, but did more to alter the composition of breeding species. Hedgerow species decreased but the total numbers of lapwings, partridges, skylarks and possibly resident seed eaters such as greenfinch, linnet and yellowhammer increased. These studies indicated that not all available niches were occupied and that, so far, farmland avifauna has proved more resilient to quite severe habitat loss than the conservationists would have us suppose.

However, there has to be a threshold limit, beyond which even the more opportunistic species cannot survive. In a recent experimental study, Arnold (1983) found that, in a variety of predominantly arable sites in East Anglia, the mean number of species encountered quadrupled from 4.5 (average number of contacts/ hectare over 12 counts) in arable fields alone to 18.3 in arable fields bounded by ditches and hedges with trees. The sites chosen for study were small and cannot reflect the situation on individual farms but, nonetheless, this study indicated what complete field boundary removal could do to farmland bird populations.

3.4 Change in populations of pest species in relation to agricultural change

Two bird species whose population change has been directly attributed to agricultural causes, apart from the skylark mentioned previously, are the wood pigeon and the rook. Perhaps this is not surprising as these are 2 of the species that rely heavily upon agricultural crops for their food. Murton and Westwood (1974) outlined the effects of several factors of the agricultural system on the wood pigeon. The reduction in area of pasture and established leys, along with the decline in autumn cereal food supply, led to a population drop of 75% from the 1950s in the study areas in Lincolnshire and Cambridgeshire.

In my own study of the rook, new information concerning the relationship between rooks and agriculture has emerged (unpublished). Drastic and rapid fluctuations in the abundance and nature of available food have accompanied the increase in arable farming. The rook has come to depend on the artificial seasonality of crop availability for its main food source, and alterations in this pattern might be expected to affect rook populations.

In 1975, when the BTO conducted a national survey of rookeries, it was discovered that the British rook population had declined since the last survey in 1944-46 (Fisher 1948; Sage & Vernon 1978). Using the results for each county, the highest rook densities (nests/km^2 of agricultural land) were associated with an optimum combination of grass and tillage crops: 55% grass (temporary and permanent excluding rough grazing) and 44% tillage (cereals, roots and vegetables). An index figure, based on deviations from the above 'optimal' proportions, was calculated for each county using the following equation:

Crop mixture index = Difference between observed % and 'optimal' % (ie 55%) of total grass + Difference between observed % and 'optimal' % (ie 44%) of tillage crops

The results suggested that rooks favoured areas of mixed farming (low crop mixture index) and were less common in specialized agricultural regimes (high crop mixture indices, Figure 1).

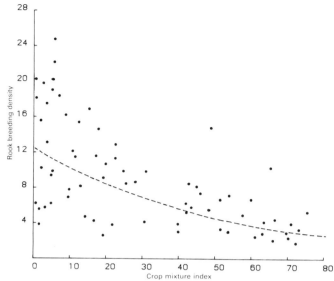

Figure 1. *The relationship between rook breeding density (nests/km crops & grass) and the crop mixture indices for all counties in Great Britain for 1975* ($y = -12.53e^{0.02x}$; $r = 0.62$; $df = 69$; $P < 0.001$)

Since 1944-46, rook populations have declined most in counties of specialized arable production, ie Cambridgeshire, Lincolnshire, Norfolk, and Suffolk, and least in regions of least agricultural change, notably Scotland. This relationship was investigated further by examining the manner in which rooks utilized crops in a variety of cropping regimes throughout Great Britain. In 9 study sites, rook feeding densities (number of feeding rooks/ha of agricultural fields surveyed) were highest in those sites where a variety of crops were available as feeding habitat throughout the year. Fields were considered unavailable as feeding habitat where the vegetation exceeded 15 mm in height, as it reduced visibility and acted as a physical barrier to ground feeding. The availability of suitable fields was critical in the summer period (May to late July). In the specialized arable regimes of eastern England, an almost total unavailability of feeding habitat for even a short period of the year is likely to confer severe limitations on the resident rook population. Rooks must either compete for what is available or be prepared to move away to find other food sources. Either way, these activities put undue stress on the birds, and this may be the time of year when population regulation occurs. Many studies have found that, in regimes of intense cultivation, the invertebrate diversity and biomass are lower than in less cultivated systems (Evans & Guild 1948; Tischler 1955; Edwards & Lofty 1977). This loss of potential food may compound the problem of food shortage in the summer months in these regions.

Changes in status of pest species are particularly good indications that the agricultural ecosystem is also changing, and for economic reasons these are amongst the first situations to be examined.

4 The use of birds as indicators in future research
It is surprising that, since Murton and Westwood's review (1974), very little research has been specifically aimed at assessing the impact of agriculture on birdlife. Birds can make very suitable indicators of change and 2 groups of birds, in particular, are identified as capable of playing a potentially valuable role in the future.

Birds whose specific feeding and nesting requirements make them slow to adapt to changing conditions are amongst the first to indicate that the agricultural system is out of balance with wildlife conservation. A national programme of bird population monitoring could be devised for the uncommon resident breeding birds which inhabit non-agricultural land, utilizing the vast store of amateur manpower available to the BTO and local ornithological groups. Such monitoring needs to be backed up by detailed ecological studies of these species, which would not only define the exact agricultural factors responsible for changes in population size or behaviour, but also provide essential information necessary for future management purposes. All these species have the potential to disappear from Britain, if agricultural development consumes much more of the natural and semi-natural habitats.

The bird species most closely associated with farmland are the second group of indicators. Their reliance on the agricultural system means that even subtle changes in farming practice are likely to affect their populations. The species that respond most quickly to changing conditions are those that are often considered pests. However, even their ecology is not always well understood, and studies tend to be initiated after economic damage has occurred. Studies of the rook, wood pigeon, bullfinch, skylark, etc, have been able to give a clearer understanding of why damage has occurred. The utilization of farmland in winter by gull, wader, goose and finch flocks is another area of research that could well indicate change.

It must be remembered that there are limitations to the use of birds as indicators. A notable response by bird populations to agricultural change may occur long after the change has taken place. This is a good reason why specific groups or individual species should be chosen as indicators because of their predicted fast reaction to change. Many common farmland birds, as found by CBC, appear to indicate that agricultural change has not greatly affected their populations.

It would be very wrong to suppose that the general trends for some of the more adaptable birds such as thrushes, tits, robin, dunnock and wren were not masking deleterious effects to other flora and fauna. As a whole, the mobility of these adaptable species allows them to use possible alternative food supplies and nest sites elsewhere; overall population changes do not then appear. More local surveys of farms, as carried out by Bull *et al.* (1976), are needed so that particular population changes can be related to specific changes in farming practice. The changing diversity of species on these farms is one good indicator of change.

Finally, birds can be used to their best advantage as indicators only when more defined objectives are made towards the problems of wildlife and agriculture. Specifically designed projects are needed to study the ways in which wildlife indicates that change has occurred. Birds are only one group of animals that should be used in this context.

5 Summary
In the past 4 decades, British agriculture has become very intensive and specialized, with major effects on wildlife. Population changes or alterations in behaviour are the types of response expected when birds react to a changing environment. Not all these reactions can be attributed to agricultural change. However, by choosing to study those groups of birds most closely influenced by agricultural development, suitable indicators may be found.

Two groups of birds, in particular, have been identified as responding quickly to agricultural change.

  i. Uncommon breeding birds, which inhabit specialized habitats outside agricultural land, decline when agricultural development is encroaching too fast.

  ii. Pest species and other birds, which have adapted to agricultural systems and now depend on them for food and nest sites, are invariably affected by changes in farming practice.

Detailed ecological studies of these birds combined with continued long-term monitoring, by methods such as the Common Birds Census, can play an important part in a defined programme of research on the impact of agriculture on wildlife.

6 References
Arnold, G.W. 1983. The influence of ditch and hedgerow structure, length of hedgerows and area of woodland and garden on bird numbers on farmland. *J. appl. Ecol.,* **20,** 731-750.

Batten, L.A. & Marchant, J.H. 1976. Bird population changes for the years 1973-74. *Bird Study,* **23,** 11-20.

Batten, L.A. & Marchant, J.H. 1977a. Bird population changes for the years 1974-75. *Bird Study,* **24,** 55-61.

Batten, L.A. & Marchant, J.H. 1977b. Bird population changes for the years 1975-76. *Bird Study,* **24,** 159-164.

Benson, G.B.G. & Williamson, K. 1972. Breeding birds on a mixed farm in Suffolk. *Bird Study,* **19,** 34-50.

128

Bibby, C.J. & Tubbs, C.R. 1975. Status, habitats and conservation of the Dartford warbler in England. *Br. Birds*, **68**, 177-195.

Bull, A.L., Mead, C.J. & Williamson, K. 1976. Bird-life on a Norfolk farm in relation to agricultural changes. *Bird Study*, **23**, 163-182.

Cadbury, C.J. 1980. The status and habitats of the corncrake in Britain 1978-79. *Bird Study*, **27**, 203-218.

Department of Agriculture and Fisheries for Scotland. 1940-1983. *Agricultural statistics, Scotland.* Edinburgh: HMSO.

Edwards, C.A. & Lofty, J.R. 1977. *Biology of earthworms.* 2nd ed. London: Chapman & Hall.

Evans, A.C. & Guild, W.J.M. 1948. Studies on the relationship between earthworms and soil fertility. 5. Field populations. *Ann. appl. Biol.*, **35**, 485-493.

Fisher, J. 1948. Rook investigation. *J. Minist. Agric. Fish.*, **55**, 20-23.

Flegg, J.J.M. 1975. Bird population and distribution changes and the impact of man. *Bird Study*, **22**, 191-202.

Fuller, R.J. 1982. *Bird habitats in Britain.* Calton: Poyser.

Gribble, F.C. 1983. Nightjars in Britain & Ireland in 1981. *Bird Study*, **30**, 165-176.

Hudson, R. 1979. Nightingales in Britain in 1976. *Bird Study*, **26**, 204-212.

Marchant, J.H. 1978. Bird population changes for the years 1976-77. *Bird Study*, **25**, 245-252.

Marchant, J.H. 1980. Recent trends in sparrowhawk numbers in Britain. *Bird Study*, **27**, 152-154.

Marchant, J.H. 1982. Bird population changes for the years 1980-81. *Bird Study*, **29**, 143-148.

Marchant, J.H. 1983. Bird population changes for the years 1981-82. *Bird Study*, **30**, 127-133.

Marchant, J.H. & Hyde, P.A. 1980a. Bird population changes for the years 1977-78. *Bird Study*, **27**, 35-40.

Marchant, J.H. & Hyde, P.A. 1980b. Bird population changes for the years 1978-79. *Bird Study*, **27**, 173-176.

Marchant, J.H. & Taylor, K. 1981. Bird population changes for the years 1979-80. *Bird Study*, **28**, 147-152.

Mellanby, K. 1981. *Farming and wildlife.* (New naturalist no. 67). London: Collins.

Ministry of Agriculture, Fisheries and Food. 1940-1982. *Agricultural statistics, England and Wales.* London: HMSO.

Moore, N. 1980. How many wild birds should farmland support? In: *Bird problems in agriculture*, edited by E.N. Wright, I.R. Inglis & C.J. Feare, 2-6. (Monograph no. 23). Croydon: British Crop Protection Council.

Murton, R.K. & Westwood, N.J. 1974. Some effects of agricultural change on the English avifauna. *Br. Birds*, **67**, 41-69.

Potts, G.R. 1970. Recent changes in the farmland fauna with special reference to the decline of the grey partridge. *Bird Study*, **17**, 145-166.

Robson, R.W. & Williamson, K. 1972. The breeding birds of a Westmorland farm. *Bird Study*, **19**, 204-214.

Sage, B.L. & Vernon, J.D.R. 1978. The 1975 national survey of rookeries. *Bird Study*, **25**, 64-86.

Sharrock, J.T.R. 1976. *The atlas of breeding birds in Britain and Ireland.* Berkhamsted: Poyser.

Shrubb, M. 1970. Birds and farming today. *Bird Study*, **17**, 123-144.

Smith, K.W. 1983. The status and distribution of waders breeding on wet lowland grasslands in England and Wales. *Bird Study*, **30**, 177-192.

Tischler, W. 1955. Effect of agricultural practice on the soil fauna. In: *Soil zoology*, edited by D.K.McE. Kevan, 215-228. London: Butterworths.

Whinstanley, D., Spencer, R. & Williamson, K. 1974. Where have all the whitethroats gone? *Bird Study*, **21**, 1-14.

Williamson, K. 1971. A bird census study of a Dorset dairy farm. *Bird Study*, **18**, 80-96.

Williamson, K. & Homes, R.C. 1964. Methods and preliminary results of the common birds census 1962-63. *Bird Study*, **11**, 240-256.

Monitoring changes in the cereal ecosystem

G R POTTS
The Game Conservancy, Fordingbridge

1 Aims

There is considerable interest in the effects of modern farming on wildlife, particularly in the side effects of pesticides. However, many pesticides have now been used for over 30 years, and very little is known about the ecological situation prior to their use. Fortunately, grey partridges were studied before crop spraying began. This paper shows how the side effects of herbicides have affected this species. It concludes that many unstudied species have been reduced in numbers in the past, that others will be threatened in future, and that research priorities must be shifted if we are to respond properly to the situation.

2 Introduction

The ecological costs of higher crop production have, at long last, begun to concern more than a tiny minority of ecologists. Nevertheless, research funding is not geared to this increased and growing concern, and in almost all countries, including our own, there is at present relatively little research work on the ecology of farmland. Moreover, almost all post-War research in cereals has been in an ecosystem constrained by pesticides, many of them in use for over 30 years. Because of this constraint and the lack of data, it is usually difficult to quantify the ecological side effects of these chemicals and of allied changes in cropping.

Cereal crops cover vast areas of our planet; wheat alone is grown on an area over 20 times the size of the British Isles. Yet, until recently, we have known very little indeed about the ecology of wheat and other cereals. Less than 10 years ago, the chapters on cereal insects written by Curtis in 1883 were still the most comprehensive available for the UK. Some pest species have been well studied and in the past few years there has been a major effort on aphids in winter wheat; workshops on grain aphid predators alone have attracted over 40 participants.

Studies on the grey partridge are different because they began before the widespread use of pesticides. Most food species eaten by partridges are much less abundant than formerly, and are still declining. The cause of these declines, a significant part cause of the decline of the grey partridge itself, is now proven almost without doubt to have been the use of herbicides in cereals. Presumably many other species have been affected but not studied; and this is probably the reason for the conclusion of Bunyan and Stanley (1983) that 'there is little evidence that the indirect effects of current pesticide usage are having serious effects on the flora and fauna . . .'. Meanwhile, even the fears about effects on game have been considered 'hysterical' and 'unjustified' (Broadbent 1980).

3 Study area and methods
The main study area consists of 62 km^2 of mixed and arable farming on the south downs in West Sussex. Maps of the area, and details of the topography, soil and farming methods are given by Potts and Vickerman (1974). Accurate counts of the grey partridge population in spring, of broods and old birds in August, and records of numbers reared and shot began in the early 1950s and give a detailed picture of events. Monitoring of insects started in 1969 and is based on the use of the Dietrick vacuum insect sampler (D-vac).

In each year, insects in 100-150 cereal fields on 17 farms were sampled using the D-vac. In each field, one sample was taken in the third week of June, each sample consisting of 5 sub-samples of 0.092 m^2, giving a total area sampled of 0.46 m^2. The samples were stored deep frozen and then sorted and identified prior to permanent storage in alcohol. In addition, data on cropping and chemical usage were retrieved from farm records. The species of weeds which were found in the cereal crop in the immediate vicinity of each D-vac sample were identified and recorded.

In a separate study in Norfolk, partridge chick faeces were collected from roost sites of radio-tracked broods in cereal crops, and the frequency of occurrence of insects in the diet was determined by micro-dissection of faeces. Insects available were sampled with the D-vac in areas of the cereal crop known to have been searched by the radio-tracked broods. Relative preferences of chicks for insect species were estimated by comparing diet and availability. Feeding trials were carried out at Fordingbridge to calibrate this method and to provide data on selection of insects by chicks. Broods spend almost all their first few weeks hidden in cereal crops, but fortunately mean brood sizes can be obtained in counts of coveys on stubbles after the cereal harvest.

These data offer a reliable indirect method of calculating chick survival rate (Potts 1980, pp21-23). A great deal of work has been done on partridges world-wide, and this paper contains material culled during a search of some 1500 others which mention or relate directly to partridges.

The basic approach to current research at the Game Conservancy is 3-fold: (i) change and associated factors are monitored quantitatively, and hypotheses concerning the causes of changes are built; (ii) the hypotheses are verified with the use of computer simulation models; (iii) hypotheses are then retained or rejected on the basis of experiments and management experience.

4 Results
4.1 Monitoring the indirect effects of herbicides on weeds: an example
At one time, cereal weeds formed a large part of the flora of the countryside because they were symbiotic with the most extensive of the cultivated plants. Even where herbicides had not been used, it was rare to find more than 20 species in any one field, but over 700 species of dicotyledonous weed occur in arable crops in Europe (Hanf 1983). In the cereal fields of the Sussex study area, the average number of dicotyledonous weeds encountered per D-vac site in 1983 was only 1.9, compared to an average of 7.5 in unsprayed plots. Herbicides have had an enormous impact and, in consequence, about a dozen species of formerly familiar weeds are now rare, examples being charlock, wild radish, pheasant's-eye, common hemp-nettle, various thistles, white campion, and sharp-leaved fluellen. The corncockle disappeared from the area in the 1920s and 1930s, and the cornflower in the 1950s.

In the present study, 45 species of dicotyledonous weed were recorded with an overall downward trend in species per D-vac site (=y)*:

$$y = 3 \cdot 78 - 0 \cdot 0225x \qquad r = 0 \cdot 19 \qquad \text{not sig.} \quad \text{........(1)}$$

where x = years after 1900, for the period 1969-83.

The black-bindweed is by far the most preferred food of adult partridges (Potts 1970a) and is potentially an important contaminant of seed grain. Its history is more quantifiable than most.

From 1898 to 1968, the average number of seeds of black-bindweed reported from partridges in autumn was 20 per bird shot. In 16 out of 17 studies, this plant species ranked in the top 3 species of weed seeds eaten. The exception was in Azerbaijan.

Weed seeds are recorded in the returns of the Official Seed Testing Station (OSTS), and from 1928-68 there is no sign of any change in status of black-bindweed in cereals; on average, about 14% of grain samples were

*NB The data on which the following regressions are based will be published separately.

contaminated with its seeds (Broad 1952; Gooch 1963; Tonkin 1968). In the Sussex study area, there was a determined campaign to control black-bindweed starting on 2 farms in 1968 with specific herbicides; returns from the OSTS show that control was very effective. By 1971, 30% of Sussex study area cereal fields still contained the weed, but the decline was statistically significant (P<0.01). By 1983, the species was reported from only 3% of the D-vac sites in cereal fields. Judging from herbicide use, these changes are likely to be typical of those in cereal growing areas.

Factors other than herbicides, such as straw burning and earlier autumn cultivations, have now also contributed to the virtual eradication of this seed as a partridge food. In 1977, the average number of seeds per bird was already down by 95%, but there was no measurable effect on the birds because alternative foods, including cereal grain, were eaten instead (Potts 1980; Pulliainen 1983). There was no increase in adult mortality which could possibly be due to food shortage. This finding contrasts with the situation in chicks.

4.2 Monitoring the change in chick survival rate

Downward trends in chick survival rates have been substantial, but the annual variation is so great that the change has only become statistically significant as a result of counts over long periods of years. Chick survival rates (=y) at North Farm in the Sussex study area have been estimated in the same way for 27 consecutive years (as before, years after 1900). During this period, the chick survival rate has fallen by 28% of the mean, yet the regression is not statistically significant, because (as we shall see later) reductions had already taken place by 1957:

$$y = 51\cdot34 - 0\cdot342x \qquad r = -0\cdot25 \qquad \text{not sig.......(2)}$$

The equivalent regression nationally, where chick survival was monitored on an average of 64 farms per year and fell only 25%, is:

$$y = 59\cdot51 - 0\cdot350x \qquad r = -0\cdot28 \qquad \text{not sig.......(3)}$$

Including the pre-1957 data, since 1932 but excluding the War-time period 1940−46:

$$y = 65\cdot39 - 0\cdot447x \qquad r = -0\cdot55 \qquad P <0\cdot01.....(4)$$

When considering the relevance of these monitored trends, it is a vital point that chick survival rates are not related to density, and therefore cannot compensate for other losses; moreover, grey partridge populations can only compensate for such declines in chick survival to a limited extent (see Potts 1980).

4.3 Causes of variation in chick survival

Analyses of choice amongst naturally available foods offered in laboratory trials, of assimilation rates of these foods, and of growth rates corresponding to the diets, show clearly that insects are essential for partridge chick survival, at least in the laboratory (Cross 1966; Potts 1980). In the field, close correlations have been shown between chick survival rate and annual and spatial/temporal variations in insect food (Potts 1974). The effects of insecticides which removed insects, but which did not kill chicks, were predicted by these correlations, thus providing further support for the belief that the correlations were the result of cause and effect (Potts 1981). In addition, detailed studies of mortality and diet in radio-tracked broods suggest that starvation through insect shortages was a main cause of chick loss (Green in press).

This summary combines the results of work ranking the preference of grey partridge chicks for various insects in laboratory trials (Vickerman & O'Bryan 1979) and in cereal fields (Green in press). The following 3 groups appear to be particularly important: plant bugs and leafhoppers; 'caterpillars' (sawfly and lepidoptera larvae); and weevils and leaf beetles. Various multivariate techniques have been tried to assess the relative importance of species within the 3 groups as a whole. They support this line of reasoning (Potts 1980), but are not satisfactory because the independent variables cannot affect chick survival independently. Among preferred insects, it appears that the attractiveness of the smaller insects (eg Jassids) is balanced by the larger food value of the less attractive species, such as sawfly larvae. The cocoons of the ant *Lasius flavus* are a favoured food, but they are not eaten much until broods are able to feed in the relatively open sites inhabited by the ants. When chicks can escape by flying, from 10-days old onwards, they eat these ants extensively where available; but by that time the value of insect foods *per se* seems much less critical to survival.

The relationship between the percentage survival of partridge chicks to age 6 weeks (=y) over the years 1969-83 in the Sussex study area, and the sum density of the preferred insects per m^2 (=x) is weaker than those which exclude inter-year effects. However, the annual variation is a most useful criterion for the study of the long-term changes. The regression equation is:

$$y = 14\cdot60 + 0\cdot710x \qquad r = 0\cdot69 \qquad P <0\cdot01 ....(5)$$

There was no significant correlation between chick survival and annual densities of the sum of non-preferred insects in the Sussex study.

4.4 The effects of pesticides on the insects preferred by partridge chicks

The indirect effects of some of the early herbicides were rather overshadowed by the direct effects. For example, DNOC was widely used in the early 1950s and was responsible for the deaths of many adult partridges (Ash 1956). Partly for this reason, its use was soon curtailed. DNOC was also directly insecticidal, and some work on its effects on insects in cereals was carried out at Rothamsted (Johnson *et al.* 1955). Some of the currently used herbicides are also directly toxic to insects, especially 2,4-D (Sotherton 1982), but here the indirect effects are often greater than the direct ones. In a series of trials in the mid-1960s,

Southwood and Cross (1969) showed that weed removal could reduce the biomass of insects in cereals by two-thirds.

Each year between 1972 and 1976, the 5 most weedy and the 5 most weed-free fields were compared in the Sussex monitoring exercise. Data from the 5 years were combined and effects on the 3 preferred insect groups ranged from −22% to −69%. In one experiment, the removal of weeds, mostly a dense stand of rough meadow-grass, changed the biomass of chick-food by −43% (Vickerman 1974). A randomized and replicated series of trials in 1983 showed significant adverse effects on preferred insects ranging from −14% to −64% (Rands in press). All these results together suggest a reduction in the sum of the most preferred insects of about 50% attributable to herbicides.

The direct effects of insecticides appear to be confined mostly to the use of aphicides in winter wheat. The effect of these insecticides on chick survival has been studied nationwide and amounted to a loss of chick survival of as much as 20% in treated areas of winter wheat, as predicted by correlations between insect food and chick survival combined with known effects of the insecticides (Potts 1981). Losses were significant in 1976 and 1980 ($P<0.02$). However, the adverse effects were confined to those winter wheats which were sprayed relatively early in those seasons. Overall, the effect was negligible in the Sussex study area, partly because farmers there used the more specific aphicides and sprayed a small proportion of the wheat.

Foliar fungicides appear to have had very substantial adverse effects on some species. For example, the density of the 5 species of the staphylinid beetle *Tachyporus*, which are cereal aphid predators, was reduced by over 95% as the foliar fungicides were introduced in the Sussex study area. Food chain destruction may have been involved, but direct effects in both laboratory and in controlled and replicated field trials have been in the order of 20-30% losses per application of foliar fungicides (Sotherton & Moreby 1984). Effects on the preferred insects, however, have not been established in the field. Trials in 1981 and 1983, with one of the most commonly used foliar fungicides, a mixture of triadimefon and captafol, showed no adverse effect on the preferred insects.

4.5 Other agricultural practices
Straw burning and hedge removal both reduced preferred insect densities locally in the Sussex study area. Conversely, the under-sowing of cereals increased densities of preferred insects (Potts 1970b, 1977; Vickerman 1979). One of the farms has maintained this traditional practice; the mean sum density of preferred insects there over the past 14 years was 63% higher than that on the other farms ($P<0.01$), and partridge chick survival was 37%, compared with 22% for all the other farms ($P<0.05$).

Since 1969, the sum density of preferred insects per m^2 ($=y$) as monitored in the Sussex study area appears also to have declined by about half, but annual variation has been high in relation to the annual rate of change. The regression equation is:

$$y = 91.13 - 0.982x \qquad r = -0.48 \qquad \text{not sig}* ....(6)$$

4.6 Decline in the frequency of insect food in partridge chicks
We have only examined 9 chicks aged less than one week since 1969; they were either killed under licence or accidentally on farm tracks. The average number of insects in the crop of chicks was 38 ± 10.5. This figure is significantly less than the figure of 98 ± 5 insects per crop obtained for 56 similar chicks in the combined results of Ford *et al.* (1938), Poyarkov (1955), Hammer *et al.* (1958) and Janda (1959). This general conclusion is further supported by the results of Launay (1975), who analysed the food in partridge chicks which had been killed by a stoat.

4.7 Chick survival prior to the use of post-emergence pesticides
The main source of data here is the first 7 years of the National Game Census, covering an average of 33 farms per year. From 1933-39 inclusive, the annual mean chick survival rate averaged 50%. Over the period from 1886-1943, 7 studies in 4 countries covering a total of 82 years gave a combined mean chick survival rate also of 50%.

4.8 The cause of the decline in chick survival
The above estimate of 50% chick survival, together with equation 4, implies a reduction in chick survival rate in the UK of 20% of the mean already by 1957, and an additional 23% of the original mean by 1983. These recent estimates are consistent with an independent estimate that the decline in partridge chick survival began between '1952 and 1962' (Potts 1970b).

The perspective is clearer if we consider the relative position at the start of the Sussex monitoring of insects using the above equations. For example, the pre-herbicide estimate of chick survival of 50% implies a pre-herbicide density of preferred insect food of $50/m^2$ (equation 5). By 1969, chick survival had dropped to 31%, 62% of the pre-herbicide mean, and chick food in cereals to $23/m^2$, 47% of the pre-herbicide mean.

These estimated changes from the pre-pesticide era, therefore, coincide almost exactly with the 50% we expect from the experiments on the effects of herbicides, and show that herbicides alone could have had effects sufficient to cause the decline in partridge chick survival.

The Game Conservancy organized a large-scale controlled and replicated experiment reducing herbicide use along the headlands of cereal fields in 1982 and

*with 1984 $P<0.05$

1983 (Plate 3). This experiment increased partridge chick survival significantly in both years (P<0.01) (Rands in press), experimental confirmation of the earlier views of Southwood and Cross (1969).

4.9 Overall result of monitoring insects in cereals

Trends for 104 species (and taxa) of insect have been examined for the 11 years 1970-80. At least 50% appear to have declined (30% at P<0.05), whereas only 4% have increased (1% at P<0.05).

5 Discussion

The partridge decline seems to indicate, a bit like the tip of an iceberg, that fundamental changes have occurred among many species of wildlife in the farmland ecosystem. Why then has so very little attention been given to the rest of the iceberg? Why has farmland ecology been so neglected? The reasons should be investigated, especially considering that most species we have monitored, several species of game, dicotyledonous weeds and insects, have declined.

One factor may be that crop entomology seems to have been over-orientated to particular pest problems, and in the early days to have been overwhelmed by the efficacy of pesticides. Side effects on the environment have often not been taken seriously, and even recently it has been considered that adverse effects of pesticides on wildlife have 'often been exaggerated out of all proportion in comparison with the benefits' (Gough 1977). Surely this was a point at which the pro-pesticide lobby could have stressed the need for the wildlife lobby to quantify their case better. I can find little evidence that this was ever done, with the possible exception of the Shell Company in defending the use of the 'drin compounds.

Russian entomologists such as Bey Bienko seem to have taken a wider view even during the 1930s, but without much result. However, when the virgin lands of Kazakhstan and Siberia were first ploughed, insect monitoring schemes were set up with a fairly broad remit (eg Grigor'yeva 1970). Pesticides were not often used, however, and the main result of the work merely echoed the view of the Canadians Turnbull and Chant (1961) that the faunas of cereal fields were, on the whole, quite well regulated. This view was widely held by Dutch entomologists monitoring the development of the field faunas of the new polders (den Boer 1977).

The concept of pesticide treadmills was introduced in the late 1950s (Commoner 1971), but the evidence came mainly from cotton fields; pesticide use in cereals was still low, and no-one seems to have thought that such treadmills might one day occur in cereals. In Britain, a key feeling was that diversity, especially in the form of weeds and hedges (Van Emden 1970), could often be undesirable, and one leading entomologist argued for bigger farms and fields (Way 1974). Indeed, there were some reasons

why entomologists should have been lukewarm about the possibilities for integrated pest control. As modern trends towards monoculture developed through the 1950s, 33 out of 39 insect pest species declined (Gair 1975). Moreover, DeBach (1964) had omitted some cases of successful biological control in cereals from his review. For good measure, at the same time, leading ornithologists argued that hedges were not important to farmland birds (Murton & Westwood 1974).

Quite simply, serious adverse effects of modern farming were not perceived, except perhaps by game conservationists, who had been aware of the problem for some time. For example, many of the osage-orange hedges of the United States were destroyed between 1910 and 1930 in a campaign to reduce insect pests in orchards. The main effect was a reduction in bobwhite quail, and over 50 years ago Aldo Leopold criticized universities for not training crop entomologists to consider environmental issues (Leopold 1931). The lessons appear not to have been learned (Lincoln 1969).

Very recent work has revealed that predatory polyphagous invertebrates are potentially of great value in integrated pest control of cereal aphids (Carter & Sotherton 1983), and that proportionally far more aphid predators overwinter in hedges than is the case with aphids; 93% of the most important cereal aphid predator, the carabid beetle *Demetrias atricapillus*, overwinter in hedges. The Game Conservancy has always realized that hedges have a tangible cash benefit to shooting farmers as nesting cover, but it now seems they may also have a cash benefit in terms of integrated pest control (Sotherton 1984). Yet there is still no research on the ecological implications of field size—why?

Our broadly based monitoring exercise in cereals on the Sussex downs has, since 1970, revealed a major decline in insect taxa. At least on this 62 km² area of cereals, which in many ways is typical of cereal growing areas in the UK as a whole, several species have apparently disappeared, while others exist in tiny remnant populations, and must be considered under threat.

On a wider scale, 20% of farms have lost grey partridges altogether. This species now appears to be as threatened as the corncrake was 50 years ago, and partridges are likely to be a barometer for many weeds and invertebrates. A first priority must surely be to see that this monitoring exercise continues. Yet after 14 years, we still cannot fund it properly; it fits unhappily between agriculture and environment, and long-term funding is especially difficult. The partridge monitoring shows that trends with very large effects often become clear after decades, rather than years. The causes of the partridge decline were in many ways discovered by techniques more analogous to those of a detective after a crime. One recalls the similar predicament of Ratcliffe in explaining the decline of the peregrine: the vital data came from egg collectors, not from ecologists. Of course, we cannot monitor everything and will always be condemned to conjecture where we do not monitor. We might be forgiven for not being able properly to quantify the effects of myxomatosis on our fauna, or for not realizing in the 1960s that DDE was toxic and not as we were told 'a harmless metabolite of DDT'. Should we be forgiven, however, for not better quantifying the effects of hedge removal on our fauna and for not finding out sooner that many of the fungicides which are now used annually on millions of hectares are also insecticidal?

A radical shake-up of lobbying for research is needed. Neither the Nature Conservancy Council, the Natural Environment Research Council nor the universities have yet perceived the urgent need for research in environmental protection in the farmed part of our countryside. One factor responsible could be the length of time needed to show that changes are important. Our insect work suggests that 10 years is a minimum for a monitoring exercise, but also that causation has to be established by experiments. A new fund should be considered specifically to prevent competition between short- and long-term interests and to cover the interface between existing research councils and MAFF. It would help us meet our commitment to monitoring recognized in the Berne Convention. However, multidisciplinary research is needed. The universities could do much to foster such research by breaking down the strong barriers between agriculture and ecology and by finding practical ways of integrating the activities of entomologists, ornithologists and the other specialized subjects. Research by industry of the sort required by the Pesticides Safety Precautions Scheme should be made available for scrutiny; like Cabinet papers, sensitive material could be withheld for a time, and there would be no point in considering chemicals and uses not cleared. Secrecy breeds suspicion.

Research in the countryside must be seen to be relevant to the concerns of ordinary people for their environment. At present, it is not. My practical recommendations are as follows.

i. The Sussex monitoring work of the Game Conservancy should continue.

ii. An independent fund should be set up to finance research on farmland wildlife.

iii. The results of research which is carried out by industry for the PSPS should be made more freely available.

iv. Universities should include courses on farming and farmland ecology in the teaching of ecology.

6 Summary

The densities and breeding success of partridge, the numbers (and taxa) of weed species, and the densities of insect species (and taxa) were monitored in cereal crops from 1969-83 on a 62 km^2 area of farmland in Sussex. Details were also kept of pesticide usage and of other agricultural techniques. These data were combined with some earlier less comprehensive material available from the literature and from the Game Conservancy archives. This paper reviews the major trends revealed by this monitoring, detailed results being published elsewhere.

Dicotyledonous weeds are far less abundant now than they were prior to the use of herbicides. The number of species per sample site is estimated to have decreased from 7·5 to 1·9. A total of 45 species of dicot weeds was recorded in cereals in the Sussex study area. The particular case of the decline of the black-bindweed is described in detail.

The survival rate of partridge chicks to 6 weeks of age is determined largely by the combined densities of plant bugs, leafhoppers, sawfly larvae, weevils and leaf beetles. The use of herbicides reduced the overall density of these invertebrates by about half, though the effect was significantly less where under-sowing was still practised.

The survival rate of grey partridge chicks has been halved since herbicides were first used. This change in chick survival is the principal cause of the dramatic decline of this hitherto common species.

Many of the fungicides used in cereals are insecticidal and adverse effects on some predators of cereal aphids have occurred. However, the implications are not clear, and there is no clear evidence, as yet, of a pesticides treadmill from cereal growing.

Trends for 104 species and taxa analysed after 12 years 1970-81 show that 50% appear to have declined (30% significant at $P<0.05$), whereas only 4% have increased (1% at $P<0.05$).

Attention is focused on the problem of why so little research is being done on farmland wildlife, despite a large interest in the subject. The needs for long-term monitoring and for multidisciplinary joint research by different organizations are stressed.

7 References

Ash, J.S. 1956. Farm chemicals. In: *Your year's work (1956)*, 46-47. Fordingbridge: ICI Game Research Station.

Boer, P.J. den. 1977. *Dispersal power and survival of Carabidae in a cultured environment*. Wageningen: Veenman & Zonen.

Broad, P.D. 1952. The occurrence of weed seeds in samples submitted for testing by the Official Seed Testing Station. *J. natn. Inst. agric. Bot.*, **6**, 275-286.

Broadbent, L. 1980. Ecological aspects of agricultural pesticide application. *Biologist*, **27**, 131-133.

Bunyan, P.J. & Stanley, P.I. 1983. The environmental cost of pesticide usage in the United Kingdom. *Agric. Ecosyst. Environ.*, **9**, 187-209.

Carter, N. & Sotherton, N.W. 1983. The role of polyphagous predators in the control of cereal aphids. *Proc. int. Congr. Pl. Prot., 10th, 1983*, **2**, 778.

Commoner, B. 1971. *The closing circle; confronting the environmental crisis.* London: Jonathan Cape.

Cross, D.A. 1966. *Approaches toward an assessment of the role of insect food in the ecology of gamebirds, especially the partridge* (Perdix perdix). PhD thesis, University of London.

Curtis, J. 1883. *Farm insects, being the natural history and economy of the insects injurious to the field crops of Great Britain and Ireland, and also those which infest barns and granaries. With suggestions for their destruction.* London: Van Voorst.

DeBach, P. ed. 1964. *Biological control of insect pests and weeds.* London: Chapman & Hall.

Ford, J., Chitty, H. & Middleton, A. 1938. The food of partridge chicks (*Perdix perdix* L.) in Great Britain. *J. Anim. Ecol.*, **7**, 251-265.

Gair, R. 1975. Cereal pests. *Proc. Br. Insectic. Fungic. Conf., 8th*, **3**, 871-874.

Gooch, S.M. 1963. The occurrence of weed seeds in samples tested by the Official Seed Testing Station, 1960-61. *J. natn. Inst. agric. Bot.*, **9**, 353-371.

Gough, H.C. 1977. Pesticides on crops—some benefits and problems. In: *Ecological effects of pesticides*, edited by F.H. Perring & K. Mellanby, 7-26. London: Academic Press.

Green, R.E. In press. The feeding ecology and survival of partridge chicks (*Alectoris rufa* and *Perdix perdix*) on arable farmland in East Anglia, U.K. *J. appl. Ecol.*

Grigor'yeva, T.G. 1970. The development of self-regulation in an agrobiocoenosis following prolonged monoculture. *Ent. Rev.*, **49**, 1-7.

Hammer, M., Køie, M. & Spärck, R. 1958. Investigations on the food of partridges, pheasants and black grouse in Denmark. *Dan. Rev. Game Biol.*, **3**, 183-208.

Hanf, M. 1983. *The arable weeds of Europe with their seedlings and seeds.* Ipswich: BASF United Kingdom.

Janda, J. 1959. Vzitecnost Juenilruch Koroptvi (*Perdix perdix* L.). *Prace Vyzkumnych Ustava Lesnickych C.S.R.*, **17**, 27-66.

Johnson, C.G., Dobson, R.M., Southwood, T.R.E., Stephenson, J.W. & Taylor, L.R. 1955. Preliminary observations on the effect of weedkillers on insect populations. *Rep. Rothamsted exp. Stn, 1954*, 129-130.

Launay, M. 1975. Disponibilité en insects dans les cultures et dans les amenagements. Ses rapports avec le regime alimentaire du poussin de perdix grise (*Perdix perdix* L.). *Bull. Off. Natl Chasse*, Special no. 4, 170-192.

Leopold, A. 1931. *Report on a game survey of the North Central States for the Sporting Arms and Ammunition Manufacturers Institute.* Madison, Wisconsin: SAAMI.

Lincoln, C. 1969. The effect of agricultural practices on insect habitats in a typical delta community. *Proc. Tall Timbers Conference on Ecological Animal Control by Habitat Management, 1st*, 13-18.

Murton, R.K. & Westwood, N.J. 1974. Some effects of agricultural change on the English avifauna. *Br. Birds*, **67**, 41-69.

Potts, G.R. 1970a. Recent changes in the farmland fauna with special reference to the decline of the grey partridge. *Bird Study*, **17**, 145-166.

Potts, G.R. 1970b. Studies on the changing role of weeds of the genus *Polygonum* in the diet of partridges. *J. appl. Ecol.*, **7**, 567-576.

Potts, G.R. 1974. The grey partridge: problems of quantifying the ecological effects of pesticides. *Proc. int. Congr. Game Biol.*, **11**, 405-413.

Potts, G.R. 1977. Some effects of increasing the monoculture of cereals. In: *Origins of pest, parasite, disease and weed problems*, edited by J.M. Cherrett & G.R. Sagar, 183-202. (Symposium of the British Ecological Society no. 18). Oxford: Blackwell Scientific.

Potts, G.R. 1980. The effects of modern agriculture, nest predation and game management on the population ecology of partridges (*Perdix perdix* and *Alectoris rufa*). *Adv. ecol. Res.*, **11**, 2-79.

Potts, G.R. 1981. Insecticide sprays and the survival of partridge chicks. *Annu. Rev. Game Conservancy, 1980*, no. 12, 39-48.

Potts, G.R. & Vickerman, G.P. 1974. Studies on the cereal ecosystem. *Adv. ecol. Res.*, **8**, 107-197.

Poyarkov, D.V. 1955. Ecology of partridges in steppes of European part of USSR. *Gorod. Ped. Inst.*, **38**, 157-213. (In Russian).

Pulliainen, E. 1983. Etela-Pohjanmaan peltopyiden syysravinnossa kahden Vvosikymmenen aikana tapahtuneista muutoksista. *Suom. Riista*, **30**, 15-21.

Rands, M.R.W. In press. Herbicide use on cereals and the survival of grey partridge chicks: a field experiment. *J. appl. Ecol.*

Sotherton, N.W. 1982. Effects of herbicides on the chrysomelid beetle *Gastrophysa polygoni* (L.) in the laboratory and field. *Z. angew. Entomol.*, **94**, 446-451.

Sotherton, N.W. 1984. The value of field boundaries to beneficial insects. *Annu. Rev. Game Conservancy, 1983*, no. 15, 72-75.

Sotherton, N.W. & Moreby, S.M. 1984. Contact toxicity of some foliar fungicide sprays to three species of polyphagous predators found in cereal fields. (Tests of agrochemicals and cultivars no. 5). *Ann. appl. Biol.*, **104**, Suppl.

Southwood, T.R.E. & Cross, D.J. 1969. The ecology of the partridge. III. Breeding success and the abundance of insects in natural habitats. *J. Anim. Ecol.*, **38**, 497-509.

Tonkin, J.H. 1968. The occurrence of broad-leaved weed seeds in samples of cereals tested by the Official Seed Testing Station, Cambridge. *Proc. Br. Weed Control Conf., 9th*, 1199-1204.

Turnbull, A.L. & Chant, D.A. 1961. The practice and theory of biological control of insects in Canada. *Can. J. Zool.*, **39**, 697-753.

Van Emden, H.F. 1970. Insects, weeds and plant health. *Proc. Br. Weed Control Conf., 10th*, **3**, 942-952.

Vickerman, G.P. 1974. Some effects of grass-weed control on the arthropod fauna of cereals. *Proc. Br. Weed Control Conf., 12th*, **3**, 929-939.

Vickerman, G.P. 1979. The arthropod fauna of undersown grass and cereal fields. *Sci. Proc. R. Dublin Soc. Ser. A*, **6**, 273-283.

Vickerman, G.P. & O'Bryan, M. 1979. Partridges and insects. *Annu. Rev. Game Conservancy, 1978*, no. 9, 35-43.

Way, M.J. 1974. Integrated control in Britain. In: *Biology in pest and disease control*, edited by D. Price Jones & M.E. Solomon, 196-208. Oxford: Blackwell Scientific.

Ecological principles in upland management

W E S MUTCH
Department of Forestry & Natural Resources, University of Edinburgh

In searching for ecological principles, whether for the uplands or elsewhere, it is tempting to look most closely at the attractive situations from which man is absent, yet to do so would be to introduce such a lack of realism as would render the study irrelevant. Nevertheless, an ecosystem model suggested as a basis of productive land management (Black 1964) envisages land resources being allocated on the basis of 2 sequential tests:

i. What uses are ecologically sustainable on this land?

ii. Which of the ecologically sustainable uses listed in (i) above offers the best economic return?

Black envisaged that the best economic use identified in (ii) would normally win acceptance and succeed, but might on various social or strategic grounds be unacceptable to the politician/administrator, so that he might decide in favour of another use already identified as ecologically sustainable in list (i). This model, however, must be regarded as unrealistic and, in essence, defective. The defect in steps (i) and (ii) lies in the assumption that the ecologist can prepare a set of ecologically sustainable productive management strategies or land uses, in the absence of financial and economic considerations. I believe that assumption is false.

The manager of land in the hills and uplands who is sensitive to the operation of the ecosystem within which he operates will indeed quickly identify ecological constraints. If he should overstep these constraints, experience tells us that the production system will fail or at least the system will show a diminution in trophic level, and hence a loss of sustention in output. For instance, a manager might unwisely decide to plant a high yielding but frost-tender cultivar in a frost-prone environment; by overstepping this ecological constraint, he would lose the crop and the management would fail. Similarly, a manager might cull an animal herd at a level which would not allow sufficient recruitment to the breeding group; by ignoring the ecological constraints, he would impose at least instability in the ouput and, if he were to persist, long-term reduction.

In practice, management essentially comprises an identification of the successive constraints acting on the land use system and a series of decisions whether or not to overcome each one. The land manager who is ecologically sensitive (and one may argue he must be sensitive if he is to be successful beyond the short term) can decide to buy out each constraint if he wishes, provided that he commands sufficient resources to do so. Whether a managed ecosystem is sustainable depends on how much the manager (or society) is prepared to pay. It is doubtful whether the ecology of any managed system can be divorced from its economics. As an extreme example, one might grow walnut trees on the top of Ben Nevis and manage the system for a sustained yield of fruit, provided enough external resources were brought in to 'buy off' the natural environment constraints. The same principle is seen, in less extreme application, in hill sheep farming, upland dairying or forestry. The managed ecosystem in the uplands is the product of nature and man's investment.

As this meeting relates to the impact of agriculture, and hence to managed ecosystems, the relevant principles are concerned less with ecology and mostly with economics. The managed ecosystems in the uplands are constrained by topography, climate and soils, which principally determine the nature and productivity of the plant communities. Typically, these ecosystems are unsuitable for conversion to arable farming and can be used best by grazing animals. The pastures are generally poor by lowland standards and the traditional set-stock grazing systems have utilized only a small proportion of the annual growth of forage. In a discussion of the ecology of the uplands, the low utilization rate of the traditional grazing systems is important to the discernment of the ecological principles, and to an understanding of the developing public attitudes to the use of hill land.

The low utilization rate of the traditional hill grazing farm was associated both with an extremely low, or negative, gross margin for the farmer apart from subsidies, and with the existence of many joint products. The low financial return to the farmer (eg Cunningham 1979; Duthie 1965; Eadie 1979) has itself been a cause of instability in the system, as farmers strove to escape from a low income; they sought to escape either by selling whole or part of the farm to another use, usually forestry, or by a radical change of farming system, involving pasture improvement, fencing and, always, an increase in the intensity of pasture utilization.

It is characteristic of low intensity management systems in the uplands that they commonly allow the provision of joint products of which neither the ecology nor the economics is simple. Multiple use of land, as this joint production is often termed, is an attractive concept, conveying as it does the idea of each unit of land serving 'double duty', as though society were receiving outputs for no input.

For the establishment of principles, it is unfortunate that the term 'multiple use' has come to cover both the deliberate decision to produce more than one good or service from a land unit and the situation where other goods and services happen to occur uninvited alongside the output that management is trying to produce. The latter condition may be regarded as casual multiple use, and is extremely common in extensive grazing systems and in forestry. On Scottish hill farms where sheep and hill cattle are the principal products, red grouse, feral goats and mountain hares share the grazings and provide subsidiary products, with public access being tolerated throughout the area. The farmer may not be aiming to produce any of these subsidiaries, and may find the disturbance of his stock by public access obviously damaging at some times of the year; nevertheless, he may accept them all, if only because he cannot afford to rid his farm of them. The subsidiaries may cost less in domestic stock production foregone than would their destruction or exclusion. The decision to change the margin at which the farmer would take action against them depends on prices and costs; an increase in the price of a major product would cause the farmer to review the cost of the subsidiaries, in principal production foregone, and hence the desirability of eliminating them.

Similar casual multiple use occurs in upland forestry; in some instances, the forester may accept the inevitable joint production (say the presence of roe deer which damage young plantations severely by browsing), and, making a virtue of necessity, may call the result multiple use.

In contrast, there are many instances where multiple use is the result of a positive management decision, as in the mixed system of timber trees and grazings (eg Knowles *et al.* 1973). Although casual multiple use and planned multiple use may appear to be quite different, both fit well enough into an optimization strategy, ie into a logical management regime for producing the desired goods at least cost, or for maximizing the yield or the profit margin of the desired system.

The foregoing describes precisely how multiple use was approached by Gregory (1955) in what is still the key paper on the economics of the subject. Gregory's model, given suitable data, would indicate whether multiple use was economically justified for a particular management situation and the amounts of the various goods considered which would yield an optimal result. As with any optimization procedure, the model requires the operator to define the criterion upon which the alternatives will be judged, ie the statement of an objective. In contrast, the adoption of multiple use as a popular panacea has allowed it to emerge, however illogically, as an end in itself, as if the yielding of many compatible products was particularly desirable and capable of maximization. This argument is vitally important in the coexistence of nature conservation and managed production systems in the uplands.

The relationships of product to product in respect of their compatibility range from supplementary production to direct competition (Lloyd 1969). These conditions are not discrete, but form a catena of compatibility which varies inversely with the intensity of management. Extensively managed land tends to produce more than one product, and capacity for multiple production (or tolerance of it) diminishes as the intensity of use increases. The fact that the farmer may receive an income from the subsidiary products of casual multiple use and extensive management arises mainly because the manager finds he has more to gain by using his scarce resources of supervision and capital on the production of his main product, X, than by diverting them to the elimination of the secondary products, Y and Z. Later, when he has intensified the system by devoting his attention, labour and capital to the most urgent improvements in system X, he finds that the increments of input factors would be more effective in eliminating system Y or Z, a stage which is commonly identified as the margin of compatibility and competition in the product/product relations.

The upland proprietor may decide to increase sheep output, eg by pasture seeding, or paddock fencing. The increased financial commitment makes the farmer intolerant of red deer and hares which clearly reduce his more valuable sheep production and may yield him little or nothing, particularly if the deer use his farm in the close season. Even public access becomes unacceptable, as people break the fences and disturb the stock. It may be necessary to take account of what the re-seeding may cost in the abandonment of the revenue-earning grouse shooting, because of the elimination of the birds' required habitat and diet of heather. As the intensity of management and capital commitment increase in any system, so casual multiple use declines. The agricultural extreme of the catena from traditional extensive sheep management is the intensive farming within a controlled environment, where not even a mouse may be tolerated, far less a red deer. These creatures, extraneous to the cultivated system, would not yield 'something for nothing', but would clearly divert inputs from the desired product, and their cost would be the reduction in sales of the harvested product.

The production functions associated with hill land are very frequently less advantageous to man than those on lowland, because the soils are thinner, less fertile or more fiercely drained, or the climate is harsher than in the lowlands; or it may be that the most productive machines cannot operate efficiently on the steeper gradients. The upland production functions being generally poorer than those in the lowlands, capital investment per unit area tends to be less attractive and is smaller than in the lowlands, so land use in the hills is generally far more extensive than on the low ground. This fact itself accounts for a high proportion of the supposed multiple product management and multiple use of hill lands; because they are not intensively managed, casual multiple use is normal.

There are clear exceptions to such a generalization, where the use of hill land is intensive, and some instances are particularly revealing as the change in management intensity has been made quite recently. An example from abroad reminds that this is not an issue confined to the United Kingdom. The change of land use in the Chianti Hills of Tuscany is an especially clear example, depending on the peculiar soil and climatic conditions which favour vine growing. In the Chianti, the intensification for viticulture produces a landscape which, to the tourist, is less attractive than the traditional Tuscan mixture of olives, corn, vines and vegetables. Under the influence of a substantial price increase for good Chianti wine, land use moves to a single product system which is much more lucrative to the proprietor. If society were to insist on continued multiple use and diversified production for aesthetic reasons, because visitors enjoyed seeing white oxen and a mosaic of crops in each field, the farmer would be denied the opportunity to increase his income from the management of his property, and a problem would be posed on how he could be recompensed for the denial of better revenue, or induced not to proceed with the change. This problem is repeated in the North York Moors National Park, the Peak District, and in the most scenically attractive upland areas of Britain to which the compensation clauses of the Wildlife and Countryside Act were directed.

Several points emerge from such evidence of change. First, there is the reminder that land use is dynamic, under the influence of changes in demand, product prices and costs; Gregory's model could test the sensitivity of the system to price and cost changes, provided data were available. The second point is that, where land is scarce (either any land or land of a particular quality), suitable hill land does attract capital investment and improvement which make intensive management profitable and multiple use unlikely; it is the existence of more attractive investment opportunities elsewhere that keeps most hill land undeveloped. Third, an artificial retention of multiple use always represents a lost opportunity for the proprietor, and a potential loss of revenue; admittedly, it may be more than offset by a non-market benefit which accrues to another person or group, but someone must sustain the revenue loss. It may fall on the proprietor or it may be shared by society. Fourth, the increase in the intensity of land uses and the accompanying reduction of multiple products present fewest problems when the proprietorship and the enjoyment of the multiple products are in a single person or few people, and they present most problems when the land is owned by one person and the multiple product services are enjoyed by society at large.

The pattern of use of the hill land in Britain has been changing quite markedly over the last 20 years, under the impetus of adverse financial circumstances in the 1950s and 1960s when labour costs rose much more rapidly than product prices. The decline in demand for mutton (as opposed to lamb), and especially for wether mutton after 1950, resulted in the withdrawal of wether flocks from the higher and more remote sheep areas, with a resulting concentration on ewe flocks to produce lambs for lowland cross-breeding and for fattening, and a marked increase in cattle numbers. The virtual withdrawal of sheep from the more remote hill areas of Scotland allowed sharp increases both in the area grazed by red deer and in their numbers, the national herd increasing by perhaps 50% in 10 years to about 300 000 head (Red Deer Commission 1976).

Concurrently with these changes, a successful programme of afforestation was followed on the lower hill slopes, up to about 500 m altitude. In some instances, afforestation was carried out by the existing landowners, but more often it followed land purchase by the Forestry Commission or a private forestry company. After 1960, the Forestry Commission planted at the rate of about 15 000 ha per annum in the Scottish uplands (Forestry Commission 1960-83), and the private sector achieved between 6000 and 17 000 ha per annum. The immediate importance of the afforestation for other uses of hill land lies mainly in 3 facts: this new forest is not in the same proprietorship as the neighbouring grazing land; in an effort to be financially successful in a relatively harsh environment, the new forest is composed principally of Sitka spruce and lodgepole pine which are productive but liable to severe damage by deer; and it is fenced against domestic stock and deer.

These 3 points imply the creation, maintenance and future increase of severe tension between the forest ecosystem and its neighbours. Personal tension between farmers and foresters has diminished greatly in recent years, but the ecological tension between their systems of land use continues.

The large areas of the Scottish uplands used almost exclusively as sporting estates for grouse and deer traditionally have provided a considerable private subsidy from the city to the country, because, large as these land holdings are, they yield a very modest revenue to set against the expense of their maintenance.

The compatibility of grouse shooting and sheep grazing has been supported by the constraints which some landlords who retain the sport shooting have placed in the leases of their tenant sheep farmers, whereby the number of sheep grazing the rented areas has been restricted. As the economics of sheep farming became more difficult after 1950, there was a strong incentive to increase the number of ewes per holding and the restriction by lease of the maximum numbers of sheep to be grazed is a practical expression of the potential competition between the systems. A move in sheep husbandry towards pasture re-seeding or more complete vegetation utilization inevitably reduces the compatibility of sheep and grouse, making a weaker case from the point of view of sheep production for the labour-intensive patch burning of heather on which grouse remain dependent. In view of the high rents currently available for grouse shooting, there is no likelihood of the grouse system disappearing, but it is probable that there will be continued specialization towards monoculture.

Systems of land use in the hills are under pressure to become more productive, to yield a higher return on invested capital, and to give more timber or more animal products in order to meet increased wages or a wider margin for the operator's income. In addition, these systems are under pressure from higher demands for non-priced recreation. This process has involved the commitment of more expenditure on roads, fences, mineral fertilizers, machinery, and for housing, purchased feed and veterinary care for stock. The case for the provision of capital from public national and EEC sources may be argued, but it should be recognized that the investment of new capital forces management to stop the leaks in the system which produces its best paying product, each becoming intolerant of the subsidiary products which represent multiple use.

A House of Commons Select Committee on Scottish Affairs (1972), considering land use in Scotland, the allocation of land resources, land improvement and multiple use, heard evidence from the Nature Conservancy that during the last 30 years there had been greatly increased pressure to maximize the potential production of land in the form of a main crop for man and a pronounced move towards monocultural systems, and undoubtedly the trend has continued strongly since then. The Select Committee found the move towards monocultures involved much that was undesirable in a heavily populated island. It was as if multiple use was ceasing just when the pressure on land systems made it especially desirable and valuable that each hectare should 'do double-duty'. In fact, increasingly specialized use is an automatic result of increased pressure, be it increased pressure from recreationists, or increased pressure from the proprietor, private or state, for the manager to produce a better financial result. The normal result of increased pressure on a land use system is a movement towards specialization.

The further loss of joint production from upland ecosystems was clearly viewed as unacceptable for society by the provision of compensation payments to proprietors under the Wildlife and Countryside Act, persuading them to forego the financial advantages of intensification in order to allow the multiple uses to persist. There is no doubt about the wide appeal of multiple use as a concept.

The model presented by Gregory (1955) is certainly relevant to the study of land use in the uplands, but over 3 decades managers have found it impossible to generate satisfactory data to use that model. They have failed to show the combinations of joint products obtainable from a range of input levels and, beyond that, to derive the expansion path of maximal benefit combinations which would be required to make Gregory's model operationally useful. Muhlenberg (1964), Helliwell (1973), and Steuer and Schuler (1979) all attempted to overcome the shortage of information on joint product combinations available to the manager, but none of their proposals is convincing.

The other substantial difficulty in analysing ecosystem management in the uplands is the fact that some of the important values involved are non-market values. For many of the important situations or output flows in the uplands, there is no market and there is no agreement on shadow-prices, for either costs or benefits: the benefit conferred by protecting rare species; the value of scarce specialized habitats; the value of interesting habitat which, though not scarce nationally, happens to be close to a population centre; the value of an indigenous source of raw material as a base for a domestic processing industry; and so on. The difficulty of such analysis without quantified values is apparent in Helliwell (1973) and in Steuer and Schuler (1979).

There has been vociferous criticism of an intensification of upland agriculture on the grounds of the change of habitats and of landscape. Three options appear to be available for positive action to avoid continued intensification: compensation, planning control, and purchase.

Compensation is the option taken in the Wildlife and Countryside Act to attempt the conservation of particular areas or objects of scientific interest. Money is paid to proprietors to equal the value of development foregone in the interests of society. Its shortcoming is seen to be its cost and open-ended nature; in particular, it is thought to be liable to abuse by proprietors who might threaten development in order to force protective payment, and it has been suggested that the sale value of land including a Site of Special Scientific Interest could be enhanced by the possibility of development blackmail.

Planning control would impose society's decisions on proprietors by regulation. It is opposed by most farmers and foresters, partly because it would reduce the value of their assets, but also because they believe there is insufficient professional competence to operate planning control and allow a productive rural economy to exist.

Land purchase to ensure public proprietorship of the areas where society wishes to foster wildlife and semi-natural habitats may be the only safe long-term solution to the tension which exists between private ownership and society's declared wish to control intensification in the uplands; the disadvantage is the high cost.

In the final analysis, the tension between agricultural and forestry development, on the one hand, and the conservation of wildlife is neither ecological nor economic; it is political. The agricultural values are largely contrived by grant-aid or fiscal legislation, and the wildlife values are non-market ones. This situation leaves agricultural development vulnerable to simple withdrawal of the fiscal or subsidy support so that the politician is able to operate not on a basis of economic analysis or ecological principle, but *ad hoc*. The relative merits of farm production and wildlife conservation must remain a value judgement by the politician, with principles not in evidence.

Summary
For a study of the impact of agricultural land use on wildlife and semi-natural habitats, it is essential to take account of the commitment of capital to the managed ecosystem. Ecological principles are less relevant than economic analysis.

The co-existence of wildlife and semi-natural habitats with agriculture, a form of joint production or multiple use, decreases as management pressure and capital investment increase. The objections by conservationists to further agricultural development in the uplands may be resolved by compensation for farmers, as allowed by the Wildlife and Countryside Act, by planning control, or by resource purchase leading to public proprietorship. In practice, the tension is neither ecological nor economic, but political. The politician can influence resource allocation decisively by fiscal regulation, as agriculture is heavily dependent on subsidies or price support, and probably must do so in view of the lack of ecological data and of non-market values of wildlife and conservation, which ecological or economic analysis would require.

References
Black, J.N. 1964. Prolegomenon to the study of natural resources. *Sylva, Edinb.*, **45**, 5-9.

Cunningham, J.M.M. 1979. The role of agriculture and its relationship with other land uses. In: *Forestry and farming in upland Britain*, 4-27. (Occasional paper no. 6). Farnham: Forestry Commission.

Duthie, W.B. 1965. *Financial results, East of Scotland farms 1963-64.* Edinburgh: School of Agriculture, University of Edinburgh.

Eadie, J. 1979. *Animal production from the hills and uplands.* (British Association for the Advancement of Science meeting, Section M). Penicuik, Midlothian: Hill Farming Research Organisation. (Unpublished).

Forestry Commission. 1960-83. *Annual reports.* London: HMSO.

Gregory, G.R. 1955. An economic approach to multiple use. *Forest Sci.*, **1**, 6-13.

Helliwell, D.R. 1973. Priorities and values in nature conservation. *J. environ. Manage.*, **1**, 85-127.

House of Commons Select Committee on Scottish Affairs. 1972. *Land resource use in Scotland.* (House of Commons paper 511). London: HMSO.

Knowles, R.L., Klomp, B.K. & Gillingham, A. 1973. Trees and grass—an opportunity for the hill country farmer. *Proc. Ruakura Fmrs' Conf. Week 1973*, 110-121.

Lloyd, R.D. 1969. Economics of multiple-use. *Proc. Conf. Multiple-use of Southern Forests, Georgia, 1969*, 45-54.

Muhlenberg, N. 1964. A method for approximating forest multiple-use optima. *Forest Sci.*, **10**, 209-212.

Red Deer Commission. 1976. *Annual report 1975.* Edinburgh: HMSO.

Steuer, R.E. & Schuler, A.T. 1979. An interactive multiple-objective linear programming approach to a problem in forest management. *For. Ecol. & Manage.*, **2**, 191-205.

Some ecological principles underlying hill sheep management

C MILNER
Institute of Terrestrial Ecology, Bangor Research Station

1 Introduction
The relationship between free-ranging hill sheep and their food resource is complex, as the sheep are polyphagous and the food is multi-species. When one includes the spatial aspects such as the presence of stable assemblages of plants occupying specific edaphic niches and the social interactions of the sheep moving between these assemblages, it is clear that there are many difficulties in producing either descriptive or predictive models. In order to reduce the scope of this review, therefore, I have confined myself in 2 ways.

First, I have considered the inter-relationship from the point of view of the effect of plant species on sheep rather than *vice versa*, although this may be a somewhat artificial distinction because the relationship is 2-way. However, this approach can also be justified on practical grounds. Conditions in Wales are dominated by grass sward (or communities with similar structure) rather than the more complex situation in which non-grass species (such as heather) are an important part of the resource.

Second, I have also been biased towards the processes of selection and utilization of food by sheep, rather than the more strictly practical aspects of upland management; and I am concerned only with sheep grazing unimproved upland areas, despite the increasing importance of combinations of improved and unimproved pasture in the economic management of the uplands (eg Hill Farming Research Organisation 1979; MacEwen & Sinclair 1983). The whole complex has been set against the background of the Pleistocene origin of sheep, a genus which evolved as grazers of stable grasslands on the fringes of the great glaciers. This evolutionary history is vital to understanding the interactions.

2 The relationship between sheep and plant communities

The observation that sheep were not distributed either uniformly or at random over the different plant communities making up the average sheep walk was first formalized by Boulet (1939), although the fact was undoubtedly known to generations of shepherds. His observation was developed further by Hunter (1962), Hughes et al. (1964), and by Rawes and Welch (1964). All these observations can be summarized simply. Sheep numbers are relatively higher on plant communities dominated by genera such as bent, fescue and clover, developed on soils of relatively high nutrient levels and without a well defined organic matter layer (the brown earths). Sheep numbers are relatively lowest, in contrast, on plant communities dominated by such species as mat-grass which occurs on soils with a well developed organic horizon. These differences in relative stocking rates are also related to differences in primary productivity, nutrient content and the amount of dead material, and are not necessarily causative but possibly the effect of differential removal of surplus plant material and the return of mineralized nutrients in dung by the selective sheep (eg Floate 1970; Welch 1982; Perkins 1978). Such preferences are understandable in the context of evolution in the Pleistocene, with its young soils and no peat development, and where the opportunist grasses formed extensive areas which to some extent were maintained by the grazing sheep.

These interactions are well understood in general terms, although more work is needed on some specific pathways in the cycle. The relative influence of volatile nitrogen compounds, for example, both directly and indirectly, and the factors influencing losses by leaching from the various soil types present major problems. However, more general features of the sheep/plant community interaction have also received little attention, and are nonetheless of considerable importance. Hunter and Milner (1963) considered the effects of changing stocking rates on the relative occupancy of the different plant communities. They showed that increased stocking rates mainly affected the less favoured communities, with the implication that social pressures within the sheep population were responsible. This effect has now been investigated in greater detail. Milner (unpublished) showed that the occupancy rate of bent/fescue communities was linearly related to overall sheep numbers (up to a maximum of 13.6 sheep/ha),

whereas the occupancy rate of mat-grass dominated communities showed no such simple relationships (see Figure 1).

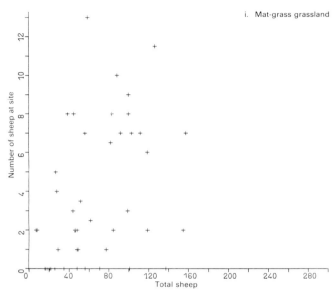

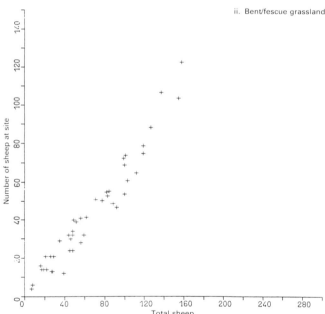

Figure 1. The relationship between sheep grazing on
i. Mat-grass grassland
ii. Bent/fescue grassland
and total sheep numbers on the sheepwalk

The reason for the differential response on different communities requires investigation. Home range behaviour has been observed in hill sheep (Hunter & Milner 1963), but no overt aggressive behaviour such as would result in territories has been observed. Nevertheless, some mechanism is necessary to explain the observed difference in occupancy rate and how individual sheep are 'prevented' from increasing the rate beyond 13.6 sheep/ha. More observation of the process of optimizing (or probably maximizing) the occupancy rates are required, and I have no realistic hypothesis for this apparent self limitation phenomenon. Whether scent (possibly via the inter-digital gland), sight, or other secondary mechanisms are involved is not known.

Our classification into simple species aggregations may be entirely inappropriate, if seen from a sheep's view of its environment. Some complex relationship between plant community, edaphic features, shelter, etc, may more appropriately determine the taxonomy of sheep environment than plant community. The interaction between overall stocking rate and occupancy is crucially important in an economic climate favouring increases in sheep numbers on the hills (in north Wales, for example, sheep numbers on hill farms have increased by between 31% and 47% since 1971).

The effects of these increases are already apparent in lower volumes of plant biomass and in increased soil surface movement, expressed as increased erosion and sedimentation in streams draining certain catchments. As yet, there is no observable decrease in the weight of sheep produced per individual (however measured), although comparative data are available.

3 The relationship between sheep and the plant species of the uplands
Animals graze selectively, and a whole range of factors interact to determine the composition of diet on a particular day. This composition may apparently be quite unrelated to the proportions of various species or plant parts present and available to the animal. In upland Britain, the plants selected show remarkable similarities from sheep walk to sheep walk. For example, the preference ratings quoted by Milner and Gwynne (1974) for sheep on the island of Hirta in the St Kilda group of the Hebrides are almost identical to the preferences shown by blackfaced sheep on the Scottish mainland (Martin 1964). Preferences are related to species occurrence in favoured communities, but selection appears to occur within such communities. The preference ratings for species of meadow-grass and Yorkshire-fog are always high, while high in summer for red fescue and bent. What is far from clear is how the preferential selection is affected by the mix of species present. This question is critical, but it is difficult to test experimentally because other factors such as herbage yield, pasture structure and overall digestibility must be constant. The possibility of using multivariate models has not been investigated, but seems plausible.

There have been many vain attempts to relate preference ratings to proximate factors in the plants, but some general agreements emerge. Leaf is preferred to stem, and green material is preferred to dead (Arnold 1964). The material eaten, when compared to the material offered and refused, is higher in nitrogen, phosphate and gross energy, and lower in 'fibre' (eg Cooke *et al.* 1956; Wallace *et al.* 1972). The relationship between selection and other factors (such as

soluble sugars, for example) is much less clear. Unfortunately, hill sheep cannot recognize, before selection, such things as nitrogen, 'crude fibre', energy, etc. Where correlations are found between any of these proximate analyses, they must relate to some other specific compounds with a particular taste or smell, or to some physical property of the plant. Even if these specific compounds can be isolated (and some attempts have been made, eg Ashton & Jones 1959), it is important to recognize that a positive or negative correlation is not proof of the unique importance or unimportance of the compound. Because of the multidimensional nature of the selection process, such simple correlations are dangerous and unlikely to have any predictive value.

It is also important to recognize that the actual form of the chemical compound, ie as grazed, is the important parameter influencing choice. The enzymes in saliva, the amount of chewing, and the volatility or otherwise of the determining compound must be considered. At least the availability of gas chromatographs now enables us to examine more quickly these ultimate determinants of species selection.

Although the problems are considerable, there is a need for such work on upland species. There is, indeed, some evidence that grazing, and saliva itself, stimulates the growth response of grasses directly, rather than by reallocating resources within the plant (Owen 1980). Whilst this effect has been disputed, it remains an intriguing and completely logical phenomenon which has important evolutionary and practical consequences.

Consideration of the ultimate factors affecting selection may seem academic. However, if we consider the interaction between a considerable increase in stocking rate and plant community occupancy, the subject becomes much more important. As available forage drops to the level from which free selection is unlikely to be possible (if sheep intake is to be maintained), then knowledge of the mechanisms of selection become important in predicting the effect on plant communities and on the sheep themselves. Whether sheep take species and parts of species in proportion to their presence or availability, or select in particular ways, will dramatically change the relative competitive ability within the plant communities grazed. There is some evidence (Peters 1980) that, even with normal stocking rates (however defined), sheep show little selectivity and only take species and plant parts in proportion to their presence in the sward. Over a short (1-2 week) timescale, the apparent differences in selectivity are expressions of the different population dynamics of tillers within the sward. This observation, if correct, has important implications for assessing the effect on upland grass swards of given stocking levels, and detailed work is required to identify individual tillers, their death rates, and the rate of production of new tillers. Peters (1980) discusses the possibility of using the tiller or part of the tiller as the unit in a production model.

4 Conclusions

The upland sheep/grass ecosystem is both a moderately productive agricultural system and the background to many other uses of the uplands such as recreation and conservation. Some of the agricultural economic problems have reputedly been solved, but much fundamental research is still required. There is some doubt whether even the economic problems of small upland farms have been solved. MacEwen and Sinclair (1983), for example, maintain that smaller farmers have suffered under the capital intensive improvement mentality induced by grants of various sorts. It is not the purpose of this review to discuss the economics, but to point out that we need to understand the production system in broad terms, if we are to predict the effect of increased (or conceivably decreased) stocking rates. In particular, we need more precise and accurate knowledge of the plant/animal system. If this information can be assembled into models of various kinds, so much the better.

Perhaps the most important feature of upland agriculture in Wales is the overall increase in stocking rate of some 30-40%. We urgently need to know how this increase affects the different plant communities, and whether the effects are irreversible. If the increase in sheep is responsible for the apparent increase in erosion, it may be an irreversible effect which needs urgent attention. Research on the sheep/vegetation/ soil interaction is still needed.

5 Summary

The way in which upland plant communities interact with sheep is of major importance in managing the upland resource. However, understanding this interaction and making predictions is not a trivial task, and requires detailed investigation. Topics to be investigated include:

  i. the preferences of sheep for different plant species;
  ii. the frequency dependent and plant density dependent changes in selection;
  iii. the effect of differential selection on competitive ability;
  iv. the social interactions between sheep influencing their spatial distribution.

6 References

Arnold, G.W. 1964. Factors within plant associations affecting the behaviour and performance of grazing animals. In: *Grazing in terrestrial and marine environments,* edited by D.J. Crisp, 133-154. Oxford: Blackwell Scientific.

Ashton, W.M. & Jones, E. 1959. Coumarin and related components in sweet vernal. *J. Br. Grassld Soc.,* **14,** 47-54.

Boulet, L.J. 1939. *The ecology of a Welsh mountain sheep walk.* PhD thesis, University of Wales.

Cooke, C.W., Stoddart, L.A. & Harris, L.E. 1956. Comparative nutritive value and palatability of some introduced and native forage plants for spring and summer grazing. *Bull. Utah agric. Exp. Stn,* no. 385.

Floate, M.J.S. 1970. Mineralisation of nitrogen and phosphorus from organic materials of plant and animal origin and its significance in the nutrient cycle of grazed upland and hill soils. *J. Br. Grassld Soc.,* **25,** 295-302.

Hill Farming Research Organisation. 1979. *Science and hill farming.* Penicuik: HFRO.

Hughes, R.E., Milner, C. & Dale, J. 1964. Selectivity in grazing. In: *Grazing in terrestrial and marine environments,* edited by D.J. Crisp, 189-202. Oxford: Blackwell Scientific.

Hunter, R.F. 1962. Hill sheep and their pasture: a study of sheep grazing in S.E. Scotland. *J. Ecol.,* **50,** 651-680.

Hunter, R.F. & Milner, C. 1963. The behaviour of individual, related and groups of south country Cheviot hill sheep. *Anim. Behav.,* **11,** 507-513.

MacEwen, M. & Sinclair, G. 1983. *New life for the hills.* London: Council for National Parks.

Martin, D.J. 1964. Analysis of sheep diet utilizing plant epidermal fragments in faeces samples. In: *Grazing in terrestrial and marine environments,* edited by D.J. Crisp, 173-188. Oxford: Blackwell Scientific.

Milner, C. & Gwynne, D. 1974. The Soay sheep and their food supply. In: *Island survivors: the ecology of the Soay sheep of St Kilda,* edited by P.A. Jewell, C. Milner & J.M. Boyd, 273-325. London: Athlone Press.

Owen, D.F. 1980. How plants may benefit from the animals that eat them. *Oikos,* **35,** 230-235.

Perkins, D.F. 1978. The distribution and transfer of energy and nutrients in the *Agrostis-Festuca* grassland ecosystem. In: *Production ecology of British moors and montane grasslands,* edited by O.W. Heal & D.F. Perkins, 375-395. Berlin: Springer.

Peters, B. 1980. *The demography of weeds in a permanent pasture.* PhD thesis, University of Wales.

Rawes, M. & Welch, D. 1964. Studies on sheep grazing in the northern Pennines. *J. Br. Grassld Soc.,* **19,** 403-411.

Wallace, J.D., Free, J.C. & Denham, A.H. 1972. Seasonal changes in herbage and cattle diets on sandhill grassland. *J. Range Manage.,* **25,** 100-104.

Welch, D. 1982. Dung properties and defecation characteristics in some Scottish herbivores, with an evaluation of the dung-volume method of assessing occupancy. *Acta theriol.,* **28,** 189-210.

Some effects of sheep management on heather moorlands in northern England

P J HUDSON
The Game Conservancy, Leyburn

1 Introduction

Since the last War, large tracts of the uplands have experienced changes in land use which have altered the distribution and quantity of their specialized vegetation and wildlife. Areas of coniferous afforestation, bracken, and grasslands are increasing, while the heather dominant vegetation is decreasing. Replacement of heather dominant vegetation appears to be permanent, and only through expensive management (eg heather planting, bracken spraying, etc) or the complete rest of the land for long periods (eg Welch & Rawes 1964) can the vegetation revert to its previous form. This paper attempts to evaluate the direct and indirect consequences of high grazing intensities on heather dominant moorland, with particular reference to the base-rich moorlands in the Pennines which contrast with the relatively poor moorlands of Scotland.

2 Grazing effects

2.1 Selection of heather

Sheep are selective grazers which concentrate on the more palatable fescue and bent grasses in preference to purple moor-grass and mat-grass (Hunter 1962; Jones 1967). The proportion of heather in the diet tends to be low when the preferred grasses are available, but as these are exhausted or die back in late summer so heather becomes a main stay of the sheep's diet over winter (Hunter 1954, 1962; Macleod 1955; Martin 1964; Hobson 1970; Grant *et al.* 1976). Its importance as a winter feed lies in its availability, being evergreen and usually exposed even during snow cover.

Diet selection by sheep operates at 2 levels, first the selection of a grazing site, and second the selection of what to bite (Milne *et al.* 1979) (Figure 1). Site selection depends on nutritional, behavioural and environmental responses by the sheep. Sheep prefer to graze on bare or small grassy patches (Grant *et al.* 1978), on young building heather (approximately 4-8 years after burning), and on areas previously grazed (Milne *et al.* 1979). Imposed on this selection are environmental effects of climate, topography and aspect, along with certain social limitations. Within a flock, individual sheep tend to live within a home range, often shared with others, which they defend against sheep from neighbouring areas (Hunter & Milner 1963). This behavioural response is used by shepherds to keep their flock restricted or hefted to

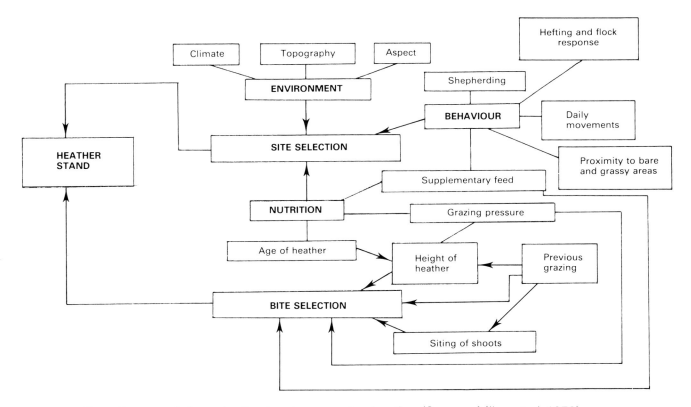

Figure 1. Flow diagram of diet selection by sheep grazing heather (Source: Milne et al. 1979)

certain parts of the hill. Daily movements of sheep are influenced by the availability of natural vegetation, supplementary feed and environmental conditions, but sheep tend to move down hill in early morning to commence grazing, and then back up hill during the day (Jones 1967; Grubb & Jewell 1974). Traditional techniques of shepherding prevent sheep from concentrating on the patches of palatable grasses, so prolonging their availability and preventing their destruction. An even grazing intensity produced by shepherding encourages shoot production and maintains the heather in a physiologically young state which is beneficial to sheep and grouse.

Bite selection is influenced by grazing pressure, previous grazing regimes, and the morphology of the plant. Sheep normally graze the growing tips of the heather shoots, but will re-graze heather when grazing pressures are high (Milne *et al.* 1979).

2.2 Effects of grazing intensity

The effects of grazing on heather dominant vegetation have been examined in a number of exclusion, controlled grazing, and clipping experiments. Hewson (1977) and Brack (1978) have demonstrated the loss of heather with high intensities of grazing in 2 areas of northern England. In Wales, Jones (1967) reports on the effects of controlled grazing on a fescue/bent sward; 2 years after the removal of stock, heather formed 20% by weight of the herbage and had increased to 88% after 15 years. The area was then subjected to grazing and, when inspected 12 years later, the heather had been reduced to just 10% of the herbage. Although grazing intensities were not monitored during this study, it does illustrate how vulnerable heather moorland is to changes in grazing intensities.

More detailed studies on the effects of grazing heather have been conducted by the Hill Farming Research Organisation (HFRO) in Scotland (Grant & Milne 1981; Grant *et al.* 1976, 1978, 1982), where sheep numbers were adjusted and clipping experiments conducted to remove varying quantities of the current season's growth. This work demonstrated that at a high level of grazing, with the removal of 80% of the current season's growth, the heather stand suffered:

  i. reduction in height;
  ii. reduction in cover;
  iii. suppression of flowering;
  iv. reduction in standing crop;
  v. reduction in new shoot production.

Furthermore, the effects of over-grazing were greater if old, as opposed to young, heather was grazed and if grazing took place in autumn rather than in summer. Autumn grazing probably prevents a build-up of carbohydrate reserves in woody stems, reduces the over-wintering green shoots and, in combination with the effects of trampling, increases the plants' water stress

(Bayfield 1979). Prolonged over-grazing will result in the loss of heather plants, and the subsequent time to recover will increase where shoot regeneration is not possible and the quantities of viable seed are reduced. Under moderate grazing pressures, where up to 40% of the weight of current shoots is removed, the productive capacity of heather is unaffected; the build-up of biomass is slowed down so that burning is needed less often than is the case with ungrazed or lightly grazed heather. The intensity of grazing which a heather dominant community can withstand depends on numerous factors and can only be assessed through the careful monitoring of the vegetation. The presence of preferred vegetation, burning regime, soil fertility, exposure, and climate will all influence the potential utilization of the heather and its recovery after periods of heavy grazing.

2.3 Changes in grazing intensity

A change in the utilization of heather by sheep can be caused by an alteration of stocking levels, or in the distribution of sheep on a moor, or in the relative availability of different feed. Within recent years, there has been a number of changes in farming techniques which have altered the grazing intensity and, consequently, the extent of heather moorland.

The numbers of sheep in England and Wales decreased between the 2 World Wars but have doubled since 1947 and are currently much the same as in the 1860s (MAFF 1968) (Figure 2). A gradual decline from 1860 to 1947 reflects a shift away from livestock production in south-eastern Britain (Yalden 1981a), while the increase since 1947 is due to an increase in stocking rates in the north and west of the country. This increase is illustrated by the figures for sheep numbers in the Peak District which have trebled since 1930 (Anderson & Yalden 1981) (Figure 2). Similarly, in a Game Conservancy survey of 63 grouse moors in the north of England, the owners of the sporting rights were asked if there had been a marked increase in the numbers of sheep on the heather moorland of their estate. Forty-nine (77%) answered the question, of whom 19 (39%, representing 311 km^2) said there had been an increase, while 30 (61%, representing 522 km^2) reported no increase. The density of sheep on the moors for which an increase had been reported was 1.57 ewes/ha, significantly greater than the 1.13 ewes/ha on moors with no increase (t test, t=2.37, P<0.02). Such data have serious limitations, but reflect the findings of Anderson and Yalden (1981) that there has been a general increase in stocking levels throughout northern England.

In the Pennines, sheep are usually on the hill for the winter so that they can utilize the heather; they are only removed when weather conditions are severe and for tupping and lambing. In recent years, there has been an increase in the use of supplementary feed given to sheep (Stern 1973). As a result, sheep are now kept on the hill for longer periods, and in some

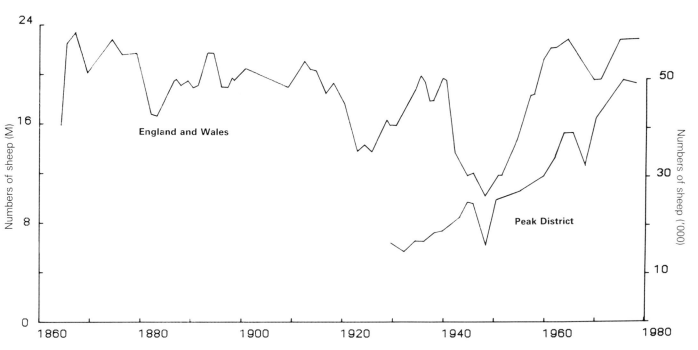

Figure 2. Sheep numbers in England and Wales (millions) from 1886-1977 (Yalden 1981a) and in the Peak District (thousands) 1930-77 (Anderson & Yalden 1981)

districts farmers even tup and lamb on the open hill. In the Game Conservancy survey, 41 of the 49 moorland estates (84%, or 761/863 km²) reported that the flock stayed on the hill all winter.

Supplementary feed is usually provided to sheep as feed blocks or hay, and was traditionally given during poor weather conditions. The Game Conservancy survey reported that 33 out of the 41 (80%) moors which wintered stock on the hill regularly provided supplementary food to sheep. Provision of supplementary food is important for flock management as the productivity of the ewe is closely linked with her plane of nutrition, especially just before and after mating. However, Ducker *et al.* (1981) found that, on average, 19% (maximum of 67%) of ewes on upland pasture did not eat any of the feed block and an average of 36% ate little or no feed block. Utilization of feed blocks is not related to the needs of the animals, but is influenced by weather conditions (Ducker & Fraser 1975) and by variations in body condition and age of the ewes. The effects of feed blocks on surrounding vegetation can be devastating. Trampling damages the heather, particularly in areas where sheep utilizing the blocks need to graze intensively to balance their intake of roughage. Hay is frequently given daily to over-wintered sheep, a practice known as 'fothering'. Observations indicate that the hay is usually left by the farmers in the late morning alongside access tracks and placed on the old heather to prevent it being blown away. This practice results in a concentration of stock at fothering sites several hours before feeding, and the consequent effects of grazing and trampling kill the heather. The loss of

heather from one area often results in the farmer moving his feeding site to another stand of heather, which in turn is destroyed (Plate 5).

In summary, there has been an increase in stocking levels and in the use of supplementary feed in moorland areas. These changes, coupled with the decline in shepherding, have resulted in a concentration of stock on areas of heather ground. High local concentrations of stock make the whole question of appropriate, overall, stocking rates on heather dominant vegetation irrelevant.

3 Initiation of erosion

In many parts of upland Britain, peat is eroding because of the combined effects of harsh weather and the nature of peat itself. Normally, erosion is stabilized by the highly tenacious moorland vegetation, but such stabilization can be prevented by increased environmental pressures, including high concentrations of sheep. Sheep prefer to graze near bare areas (Grant *et al.* 1978) and, due to their shape and size, their hooves exert a cutting action with a high pressure, relative to humans (Yalden 1981b). This action can prevent stabilization and encourage erosion. In the Peak District, a Moorland Erosion Study (Phillips *et al.* 1981) reports large areas of sheet erosion where the natural balance between instability and restoration had been altered. This erosion was associated with a marked increase in sheep numbers (Anderson & Yalden 1981). The nature of peat erosion is such that, once the natural balance is altered, it can spread at an alarming rate. Without suitable management control and the removal of the causal agent, large areas could be rapidly destroyed.

4 Heather burning

Heather burning is an essential aspect of moorland management. It is usually conducted on a 12-year (5-25 year) rotation, but the timing can vary considerably and depends on the labour available and on environmental conditions. The main purpose of burning is to remove the old heather and to encourage the growth of young nutritious shoots which are beneficial to the production of grouse (Miller 1980) and sheep (Lance 1983). Grouse management requires small fires which provide edges and a variation of heather age within the territory of each pair. Although beneficial to them, small fires are not essential for sheep, and farmers tend to burn off large areas of heather. Burning can be destructive, particularly if used too frequently or when high temperatures are reached. Large, uncontrolled fires can result in surface drying, wind-blow, increased runoff, gulleying, freeze/thaw and trampling effects which prevent stabilization and increase erosion (Brown 1982).

Burning favours the fire resistant species, and in particular the ericoids and their associated flora. However, burning in conjunction with high grazing intensities results in selection of plants tolerant to both pressures and can lead to large-scale vegetational changes, with the replacement of heather by purple moor-grass and cottongrass in wet habitats and fescue and bent in dry habitats.

5 Moorland drainage

Drainage is conducted in moorland habitats to improve runoff and lower the water table. It is assumed that this measure will improve the growth and cover of heather, and in turn the productivity of livestock and grouse. It is currently grant-aided at 60% of costs, the highest rate payable for any form of capital expenditure on farming, and costs approximately £40/ha. In England and Wales, drainage statistics are not available. However, in a Game Conservancy survey in 1979 in the north of England, 28 of 51 grouse moor owners (55%) had drained parts of their moorland estates in recent years. In Scotland, hill drainage, which includes field and moorland, was about 200 km² per year in the 1960s and 1970s. Stewart and Lance (1983) have reviewed the literature available on the effects of drainage on moorland ecology and found little evidence of vegetation change after drainage on blanket bog. Other unpublished work indicates that heather grows taller and denser within 2 m of drains. Improvements in sheep and grouse production are only anecdotal; drainage is often associated with changes in grazing and burning management, so confounding the true effects of drainage without adequate controls for comparison.

6 Repercussions from the loss of heather

Loss of heather dominant moorland alters the ecology and land use of upland areas. Some effects are a direct consequence of change in the habitat, but other repercussions affecting the future of the uplands may be less obvious.

The loss of heather as a winter feed for sheep will reduce the ewe's plane of nutrition and so the productivity of the farms. Output from the land can only be maintained through improving the sward, which, at the current time, would not be viable or even possible in many upland areas. Furthermore, a decline in the extent of heather reduces the numbers of red grouse and the valuable sporting interests (Peel 1983); coupled with the decline in farming output, this will result in a fall in the value of the land, so that the only viable alternative is afforestation. The replacement of moorland with Sitka spruce and lodgepole pine will have far reaching repercussions on the ecology of the area, its aesthetic value, and the social fabric of upland communities.

The ecological effects of afforestation can be disturbing, particularly in the light of Forestry Commission (1977) recommendations to plant a further 1.8×10^6 ha by the year 2025, mostly in upland areas. The spread of forestry can result in an increase in the density of breeding passerines (Lack & Lack 1951; Moss 1979; Yapp 1979), which is often to the detriment of specialized upland birds, in particular upland waders (Table 1). Densities of waders are low in the uplands; they rarely exceed 3.5 pairs/km² (Campbell 1982), while the lowland waders, such as the redshank, reach 75 pairs/km² in areas of northern England (Hale 1980). Furthermore, the distribution of upland waders is uneven, reflecting variations in the upland habitat (Campbell 1982). Plantations can also influence the distribution of birds in nearby areas. They tend to act as a refuge for predators of upland birds (particularly the fox and carrion crow), which can reduce the productivity of grouse and may explain the absence of waders from apparently suitable habitat alongside

Table 1. The habitat use of the principal bird species nesting on British moorlands. Included are the species whose main nesting habitat is on moorland at an altitude of 300–900 m. It does not include montane species (eg dotterel, ptarmigan), species nesting on crags (peregrine, golden eagle, raven), species which nest in the uplands as a secondary habitat (eg yellow wagtail, mallard) or those dependent on water (red-throated diver, greylag goose)

Species	Open heather or grass moor	Young plantations	Mature plantations
Hen harrier	------------------	------------------	
Merlin	------------------	------------------	
Red grouse	----------		
Golden plover	----------		
Lapwing	----------		
Dunlin	----------		
Snipe	----------		
Curlew	----------	----	
Greenshank	----------		
Short-eared owl	------------------	------------------	
Skylark	------------------	----	
Meadow pipit	------------------	------------------	
Stonechat	------------------	------------------	
Wheatear	----------		
Ring ousel	------------------	----	
Twite	----------		

plantations (T M Reed pers. comm.). Areas of trees can also put limitations on management procedures on neighbouring ground; for example, heather burning is too much of a fire risk close to plantations. In this respect, care must be take to site forestry plantations away from areas of conservation interest, or where they could fragment the habitat, or in other places which, if managed correctly for heather, could continue to produce a healthy sheep, sporting and tourist industry.

In summary, the replacement of heather by vegetation such as bracken and purple moor-grass results in a decline in sheep farming and a change in upland land use. To prevent such degradation, it is clear that the land use interests favouring heather habitat (sheep, grouse shooting, conservation, tourism and water catchment) should be encouraged to reconcile their conflicts and maintain multiple use.

7 Conclusions

7.1 The problems

Over-grazing of heather can be caused by high stocking levels, and more usually by the concentration of sheep in autumn and winter on small areas. These 2 activities have been intensified by the current grants and subsidies paid to the Less Favoured Areas (LFA) established under the EEC Directive 75/268. The system encourages farmers to increase stocking levels which their in-bye land cannot support. As a result, they are forced to leave stock on the hill for longer periods, and the stock become dependent on hay, often brought in from other areas. With a low plane of nutrition, lamb production is low, which may explain partly why lambing rates are currently at 90-100% or less on most hill farms, while the traditional Swaledale ewes are known to be capable of 180%. Another trend aggravating the situation is the amalgamation of farms into larger units requiring less labour, which results in a decline of traditional shepherding techniques (Sinclair 1983).

Not all the blame lies within the farming system. Other interests in the uplands should work more positively in conjunction with the farming concerns to maintain multiple use and acceptable financial returns. Burning and maintenance of the heather are a responsibility usually undertaken by the shooting interests. A poor burning programme will result in the concentration of stock on burnt ground and lead to over-grazing. Similarly, the spread of bracken can cause the aggregation of stock and should be controlled for the benefit of all interested parties.

7.2 The solutions

The EEC directive for support of agriculture in the LFAs was instigated first to stem depopulation of the uplands, and second for conservation reasons which would encourage tourism and produce better economic prospects than agriculture or forestry alone (EEC 1973). In practice, the EEC directive has encouraged

farm amalgamation (Sinclair 1983), labour shedding and, as indicated here, the loss of heather moorland. Clearly, the EEC directive is failing to meet its aims, and a restructuring of headage payment is needed. An alternative system, reflecting control of stocking numbers and of grants which conflict with conservation interests, has been advocated by MacEwen and Sinclair (1983). Although an ambitious system, it is a workable alternative which needs careful consideration.

The ultimate aim of any new system for the uplands should be to maintain farming as the principal land use, but at the same time to conserve the natural resources. There is currently a wealth of information on ewe nutrition which could improve the performance of hill ewes. Some examples of how this improvement could be achieved are:

i. use winter housing for ewes;
ii. wean one of a pair or even both lambs when 6-weeks old and then feed concentrated food;
iii. finish lambs at home or through a local co-operative;
iv. cull stock effectively and select for twinning;
v. provide incentives to improve certain in-bye land, and to control bracken, purple moor-grass and mat-grass;
vi. incorporate sown grass on some moorland areas.

7.3 Research requirements

This review has concentrated on the need for multiple land use in the uplands and for grazing intensities to be set at a level which does not conflict with nature conservation. Although there is ample information on ways to improve ewe nutrition, there is still a need for ecological research of moorland habitats to assist in management planning. Twelve of the more important research requirements are listed below.

7.3.1 Moorland classification

The response of heather dominant vegetation to grazing and burning regimes varies according to numerous environmental factors, in particular soil fertility, peat depth, altitude and rainfall. Generalizations in upland ecology are difficult and it is often not possible to extrapolate research findings from one area to another. In this respect, there is a need to classify blocks of heather dominant moorland.

7.3.2 Optimal grazing pressures

The estimation of optimal grazing intensities on heather dominant vegetation is complex and depends on the interaction of many factors. Further research along the experimental lines of the HFRO study (described earlier) is required to produce models of optimal heather utilization. However, such models need to be robust and applicable to different moorland areas with inputs of competition from other species, such as red deer, and could encompass the grazing effects of adjacent habitats such as bilberry and birch scrub.

7.3.3 Burning and grazing interactions

Burning heather in conjunction with high grazing pressures can result in vegetational changes. However, the interaction of the 2 pressures is not clearly understood and requires detailed study, with the ultimate aim of producing clear guidelines for which habitats should be burnt and when.

7.3.4 Moorland restoration and the control of bracken and purple moor-grass

The spread of bracken and purple moor-grass through mis-management and, in particular, poor burning is of concern to conservationists, farmers and game managers. Further research is needed to develop cost effective control and management of these species. In addition, we need to develop effective ways of re-establishing heather moorland after severe burns and to control unwanted vegetation.

7.3.5 Moorland drainage

Moorland drainage is a recognized part of moorland management and yet its influence on sheep and grouse production is based on anecdotal evidence. The significance of drainage and its impact on moorland ecology need to be tested through experimentation.

7.3.6 Influence of afforestation on wildlife

Afforestation is a major agent of change in the uplands and its influence on wildlife needs further investigation to elucidate optimal plantation size and to identify the areas suitable for planting. Such work needs to be conducted in conjunction with studies of the flora and site requirements of upland animals.

7.3.7 Pollution

Pollution has influenced the distribution of *Sphagnum* and lichen in areas of the Pennines and has been a causal agent of serious erosion. Pollution from other sources, such as Fenitrothion used to control pine beauty moth of lodgepole pine, may be influencing upland ecology and needs further study.

7.3.8 Decline of grouse

The decline of grouse in Scotland and the factors causing the decline need further investigation. The problem is of environmental importance as the economic equation of multiple land use is bound together by the sporting interests.

7.3.9 Ticks (Ixodes ricinus) and tick-borne diseases

Ticks and tick-borne diseases are causing serious economic losses to hill farmers and grouse moor owners, and yet the current state of knowledge on the population dynamics of this parasite is poor and control techniques appear ineffective. A detailed population study investigating the mortality factors is urgently needed (Plate 6).

7.3.10 Interactions of land use and wildlife

Grouse moor management involves the control of foxes and crows in upland areas, while high stocking levels inadvertently provide carrion for raptors and crows. The effects of these practices could well be beneficial to many forms of wildlife and need further research.

7.3.11 Recreation

Recreation in moorland areas is increasing, bringing with it direct and indirect disturbance. It is possible that such effects could become a problem in the future and research is needed to elucidate optimal levels.

7.3.12 Fragmentation and co-ordinated management of moorlands

It is clear from research on upland birds that many of the principles of conservation in lowland areas cannot be applied to the uplands. Conservationists, planners and consultants need research to discover the optimal and minimal size of moorland areas for socio-economic and wildlife interests.

8 Summary

The effects of sheep management on heather moorlands are reviewed. Heather is an important winter feed for sheep but high stocking rates, the concentration of stock and grazing, in conjunction with burning, can kill heather stands. Severe burns and high stocking levels can also encourage the spread of erosion. A number of changes in upland farming has resulted in over-grazing and the loss of heather habitat. In the long term, this could result in habitat degradation and the consequent loss of good farming land and grouse moorland to commercial afforestation. There are techniques available which could improve the performance of ewes without conflicting with nature conservation; but they would require a restructuring of grants and subsidies paid to upland farmers. Twelve of the more important research requirements for the uplands are outlined: in particular, the need to elucidate the effects of drainage, afforestation and burning, in conjunction with different grazing intensities, on the nature, rate and reversibility of changes in vegetation and associated fauna. Upland research should be directed towards encouraging multiple land use and reconciling conflicts with conservation.

9 References

Anderson, P. & Yalden, D.W. 1981. Increased sheep numbers and loss of heather moorland in the Peak District, England. *Biol. Conserv.*, **20**, 195-213.

Bayfield, N. 1979. Recovery of four montane heath communities on Cairngorm, Scotland from disturbance from trampling. *Biol. Conserv.*, **15**, 165-181.

Brack, E.V. 1978. Vegetational changes in upland landscapes. *Landsc. Res.*, **3**, 8-10.

Brown, R.W. 1982. Moorland fires and their aftermath. In: *Moorlands, wild life conservation, amenity and recreation*, edited by K.A. Hearn, 37-44. (RERG report no. 8). Wye: Recreation Ecology Research Group.

Campbell, L. 1982. Characteristics of the moorland breeding bird community with particular implications for nature conservation. In: *Moorlands, wild life conservation, amenity and recreation*, edited by K.A. Hearn, 55-65. (RERG report no. 8). Wye: Recreation Ecology Research Group.

Ducker, M.J. & Fraser, J. 1975. Some initial observations on the effect of weather on the consumption of feeding blocks. *Expl Husb.,* **29,** 113-117.

Ducker, M.J., Kendall, P.T., Hemmingway, R.G. & McClelland, T.H. 1981. An evaluation of feedblocks as a means of providing supplementary nutrients to ewes grazing upland hill pastures. *Anim. Prod.,* **33,** 51-57.

European Economic Communities. 1973. EEC council resolution 15, May 1973. *Off. J. eur. Communities, C. Inf. Not.,* 33/1.

Forestry Commission. 1977. *The wood production outlook in Britain—a review.* Edinburgh: FC.

Grant, S.A. & Milne, J.A. 1981. Heather management. *Blackface J.,* **33,** 13-17.

Grant, S.A., Lamb, W.I.C., Kerr, C.D. & Bolton, G.R. 1976. The utilization of blanket bog vegetation by grazing sheep. *J. appl. Ecol.,* **13,** 857-869.

Grant, S.A., Barthram, G.T., Lamb, W.I.C. & Milne, J.A. 1978. Effects of season and level of grazing on the utilization of heather by sheep. 1. Responses of the sward. *J. Br. Grassld Soc.,* **33,** 289-300.

Grant, S.A., Milne, J.A., Barthram, G.T. & Souter, W.G. 1982. Effects of season and level of grazing on the utilization of heather by sheep. 3. Longer term response and sward recovery. *Grass Forage Sci.,* **37,** 311-320.

Grubb, P. & Jewell, P.A. 1974. Movements, daily activity and home range of Soay sheep. In: *Island survivors: the ecology of the Soay sheep of St Kilda,* edited by P.A. Jewell, C. Milner & J.M. Boyd, 160-194. London: Athlone Press.

Hale, W.G. 1980. *Waders.* (New naturalist no. 65). London: Collins.

Hewson, R. 1977. The effects on heather *Calluna vulgaris* of excluding sheep from moorland in north east England. *Naturalist, Hull,* **102,** 133-136.

Hobson, P.N. 1970. Some field experiments on the rumen functions of red deer, hill sheep and reindeer. *Deer,* **2,** 450-452.

Hunter, R.F. 1954. The grazing of hill pasture sward types. *J. Br. Grassld Soc.,* **9,** 195-208.

Hunter, R.F. 1962. Hill sheep and their pasture: a study of sheep grazing in south eastern Scotland. *J. Ecol.,* **50,** 651-680.

Hunter, R.F. & Milner, C. 1963. The behaviour of individual, related and groups of south country Cheviot hill sheep. *Anim. Behav.,* **11,** 507-513.

Jones, L.I. 1967. Studies of hill land in Wales. *Tech. Bull. Welsh Plant Breed. Sta.* no. 2.

Lack, D. & Lack, E. 1951. Further changes in bird life caused by afforestation. *J. Anim. Ecol.,* **20,** 173-179.

Lance, A.N. 1983. Performance of sheep on unburned and serially burned blanket bog in western Ireland. *J. appl. Ecol.,* **20,** 767-776.

MacEwen, M. & Sinclair, G. 1983. *New life for the hills, policies for farming and conservation in the uplands.* London: Council for National Parks.

Macleod, A.C. 1955. Heather in the seasonal dietry of sheep. *Proc. Br. Soc. Anim. Prod. 1955,* 13-17.

Martin, D.J. 1964. Analysis of sheep diet utilizing plant epidermal fragments in faeces samples. In: *Grazing in terrestrial and marine environments,* edited by D.T. Crisp, 173-188. Oxford: Blackwell Scientific.

Miller, G.R. 1980. The burning of heather moorland for red grouse. *Bull. Ecol.,* **11,** 725-733.

Milne, J.A., Bagley, L. & Grant, S.A. 1979. Effects of season and level of grazing on the utilization of heather by sheep: 2. Diet selection and intake. *Grass Forage Sci.,* **34,** 45-53.

Ministry of Agriculture, Fisheries and Food. 1968. *A century of agricultural statistics, Great Britain 1866-1966.* London: HMSO.

Moss, D. 1979. Even-aged plantations as a habitat for birds. In: *The ecology of even-aged plantations,* edited by E.D. Ford, D.C. Malcolm & J. Atterson, 413-427. Cambridge: Institute of Terrestrial Ecology.

Peel, Rt Hon. The Earl. 1983. Integrated management of upland environment. In: *Management of natural and semi-natural vegetation,* edited by J.M. Way, 155-167. Ashford: Wye College, Centre for European Agricultural Studies.

Phillips, J., Yalden, D.W. & Tallis, J. 1981. *Peak District Moorland Erosion Study Phase 1 report.* Bakewell: Peak Park Planning Board.

Sinclair, G.A. 1983. *The upland landscape study.* London: Countryside Commission.

Stern, E. 1973. Upsurges in block feeding expected as more turn to low-cost roughage. *Livestock Farm.,* **10,** 34.

Stewart, A.J.A. & Lance, A. 1983. Moor draining: a review of impacts on land use. *J. environ. Manage.,* **17,** 81-99.

Welch, D. & Rawes, M. 1964. The early effects of excluding sheep from high level grasslands in the northern Pennines. *J. appl. Ecol.,* **1,** 281-300.

Yalden, D.W. 1981a. Sheep numbers in the Peak District. In: *Peak District Moorland Erosion Study Phase 1 report,* edited by J. Phillips, D.W. Yalden & J. Tallis, 116-124. Bakewell: Peak Park Planning Board.

Yalden, D.W. 1981b. Sheep and moorland vegetation—a review. In: *Peak District Moorland Erosion Study Phase 1 report,* edited by J. Phillips, D.W. Yalden & J. Tallis, 132-141. Bakewell: Peak Park Planning Board.

Yapp, W.B. 1979. Specific diversity in woodland birds. *Fld Stud.,* **5,** 45-58.

The impact of upland pasture improvement on solute outputs in surface waters

M HORNUNG

Institute of Terrestrial Ecology, Bangor Research Station

1 Introduction

This paper outlines some of the major factors influencing solute outputs from sites following land improvement, and then considers data from improved catchments in mid-Wales.

Over the past 30 years, considerable areas of former rough grazings in the uplands of Britain have been converted to improved pasture. For example, Jones (1978) calculated that 100 000 ha of land were improved in the Welsh uplands in the 25 years prior to 1978, an area equivalent to 20% of the hills and uplands of the Principality. The replacement of natural vegetation of low productivity and low nutrient content with more productive, higher nutrient status, grass/clover swards can only be achieved if the inherent problems of soil acidity and nutrient deficiency are overcome. In most situations, this requires the addition of relatively large quantities of lime and fertilizers with, in many instances, some form of cultivation. A proportion of the readily soluble fertilizer compounds and lime, plus elements rendered more mobile as a result of cultivation, inevitably find their way into streams draining the improved ground. This added load of solutes may have impacts on water quality in areas which are important as water gathering grounds. The changes in water chemistry may also affect freshwater biota in otherwise unpolluted streams.

These impacts on surface water chemistry and freshwater biota are generally assumed to be insignificant (Baldwin 1978). These assumptions, however, are not based on actual case studies. A recent extensive review of the British literature on the influence of land use on water quality in upland Britain (Roberts in press) revealed a total absence of papers on the impact of land improvement. Data may exist in Water Authority records, but they are not readily available. Similarly, there has been little attempt to evaluate fertilizer losses to drainage waters or to consider possible loss from the soil capital of nutrients as a result of improvement.

2 Factors influencing solute outputs

The output of solutes in the stream draining any given improved area will be influenced by the interaction of many factors, important amongst which are:

    i. method of improvement;
    ii. chemical and physical properties of the soils;
    iii. catchment hydrology;
    iv. climate.

2.1 Methods of improvement

The method of improvement used is mainly determined by the soils and vegetation of the site (East of Scotland College of Agriculture 1980; Newbould 1983). On the more favourable brown soils with bent/fescue swards containing some white clover, significant sward improvement can be achieved simply through intensive controlled grazing (Floate 1972). This process produces the quicker and more efficient cycling of plant nutrients, especially nitrogen, phosphorus, and potassium, needed to maintain a relatively high productivity, high nutrient content sward. Floate (1972) suggests that this approach may result in small losses of phosphorus and nitrogen from the site. These losses are unlikely to have a significant impact on drainage water chemistry or on the capital of these nutrients held on the site.

In contrast, most pasture improvement schemes involve the addition of lime and fertilizers, and reseeding with a grass/white clover seed mix. The treatment may also include cultivation and, on wetter sites, drainage. The detailed prescription for the improvement will depend on the soil type, vegetation, and climate. The lime is added to reduce soil acidity and the levels of soluble aluminium in the rooting zone, although these 2 problems are inter-related (Floate 1977; Munro *et al.* 1973). The quantities used are usually based on the amount required to raise the pH to 5.5-5.8 or to produce 50% base saturation, and depend, therefore, on the initial soil chemistry. The lime is usually added as magnesium limestone and a typical treatment for a soil with a peaty surface horizon would be between 5-8 t/ha. The liming, therefore, provides a large potential source of calcium and magnesium for output to drainage waters.

Additions of phosphorus and nitrogen are also usually required for establishment of the sown grasses and the white clover. The quantities used are broadly determined by the demands of the white clover and will vary somewhat with soil type. Usually, some 60-80 kg P/ha are added. Phosphorus was formerly added as basic slag, which had the added bonus of its considerable acid neutralizing capacity, but, today, rock phosphate-super-phosphate mixtures are generally used. Recommendations on the quantities of nitrogen to be added vary widely, but 40-80 kg N/ha are probably the most common. It is usually added as ammonium nitrate. White clover also has a high potassium demand and additions of up to 100 kg K/ha may be needed on peats or peaty surfaced soils: it is usually added as potassium chloride. The timing and method of application of the lime and fertilizers vary regionally, and with the type of cultivation used, and may influence the loss in drainage waters.

Following the initial improvement, further additions of lime and fertilizers are required to maintain the new sward. Typically, 2-4 t/ha of lime are added every 4-5 years, 40 kg P/ha every 3-4 years, and, on peats, 60 kg K/ha every 3-4 years. The initial and maintenance inputs, therefore, provide a large readily soluble pool of phosphorus, nitrate and potassium, plus, depending on the form of the fertilizer, ammonium, chloride and sulphate which may be transferred to drainage waters.

In open swards, the seed mixture and fertilizer may be surface spread with surface scarification or trampling by stock to produce some penetration. Alternatively, surface applications may follow suppression of existing vegetation by burning, cutting or the use of herbicides. Most reclamation systems involving re-seeding and fertilization, however, also involve some form of cultivation. Deep ploughing, the standard technique in the early reclamations, is now used mainly on freely drained acid brown soils and brown podzolic soils. Rotavation of the surface is generally used on peats, stagnopodzols, stagnogleys, gleys and peats. On these soils, ploughing reduces the surface bearing strength, and can lead to germination of seeds of unwanted rush species, while the buried organic layers can cause drainage problems. Seed bed preparation will also involve disking and rolling, following the ploughing or rotavation. These various cultivations will change the patterns of water penetration and movement through soils. New surfaces will also be exposed to weathering, with possible release of elements to solution. The opening up of organic surface horizons may lead to an increased rate of decomposition and element release. The organic horizons may also dry out more readily, with consequent production of sulphate by oxidation of organic sulphides, and may result in raised sulphate levels in drainage waters and the leaching of balancing cations.

Drainage systems may also be installed on wetter sites. The type of drainage system used will depend on the cause of the problem, ie springs or seeps, surface water or groundwater. The aim of all systems, however, is to facilitate the removal of as much water as possible from the site by the shortest route, but such removal can lead to increased losses to drainage waters of fertilizers, lime, and supplies of available elements generated within the soil. Although open drains would rarely be used in agriculture, it is worth noting that, on a site fertilized with phosphorus and drained prior to afforestation, the main increase in P concentrations in drainage waters took place following the drainage (Robinson 1980).

2.2 The soil factor

The output of solutes derived from added lime or fertilizers, or released as a secondary effect of the improvement, is strongly influenced by the chemical and physical properties of the treated soils. As waters move through soils, they are influenced by many reactions and processes. These include cation exchange, anion adsorption, oxidation/reduction reactions, complexation, precipitation and fixation in clay lattices. Detailed consideration of these various reactions is outside the scope of this paper, but a few illustrations will be given of their impact. Hydrous iron and aluminium oxides are very efficient scavengers of phosphate anions from solution (Bohn et al. 1979). The phosphate is held on the oxides by anion adsorption or ligand exchange. The Bs horizons of podzolic soils, which are widespread in the uplands, have a high content of hydrous iron and aluminium oxides and can fix large quantities of phosphorus. Fertilizer phosphate not taken up by plants is, therefore, readily fixed by these soils, and one would predict that little will be lost from them in drainage waters. Similarly, phosphate can be immobilized as calcium phosphate in, for example, calcareous subsoils, thus limiting output from a site.

Potassium can be fixed in the lattices of some clay minerals and micas and is then not exchanged in cation exchange reactions with salt solutions. The loss of fertilizer potassium from mica and clay-rich soils will, therefore, be minimized by these fixation reactions. The ammonium ion is similarly fixed by vermiculite clays and weathering trioctahedral micas; like the other cations, it can also be held on clays and humic complexes in sites affected by cation exchange reactions. These processes will tend to reduce losses of potassium and ammonium from fertilizers. The nitrate anion, in contrast, is highly mobile, being little affected by anion adsorption reactions. Nitrate in solution at levels in excess of the demands of the surface vegetation will probably be lost in drainage waters. The nitrate ion lost, and the chloride derived from added potassium chloride, will also carry a balancing cation out of the system.

The sulphate added in some forms of phosphatic fertilizers, or produced by oxidation of sulphides in organic horizons, will certainly be present at levels in excess of the vegetation requirements. It is relatively mobile but is affected by anion adsorption on to the iron and aluminium oxides found in the podzolic B horizons. This adsorption is much less efficient than that of the phosphate anion, so that much of the sulphate will be lost. In addition, recent work has shown that added lime may result in the release of adsorbed sulphate from podzolic B horizons, and could lead to a further increase in sulphate levels in drainage waters.

The soil/water reactions will also be strongly influenced by the inter-related factors of the residence time and pathways followed by the waters. Short residence time, rapidly moving, waters in macropores will attain very different equilibria from the long residence time water in fine pores. Thus, although excess potassium or phosphate could, theoretically, be removed from solution and fixed in soils, this process may not take place from rapidly transmitted waters such as that moving through natural soil pipes. The proportion of infiltrating waters which move through the whole body of a profile will also vary. In stagnogleys and stagnopodzols, and other soils with an impermeable layer within the soils, much of the infiltrating water will move laterally through the upper horizons. It will not, therefore, be affected by reactions in the lower horizons. In freely drained brown soils, in contrast, a large proportion of the infiltrating water may move through the soil to the groundwater table.

2.3 Catchment hydrology

The considerations here are an extension of those outlined above when noting the influence of water pathways. The chemistry of any stream reflects the relative mix of water from a number of contributing sources within the stream catchment. Water may be input to the stream from, for example, groundwater sources, throughflow, soil pipes or overland flow. Each of these types of water may have a very different chemistry, as a result of their different residence times and contact with differing materials. Elements released from fertilizers, or as a result of cultivation, may persist in water from one source but not in that from another. For example, phosphate may remain in solution in overland flow but be removed by adsorption or precipitation reactions from throughflow or groundwater. Similarly, potassium may be present in overland flow, pipeflow, or throughflow from upper horizons, but be absent, due to fixation or cation exchange reactions, in throughflow from lower horizons or groundwater. Nitrate, once in solution, will tend to persist in all types of water, unless affected by biological processes. Liming will have a major effect on the pH of overland flow and upper soil throughflow, but may hardly alter lower soil throughflow or groundwater. The proportions of the streamwater derived from the different contributing sources will also vary with streamflow. At very low flows, groundwater may provide the only input, while at very high flows throughflow plus overland flow may dominate.

The derivation of the waters in the improved catchment will, therefore, be a major factor influencing the impact on the outflow chemistry. The most important factor, however, may be the proportion of the catchment affected by the improvement.

2.4 Climate

The major impact of climate is the amount and type of rainfall. Compared to the lowlands of Britain, all the areas likely to be affected by land improvement have a high rainfall. Within the hill and upland area, there is, however, enormous variation in rainfall from 800 mm in the North York Moors to over 2000 mm in mid-Wales and other western sites. The loss of lime and fertilizers is potentially higher in the high rainfall

areas; allowance is usually made for this loss in calculating the rates of lime addition. The concentrations of the elements derived from solution of fertilizers may, however, be no higher in the streams of these areas because of the dilution effect.

Rainfall intensity will also influence losses of fertilizers to drainage waters. Losses will be greater as a result of high intensity rainfall, but, once again, may not produce high concentrations of fertilizer derived elements in the outflow streams because of dilution.

3 An example from mid-Wales

As part of a geochemical cycling study, we have monitored solute inputs and outputs of a number of first and second order stream catchments in mid-Wales. The following report covers the solute chemistry of one catchment (C2) draining unimproved upland grazing and 2 catchments (C7 and C17) which drain areas of improved pasture (Figure 1). The catchments are located in the headwaters of the River Wye at 450 m above sea level on the eastern slopes of the Plynlimon massif. The area is underlain by Ordovician and Silurian mudstones and the catchments are dominated by stagnopodzols. The unimproved area has a mat-grass/bent/fescue vegetation with smaller areas of a heather/cottongrass community. One im-

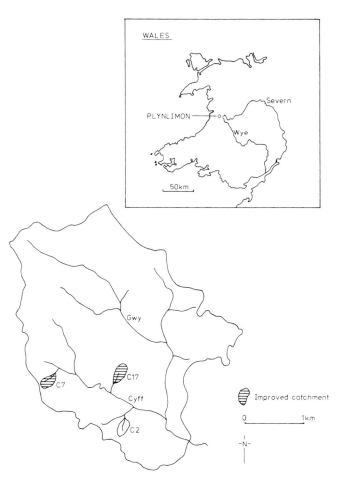

Figure 1. Map showing location of catchments in mid-Wales

proved catchment (C7) was ploughed some 40 years ago, magnesium limestone and basic slag added, and re-seeded. The vegetation has largely reverted, but some white clover remains. The other catchment (C17) was improved in the mid-1970s with surface cultivation, additions of limestone and compound fertilizers, and re-seeding; it has also received maintenance additions of lime and fertilizers.

The mean solute concentrations for the streams for a 2-year period are given in Table 1. The concentrations of most solutes were higher in the improved catchment drainage. Phosphorus concentrations, however,

were below the detection limit of 0.005 mg/l throughout the 2 years in all 3 streams. Any excess phosphorus entering solution from fertilizers was probably immobilized in the stagnopodzols. Nitrate concentrations were raised in both streams draining improved catchments, and in catchment C17 could have been due to solution and loss of fertilizer. Nitrogen fertilizer was not added in catchment C7, and the higher concentrations here must have been due to a higher rate of nitrate production in the soils, perhaps as a result of the presence of white clover and the effects of liming and cultivation. These latter factors would also be operative in the C17 catchment.

Table 1. Summarized chemical data for streamwater in one unimproved (C2) and 2 improved (C17 and C7) catchments

	Na	K	Ca	Mg	Si	NO$_3$-N	SO$_4$-S	Cl	μeq/l HCO$_3$	pH	μeq/l H
C2	3·1	0·10	1·1	0·7	0·8	0·07	1·6	5·0	53	5·27	5·4
C17	3·6	0·11	1·6	1·8	1·6	0·28	2·2	5·8	100	6·12	0·8
C7	3·1	0·13	1·6	1·6	1·4	0·18	3·2	4·9	45	4·83	14·8

Figures are arithmetic mean values for weekly samples over a 2-year period, 27 November 1979–24 November 1981

Potassium concentrations showed no significant difference between the 3 streams. The potassium added in fertilizers in catchment C17 must have been utilized very efficiently or any excess which entered solution was retained in the soil by cation exchange or fixation. The small, but significant, increase in chloride concentrations in C17 was probably due to solution of the potassium chloride fertilizer, but with little retention of chloride in the soil. The higher calcium and magnesium concentrations in the streams from the improved catchments will have been caused by solution of the added lime. It is surprising, however, that the magnesium concentrations increased more than the calcium. Differential retention within the soil system may have taken place or increased magnesium release from weathering, perhaps as a result of the cultivation. It is interesting that the effect of liming was still detectable in catchment C7 some 40 years after the initial treatment. The raised pH in stream C17 compared to C2 was also attributable to the effects of liming. Stream C7, however, had a lower pH, and it is thought that the more acid groundwater in this catchment masked the effect of the liming.

The higher sulphate concentration in catchment C17 was probably due to solution of fertilizers, but superphosphate was not added in C7. Sulphate displacement from the Bs horizon as a result of liming (Korentajer *et al.* 1983) might also have been oper-

ative, but sulphate input from groundwater sources probably explained the higher concentration in C7. The increased silica concentrations in the improved catchment streams were probably due to increased solution from soil mineral sources.

Solute budgets for the 3 catchments (Table 2) give an indication of possible loss of lime, fertilizers or the soil capital of nutrients. The additional calcium output from the improved catchments is small compared with lime inputs. If outputs of magnesium from C7 had continued at the rates measured here since improvement, the added magnesium would have been exhausted. This observation provides some support for the suggested increased rate of release of magnesium from mineral weathering. The increased potassium deficit in catchment C17 was also small compared with fertilizer addition, but the higher output from C7, compared with C2, must represent a real loss from the soil capital. Losses at this rate, however, are probably insignificant in terms of the nutrient demand of the natural vegetation.

It is not possible to calculate a full nitrogen budget from the data presented here, as only inorganic solutes were measured. There would also be a nitrogen input through fixation by the white clover, an organic nitrogen output, and possible gaseous losses. The inorganic solute budget indicated a change from

Table 2. Solute budgets (kg/ha/yr) for the 3 study streams (C2, unimproved; C17 and C7, improved)

	Na	K	Ca	Mg	Si	NO$_3$-N	SO$_4$-S	Cl	HCO$_3$	H
C2	−28	−0·5	−20	−10	−24	+1·4	−15	−41	−64	+0·6
C17	−47	−2·0	−37	−39	−53	−8·7	−37	−78	−127	+0·9
C7	−28	−1·2	−37	−33	−35	−0·2	−62	−37	−72	+0·6

net accumulation in the unimproved catchment to a net deficit in the improved catchments. The deficit in catchment C17 was very small, and even the small remaining amount of white clover probably fixed enough nitrogen to balance the loss. The larger apparent deficit in C17 is probably still balanced by fixation inputs as clover is an important component of this sward.

There were apparent chloride deficits in all 3 catchments because of an under-estimate of particulate inputs such as sea salts. There was an increase in the net output of chloride and sodium from catchment C17 compared with the other 2 catchments; this increase was due to fertilizer solution and would not produce stress in the vegetation. Similarly, the apparent increases in sulphate and silica output were small compared to the site capital and would not produce significant changes in the soil/plant system.

The data showed differences in streamwater chemistry which apparently resulted from pasture improvement, some of which persisted long after improvement. The changes in chemistry were, however, unlikely adversely to affect freshwater communities or water quality and would soon be masked in a larger catchment. Nitrate concentrations were well below the 11 mg/l maximum recommended by the World Health Authority, with peak concentrations around 3 mg/l. Phosphorus concentrations, the other major concern for water quality, remained at concentrations below 0.005 mg/l. The systems examined here had returned to an equilibrium, and data are needed for the actual period of cultivation. Preliminary results from a lysimeter study by Institute of Hydrology staff showed nitrate concentrations of 6 mg/l nitrate during drainage operations prior to fertilizer additions. The element budgets for the catchments also indicated that losses would not lead to significant depletion of the site capital of nutrients.

4 Future research needs

There is a clear need for further data on the impact of upland pasture improvement on streamwater chemistry and on the export of elements from catchments. As shown above, the solute outputs following improvement are the result of the interaction of a number of factors, including method of improvement, soil type, catchment hydrology and climate. The one small study reported here, however, was restricted to one soil type and one modern method of improvement, and did not cover the period of cultivation and fertilizer addition. Another study just completed in mid-Wales by Institute of Hydrology staff, and work in progress by Ministry of Agriculture staff at Pwll Peiran experimental farm will increase the available information but will still only cover a limited range of upland sites. Further studies are needed, particularly in other regions and with contrasting methods of improvement, before broadly applicable predictive models can be developed. It is also important that some of these

studies use an integrated approach with inputs from agronomists, soil scientists, hydrologists and freshwater biologists. Such an approach would enable us to examine processes, as well as monitoring effects, and thus strengthen any interpretation and application of the results.

5 Summary

Pasture improvement in the uplands generally involves addition of lime and fertilizers, plus cultivation. Loss of lime and fertilizers to drainage waters, plus increased solute outputs due to the changed soil conditions, may produce changes in the chemistry of otherwise unpolluted streams. There are virtually no published data on the magnitude of these changes or their impact on freshwater communities or water quality. A study in mid-Wales detected increases in the concentrations of a wide range of solutes in drainage waters, apparently as a result of improvement, but these were not large enough to have significant effects on freshwater communities or water quality. Element budgets also suggested that increased outputs would have little impact on the site capital of nutrients and, for those elements added as fertilizers, were small compared to inputs. Solute outputs following improvement will be a function of method of improvement, soil type, catchment hydrology and climate. The reported study only concerned one soil type and one modern method of improvement, and did not cover the actual period of cultivation and fertilizer addition. Further studies are needed, covering a range of upland site types and methods of improvement. These studies should be multidisciplinary, involving agronomists, soil scientists, hydrologists and freshwater biologists.

6 References

Baldwin, A.B. 1978. Quality aspects of water in upland Britain. In: *The future of upland Britain*, edited by R.B. Tranter, 322-327. (CAS paper no. 2). Reading: Centre for Agricultural Strategy, University of Reading.

Bohn, H., McNeal, B. & O'Connor, G. 1979. *Soil chemistry.* New York: Wiley.

East of Scotland College of Agriculture. 1980. *Hill improvement.* (Bulletin no. 26). Edinburgh: East of Scotland College of Agriculture.

Floate, M.J.S. 1972. Plant nutrient cycling in hill land. *Proc.N. Engl. Soils Discuss. Group*, no. 7, 11-27.

Floate, M.J.S. 1977. British hill soil problems. *Soil Sci.*, **123**, 325-331.

Jones, W. Dyfri. 1978. A review of some economic aspects of hill and upland farming. In: *The future of upland Britain*, edited by R.B. Tranter, 50-74. (CAS paper no. 2). Reading: Centre for Agricultural Strategy, University of Reading.

Korentajer, L.B.H., Byrnes, B.H. & Hellums, D.T. 1983. The effect of liming and leaching on the sulphur-supplying capacity of soils. *Soil Sci. Soc. Am. J.*, **47**, 525-530.

Munro, J.M.M., Davies, D.A. & Thomas, T.A. 1973. Potential pasture production in the uplands of Wales. 3. Soil nutrient resources and limitations. *J.Br. Grassld Soc.*, **28**, 247-257.

Newbould, P. 1983. Reclaiming the hills. *Soil and Water*, **11**, 27.

Roberts, G. In press. The effects of different land uses and changes in land use on water resources in upland Britain. In: *Proc. Man and the Biosphere (MAB) Workshop No. 5, Budapest, 1983.*

Robinson, M. 1980. *The effect of pre-afforestation drainage on the streamflow and water quality of a small upland catchment.* (Report no. 73). Wallingford: Institute of Hydrology.

Stevens, P.A. 1981a. *A bulk precipitation sampler for use in a geochemical cycling project.* (Bangor occasional paper no. 7). Bangor: Institute of Terrestrial Ecology.

Stevens, P.A. 1981b. *Modification and operation of ceramic cup soil solution sampler for use in geochemical cycling study.* (Bangor occasional paper no. 8). Bangor: Institute of Terrestrial Ecology.

Studies by ITE on the impact of agriculture on wildlife and semi-natural habitats in the uplands

D F BALL
Institute of Terrestrial Ecology, Bangor Research Station

This paper considers the following 3 questions.

1. What are the major impacts of agriculture on upland habitats and wildlife?

2. What work relevant to these impacts has been done or is currently in progress in ITE?

3. What are the main needs for research in this field, and how should ITE contribute?

1 Factors influencing upland agriculture
Economic factors arising from EEC and UK agricultural support policies are dominant, but are discussed elsewhere in this volume (eg Marsh 1984). Climatic, geological and physiographic variety, and the consequent diversity in soil types and fertility give contrasting natural environmental characteristics that affect the regional applicability of the economic spurs to, and constraints on, agricultural methods and their potential for profitable change. Historical and social aspects of land ownership, farm tenure and structure, and of regional non-agricultural activities, also create conditions locally which can modify the rate or direction of responses to economic stimuli in similar physical environments. Where climate, land form, soils and farm structure in the uplands combine to give conditions marginally suitable for mixed or even arable farming, current economic policies tilt the balance away from pastoral systems. Changes in land use then involve the conversion of ley grassland to arable cultivation, the decay or removal of superfluous hedgerow or wall boundaries, more use of fertilizers, herbicides and pesticides, increased land drainage, and the removal of unwanted small copses and decline of farm woods. Stock that are retained are transferred to cultivated and re-seeded former rough pastures, and seasonally to remaining fragments of rough grazing and moorland, the latter's vegetation having changed from heather to grass by intensified grazing and burning.

More widely, in areas environmentally only suitable for pastoral farming, the certainty of financial returns from grants and subsidies increases stock numbers within farming systems unchanged in principle. Beyond an expanded zone of improved pastures, this increased grazing intensity again results in heather moorland being transformed into grass moors, with consequent changes in wildlife.

Extensive changes in the uplands also result from taxation policies. It becomes worthwhile to alter current upland farm/moor mosaics by linking agricultural change with zones of forestry planting on rough pastures and moorland. The possibility of agricultural intensification in parts of an upland area may thus be an essential trigger to the more wide-ranging effects on semi-natural habitats caused by associated extensive forestry enterprises.

In summary, these trends, if current support and taxation policies continue, will create uniformity in the more climatically amenable, lower altitude, sectors of the British uplands, through the disappearance of a high proportion of their characteristically varied semi-natural habitats (Plate 7). In the middle altitude ground, surviving semi-natural moorlands will be broken up into separated and declining fragments. The present typical upland landscape contrast, between diverse vegetation on an agricultural fringe, and expanses of uniform open moorland and hill, will persist only where the wishes of local landowners or administrative constraints check the tide of change in temporary museum pieces. Ultimately, only the highest hills, environmentally unsuitable for intensified agriculture or economic forestry, will remain visually rather as they are today, as open mountain and moor. In this fragile environment, even wildlife must compete with increasingly concentrated recreational pressures and now, apparently, also with development demands arising from the compensation principle of the Wildlife and Countryside Act.

2 Relevant research by ITE staff
2.1 Evaluation of upland land and biological resources
In the assessment of national land resources and their use, computer-stored data inventories co-ordinated from a wide range of data are an essential tool. Although the national land data bases set up in ITE were not directly aimed at relating habitats and wild species to agriculture, their availability can assist

evaluations of relationships between the physical environment, the distribution of plant and animal species, and current and potential land uses, including those in the uplands. In the Biological Records Centre (BRC), the primary source of information on species distribution in Britain, data sets record the presence of plant, animal and insect species in each 10 km x 10 km grid square of the Ordnance Survey national grid (Heath & Perring 1978). This data bank currently holds more than 2.5M records of over 6000 species (Harding *et al.* 1983). The 10 km x 10 km scale of data collection and storage has also been used for a national land characteristics and classification data set of land physical and use characteristics drawn from map and statistic sources; 126 attributes in groups of physiography, climate, geology, soils, topography, land use, agricultural land classification, and conservation status have been quantitatively recorded and computer-stored for each of the 2858 10 km x 10 km Ordnance Survey grid squares containing land in Great Britain. Analyses of inter-relationships between physical environment factors and land use can be made within the national land characteristics data set, and comparisons between physical land character or broad types of land use, and species occurrence, are possible through the linking of this data set with those of the BRC. Classifications of land strata derived from the 10 km x 10 km land data set are now being generated and tested as one basis for regional and national analyses of land use related to the physical environment, and as a framework for stratified sampling in extrapolation of existing data and for future studies.

At a 1 km x 1 km grid square scale in the ecological survey of Britain project, map-derived data from a sample of one square in every 225 (1228 squares) were used to give a classification into 32 land classes (Bunce *et al.* 1981a, b). The key from this classification was then applied to allocate a further sample of 4800 squares to classes, in order to strengthen identification of class geographic distribution. Within each class, field data on plant species, habitat type, soils, land use and landscape features have been collected in 8 sample 1 km x 1 km squares. These data have been extrapolated to quantify the characteristics of each class.

These 3 national land data sets, which are being actively maintained and developed, reinforce each other by their different scales and types of information.

In considering geographic data bases, it is possible to argue in favour of digitized computer-stored 'vector' formats which can retrieve the exact location of any desired feature, rather than the cell-based 'raster' format used in these data sets and in other 'local' land data banks mentioned later (2.3), which only locate the feature as present somewhere in the cell. However, practical considerations justify the raster format (see discussions on the national land characteristics data set in Ball 1983; Ball *et al.* 1983).

2.2 Process studies

Early work in Snowdonia had demonstrated the control exerted by geology and climate, through soils, on the vegetation of open grazings in a geologically diverse hill area (Hughes 1958). Quantitative observations followed on the grazing intensities supported by the contrasting vegetation (Hughes *et al.* 1975b). Selective grazing between grass and heather moorland vegetation types has been studied also in Scotland (Welch 1981). To follow botanical changes in the absence of sheep grazing, exclosure plots were set up and maintained on hill grassland types in Snowdonia (Hughes *et al.* 1975a; Hill 1983) and at Moor House in the northern Pennines (Welch & Rawes 1964; Rawes 1981, 1983). The early stages of vegetation responses to grazing removal recorded so far on these plots show generally slow, and probably readily reversible, changes, with an emphasis on an altered balance among plant species already present. The entry of heath species that are less resistant to grazing is limited, often because local seed sources are lacking, but also by the inability of any seed present to germinate in the close grass herbage. Work on the effects of grazing on vegetation was extended to include quantitative detailed measurements of the productivity of flora and fauna during studies under the International Biological Programme (IBP) in the 1970s. Results from these studies, concentrated on grassland on Snowdon and on blanket bog at Moor House, are recorded in an IBP volume (Heal & Perkins 1978) and summarized by Heal and Perkins (1976).

Unfortunately, the intensive studies at Moor House and in Snowdonia in the 1950s to 1970s were not closely integrated in their planning, timing and methods with work in Scotland (eg Miller & Watson 1978), and were not extended to south Wales and south-west England. A co-ordinated study of the effects of soil and climate on the responses of hill heath and grassland communities, and of local ecotypes of key species, to different grazing regimes at a wide range of sites would have given a clearer quantitative picture of regional similarities and differences.

The grazing exclosure plots in Snowdonia and the Pennines allowed direct observation of the locally variable course of vegetation change in the early stages after cessation of agricultural management of hill grazings. An indirect assessment of the longer term response of upland vegetation to a reduction in the intensity of agricultural management was one aspect of a recent study on the ecology of vegetation change in upland landscapes, carried out in England and Wales under contract to the Department of the Environment (Ball *et al.* 1981a, b, 1982). This work took place in 12 parishes designated by the customer, from Alwinton in Northumberland to Widecombe in Devon. The study combined field records of botanical data, and a vegetation classification derived from them, with a land type analysis, an investigation of the history of land use over the past 200 years, and a review, from existing ecological knowledge, of the impact of different management methods which bring about relatively gradual vegetation change.

The historical analysis identified, from map, archive, and air photo interpretation, locations which had been more intensively managed at one time and then allowed to revert to less intensive grazing use only. The sequence of change from improved pastures through rough pasture vegetation types to grassy heaths and ultimately shrubby heaths (heather moorland types) was found to be generally slow. Though some sites had reverted to shrubby heaths within 40 years, others only developed heath vegetation comparable to adjacent undisturbed moorland after more than 130 years. The proportion of shrubby heaths on sites of this age remained lower than in sites on moorland for which there is no evidence of intensified use within the past 200 years. While conversion of moorland to grassland can be achieved virtually overnight, its restoration by natural means, if intensified use is abandoned and only grazing maintained, is very slow. A non-sustainable improvement encouraged by artificial economic inducements can thus have an effect on the landscape and on wildlife habitats that will persist for more than one generation. Predictive interpretations of future vegetation type frequencies in these study areas, a main aim of the work, are considered later (2.3).

Among the sources of data from which the account of the impact of non-cultivation agricultural practices was prepared in the vegetation change study were quantitative investigations of the effects of grazing, burning and nutrient regimes on heather moors in Scotland (Miller 1979). Subsequent work has also identified potential losses of heather moor of landscape importance through fragmentation and inadequate management, losses equivalent to those attributable directly to agricultural improvement, on the moorlands of the Exmoor National Park (Miller et al. 1984).

In north-east Scotland, local mosaics of heather moorland and birch woodland occur. Studies have shown the importance of birch, through its more active nutrient cycling and enhanced soil biological activity, in modifying soil conditions from those of heather moorland to ones of higher fertility (Miles 1981). In a low input management system for extensive moors, incorporating in its aims stock grazing, grouse management, maintenance of fertility in the soils, and of conservation and landscape interest through habitat diversity, the potential of successional change between birch woodland and moor in such mosaics has considerable interest.

Reviewing this vegetation distribution and management work as a whole, there would appear to be an adequate general understanding of the directions of upland vegetation change through alternative manage-

ment. A remaining need is for integrated studies between different upland areas to monitor actual courses and rates of change from control sites and through experiment, so that specific management recommendations can be made with greater certainty for particular situations (cf Hudson 1984). As noted earlier, loss of heather moor through cultivations and liming is easily achieved, but its restoration, if agricultural improvements turn out to have been ill-judged and impossible to sustain, is another matter entirely.

Another gap in past work, which has repercussions now, relates to a failure to follow up the general picture of upland rock/climate/soil/vegetation relationships with adequately sampled soil and plant chemical data from a geographic spread of contrasting soil parent materials and semi-natural vegetation types maintained on sites with long-term security. Had such data been obtained, preferably at different times, then the present conspicuous absence of accurate information applicable to the question of the environmental impact of 'acid rain' might have been alleviated. Although media attention is directed to effects on upland lakes, rivers and plantation forests, if there is a clear 'acid rain' problem it could also be reducing plant nutrient levels in upland grazings with poorly buffered soils below those due to their natural unpolluted environment, thus increasing the costs of sustaining particular fertility and productivity levels.

In association with the Institute of Hydrology (NERC) and the University College of North Wales, ITE is obtaining detailed data on chemical transfers between inputs from rain and rock weathering, cycling in the soils, and outputs in streams (Hornung et al. 1983; Hornung 1984). One objective is a comparison of pathways and levels of plant nutrients under agricultural grazing and forestry uses. Contrasts between fertilized and unfertilized grazings also show the long-term residual effects of fertilizers and may help in assessing the long-term economic viability of agricultural improvements that depend on regular lime and fertilizer inputs in similar upland environments.

Turning from upland vegetation to fauna, a large part of ITE work in the uplands has been on grouse and deer. Because there has been less direct interaction with recent agricultural intensification in the types of hill land in which these species occur than in the more agriculturally favourable parts of the British uplands, reference to these studies here is brief. This brevity does not reflect the importance of the work done in long-continuing investigations of management, nutrition, and population dynamics of grouse (eg Jenkins et al. 1963; Moss & Miller 1976; Watson & Moss 1978) and of red deer (eg Nicholson 1974; Mitchell et al. 1977; Red Deer Commission 1981; Staines et al. 1982). Both species play an important economic role in conjunction with, or as an alternative to, agricultural stocking on hill ground. Moorland management for grouse must be reconciled with the demands of grazing livestock, while deer can conflict in winter with agriculture and forestry (Plate 4).

Birds of particular conservation importance, eg merlin, red kite and buzzard (Newton et al. 1981a, b, 1982), have been studied in relation to the substantial habitat changes in upland areas that have occurred through modifications of rough grazing and expansion of forestry. Related research, continuing from its prominent role in earlier years, has concerned the effects of agricultural chemicals on birds, including birds of prey in upland areas (Cooke et al. 1982).

2.3 Predictions of ecological change

Resource and process studies in ITE, together with data from other sources, have in recent years supplied a means of predicting the results of likely courses of land use change in Britain, and of modelling alternative land use options.

In the mid-1970s, a desk study on upland land use in England and Wales, under contract to the Department of the Environment (ITE 1978), reviewed the distribution of different land uses, the factors influencing them, and the changes in land use that were likely. It used a data collection approach linking national, regional and local scales of study that involved Ordnance Survey grid squares of appropriate scales as the unit of measurement (2.1). At the national scale, an upland land classification for England and Wales derived from 10 km x 10 km grid square data (a data set and classification now superseded by the later comprehensive Great Britain set (2.1)) was used to predict sectors in which agricultural activity was likely to expand or contract. At the regional scale, a 1 km x 1 km data set and land classification of Cumbria (Bunce et al. 1975; Bunce & Smith 1978) were used to interpret the current use and potential for change of different sectors of the county. At the local scale, 0.25 km x 0.25 km grid squares were employed in analyses of agricultural and forestry potential of a small area in Snowdonia, using data involving progressively greater scales of effort to obtain. Results suggested that land use potential could be effectively assessed from a land classification based on readily available map attributes, with the greater precision of detailed soil and vegetation maps only offering benefit at the site level.

Land classifications in Cumbria have subsequently been applied, with the incorporation of economic data, to resource assessments and land use strategy interpretations at county and district levels in collaboration with staff of Cumbria County Council (Smith 1982). The initial county land classification was expanded through sample field survey to quantify the characteristics of each land class. Combining these data with economic criteria for alternative land uses permitted evaluation of alternative planning strategies in relation to changing economic returns and to social and other constraints on land use. A linear programming model (Bishop 1978) was used to produce land use patterns which maximize particular types of output for the county. The effects of alternative strategies on factors not involved in their formulation could be assessed, for example on wildlife and habitat conservation. At a district level, the same approach was applied to a study of the Sedbergh district. Both scales of analysis suggested that there is potential for significant increases in forestry without detrimental effects on other land uses.

One shortcoming of subsequent ITE work is that the validity of predictions made has not been re-evaluated in the light of data from subsequent actual changes in land use, or altered economic conditions.

From a framework of a land classification in which each class is quantitatively defined by the mean and range of its land characteristics, an assessment can be made of land potential for uses not now practised. An example is the application of current land use and environmental data for the 256 sample squares in the land classes drawn from the ecological survey of Britain data set (2.1) to estimate the area of Great Britain that could be utilized for the production of wood as an energy crop under various constraints (Barr & Bunce 1983). The extreme possibility of 35% of Britain being available for this use, or a more realistically constrained option of 8% being economically applicable, can be suggested from a combination of land, land use priority, and economic data. The model from which these figures are drawn supplies estimates of wood output and its energy capacity for the area of land potentially available under varying constraints. Another potential energy source which might be manageable as an agricultural 'crop' is bracken (Callaghan et al. 1982).

The upland land use desk study included a summary of the effects of grazing, burning, and other non-cultivation agricultural management methods on semi-natural grassland and moorland vegetation in the uplands. An expanded analysis has been made in the vegetation change in upland landscapes project (2.2) (Ball et al. 1981a, b). The generalized courses of change suggested by this analysis under broad criteria of agricultural expansion or contraction were applied to the present frequencies of the vegetation classes at recorded sites in the 12 upland study areas of England and Wales. If the recent level of agricultural expansion continues over the next 10-20 years, it is estimated, for the study areas combined, that there would be a loss of some 4% of their present total moorland, but a loss of 15% of the current area of 'shrubby heaths' (heather moors in a general sense) (Ball et al. 1982). Grassy heath and rough pasture vegetation groups would remain similar in extent to their present situation, but would occur in different locations. Grassy heaths would develop from shrubby heaths, and rough pastures from grassy heaths, as grazing pressures intensify, while improved pastures would be increased by more active change along the moorland fringe. In individual study areas, the effects would vary because of their contrasting land character, farm structure, and non-agricultural constraints. An alternative possibility to the continuance of present trends of change could be a substantial intensification of agriculture (in the order of a 50% livestock increase over 10-20 years). Calculations of the possible changes from present vegetation frequencies under such a 'maximum change' scenario suggest increases in improved pastures by about 60% and rough pastures by 18%, with a reduction of the heather moors to around one third of their present area. The balance of recorded sites, respectively 27%, 17%, 23% and 33% for improved pastures, rough pastures, grassy heaths and shrubby heaths in 1977-78, could change to levels of 44%, 20%, 24% and 12%.

Intensification of agriculture to the maximum scale envisaged would eliminate or severely reduce many vegetation types and the fauna they support. Except where special constraints operate, this intensification would substantially alter the habitats and wildlife of the majority of upland areas of England and Wales and of comparable parts of Scotland. As such agricultural expansion would, for economic reasons, be likely to be accompanied by new forestry plantings so far as land requirements for increased grazing permitted, there could well be additional losses of moorland (Plate 7). On simple assumptions of land type suitability for forestry, this use could occupy some 37% of the study areas as a whole, rather than its present 10% of their area.

If, at the other extreme, upland agriculture were to decline substantially (by a fall in livestock of the order of 50%), the estimates suggest an ultimate possible decline in improved pastures by 25%, in rough pastures by 40%, in grassy heaths by 45%, but an increase in shrubby heaths by 70%. Many of the additional reverted rough grazing and moorland areas would then become scrub woodland, if they were not positively taken into plantation forestry.

The opportunity afforded by the detailed records of plant species at some 1000 sites in these study areas in 1977-78 can be followed up by re-recording sample sites in some areas, to monitor where change has actually occurred in relation to identified stable or changing management, and thus provide comparisons with the generalized predictions.

3 The main needs for research
A pessimistic view is that, if present policies continue, ecological research in all but the least agriculturally suitable hill land would only be able to guide management of the few specially protected 'museum' sites and areas, or record what upland habitats have been like in recent times before the current agricultural changes have taken place. From a more optimistic view point, there is still room for hope that a less narrow attitude towards support for upland communities and environments may develop. This view may be dismissed as a pious platitude that overlooks political realities, but an alternative approach to marginal farming and the welfare of upland communities, biased towards the small unit, traditional methods, and habitat restoration, is having different, and in many ways more environmentally and socially favourable, effects in France (Mills 1983).

Neutrality between conflicting interests is always difficult, and usually unpopular. However, a body such as ITE which aims to gather objective information through research on ecological systems, and to assess independently the ecological effects of actions carried out and policies advocated by agriculturalists, foresters, nature conservationists, recreation interests, water supply bodies, and others concerned in using the uplands, is an essential element in the checks and balances of the diffuse British Governmental system. The Director has stated that 'any future policy must be based on a sound scientific knowledge of the ecology of the uplands, and any policies which are proposed should be fully tested against the best model available to predict the consequences of these policies. Similarly, the results of such policies should be monitored carefully' (J N R Jeffers pers. comm.).

Resource assessment, process investigation, and modelling the effects of actual and potential policies, proceeding in a parallel in a co-ordinated programme, comprise the ITE approach to contributing to such knowledge. In terms of resource inventories and evaluation, more detailed answers are needed to the question: what is present now? These answers will require improvements to the existing land data inventories, and greater integration of national, regional and local physical, management, and economic data to give a co-ordinated base-line of national information on land resources. Expansion of the use of air photography and development of applications of satellite imagery will support or supplant field work in updating information and monitoring change in stratified sample locations. As part of 2 linked research programmes in which ITE work is now involved, *Land resources and land uses* and *Survey and monitoring*, an objective is to produce in 5 years a handbook that will analyse the environmental characteristics of the land resources of Britain, how these resources are now used, and why this land use pattern has developed. It will also include modelling of the ecological impacts of trends in land use change and of alternative options.

Efficient resource evaluation from land data sets depends on understanding the ecosystem processes that link the physical and biological aspects of upland environments to discover why upland habitats are as they are, and how they work. Detailed site studies must be applicable to broader evaluations. A survey census approach based on sound sampling strategies must follow changes in habitats, their soils, and plant and animal populations, on control sites and areas, as well as on sites affected by changes in management in otherwise similar environments. Too many past studies have been concerned only with parts of an ecosystem and have been carried out in isolation from other aspects. The need is for more integrated studies, which should include experimental manipulations of the factors that control soil, plants and fauna in major upland vegetation types, emphasizing both rare and widespread habitats in farmlands, woodlands, moorlands and hill ground.

Long-term geochemical studies, though laborious and expensive, can provide a quantitative nutrient balance assessment for particular land form, climate, soil and land use conditions. Through these data, the costs and benefits can be considered of higher fertility, higher production agricultural systems achieved by increasing the soil nutrient status in inherently unfavourable environments. Is the result of introducing such systems and attempting to sustain them worth the effort? What will the effort cost? What is lost to the upland environment in other ways? What alternative might be preferable? These are among the questions to which answers for particular upland situations would be helpful from an ecological view point.

Although a wide measure of knowledge has been gained on the management of grouse and deer and their interactions with other land uses, if agricultural and forestry encroachment on the hill ground in Scotland increases, conflicts between uses will also increase and their resolution is likely to need further experimental and observational studies. Attention throughout this paper has been concentrated on considering agricultural intensification as the main trend of change in the uplands. However, in a large area of hill land in north-west Scotland, agricultural production will not only never be truly economic under modern conditions, but will remain inefficient even under the criteria of current agricultural support. Alternative options and their ecological implications should be investigated in theory and experimental practice. Could local communities in such areas be as effectively sustained as they are now, if the attempt to maintain any significant level of supported agriculture were withdrawn and replaced by other land uses concentrated on utilization of wild species, and on the economic values in recreation carefully allied to positive conservation?

In prediction and modelling studies, in order to answer the question: what will happen if?, data inventories and the type of data provided by process studies will need to be appropriate for a wider range of modelling methods than those previously employed. More use of economic and social science expertise is essential, with greater interaction with other organizations in the formulation of viable models of the ecological, economic and social consequences of action or inaction. The clear definition of land and land use features that

are of importance, measurement of their regional and national variation, and appropriate sampling programmes to relate site, region and national assessments, all require the most careful consideration, if observations are to be used to set up models of ecological impacts and changes and then to refine them by monitoring control sites. Modelling should extend to proposing balances of land use in particular regions or upland environments that optimize alternative interests, rather than concentrating on one, however important. The potential practicality of proposals should be examined thoroughly and then, if appropriate land holding structures are available, be tested by co-operation between ecologists, land managers, and administrators.

To some extent, these suggestions could be seen as a continuation of what ITE has done in the past, but they should rather be thought of as an intention to use what has been done as a basis for a more co-ordinated research effort in the future, in line with ITE's current strategy for integrated research in key programme fields. Impacts of agriculture in the uplands are a live political issue and also a live, interesting, and essential field for scientific study.

4 Summary
Past and current work in ITE on impacts of agriculture on upland habitats includes: land resource evaluation, process studies of the interactions of land use with wild species, and the prediction and modelling of the ecological results of alternative land use trends and options. Data banks at national, regional and district scales display and analyse the links between land character, land use, and species and habitat distributions. Process studies have included experimental monitoring of changes in vegetation, as a result of altered grazing and burning regimes, major studies of management and of population dynamics of economically important upland species (grouse and deer), and investigation of the impact of agricultural chemicals on upland birds of prey. Studies involving prediction and modelling of change have included generalized forecasts of the potential trends of vegetation change in upland grasslands and moorlands, applications of land data and classifications to county and district planning strategies under alternative land use options, and the assessment of land potentially available for novel forms of land use, such as the growth of energy crops. Work that should now be undertaken by ITE in this field should look beyond the necessary ecosystem studies in surviving semi-natural habitats to seeking a wider understanding of ecological factors and processes in the general countryside in relation to particular land use systems. Data from such studies, allied to existing material, can be co-ordinated in analysable land resource data sets, to enable predictions of the impact of alternative policies to be made with increased confidence. The current ITE research programmes provide foundations for upland ecosystem process studies linked to regional and national

sampling frameworks, for integrated multiscale land data bases, and for the application of modelling methods combining ecological, technical and economic criteria to assess the acual and potential impacts of policies.

5 References

Ball, D.F. 1983. National land characteristic data bank. *Annu. Rep. Inst. terr. Ecol. 1982*, 103-106.

Ball, D.F., Dale, J., Sheail, J., Dickson, K.E. & Williams, W.M. 1981a. *Ecology of vegetation change in upland landscapes. I: General synthesis.* (Bangor occasional paper no. 2). Bangor: Institute of Terrestrial Ecology.

Ball, D.F., Dale, J., Sheail, J. & Williams, W.M. 1981b. *Ecology of vegetation change in upland landscapes. II. Study areas.* (Bangor occasional paper no. 3). Bangor: Institute of Terrestrial Ecology.

Ball, D.F., Dale, J., Sheail, J. & Heal, O.W. 1982. *Vegetation change in upland landscapes.* Cambridge: Institute of Terrestrial Ecology.

Ball, D.F., Radford, G.L. & Williams, W.M. 1983. *A land characteristic data bank for Great Britain.* (Bangor occasional paper no. 13). Bangor: Institute of Terrestrial Ecology.

Barr, C.J. & Bunce, R.G.H. 1983. The land potentially available for wood energy production in Great Britain. *Annu. Rep. Inst. terr. Ecol. 1982*, 106-109.

Bishop, I. 1978. *Land use in rural Cumbria—a linear programming model.* (Merlewood research and development paper no. 75). Grange-over-Sands: Institute of Terrestrial Ecology.

Bunce, R.G.H. & Smith, R.S. 1978. *An ecological survey of Cumbria.* Kendal: Cumbria County Council and Lake District Special Planning Board.

Bunce, R.G.H., Morrell, S.K. & Stel, H. 1975. The application of multivariate analysis to regional survey. *J. environ. Manage.*, **3**, 151-165.

Bunce, R.G.H., Barr, C.J. & Whittaker, H.A. 1981a. An integrated system of land classification. *Annu. Rep. Inst. terr. Ecol. 1980*, 28-33.

Bunce, R.G.H., Barr, C.J. & Whittaker, H.A. 1981b. *Land classes in Great Britain: preliminary description for users of the Merlewood method of land classification.* (Merlewood research and development paper no. 80). Grange-over-Sands: Institute of Terrestrial Ecology.

Callaghan, T.V., Lawson, G.J. & Scott, R. 1982. Bracken as an energy crop? In: *Solar world forum,* edited by D.O. Hall & J. Morton, vol. 2, 1239-1247. Oxford: Pergamon.

Cooke, A.S., Bell, A.A. & Haas, M.B. 1982. *Predatory birds, pesticides and pollution.* Cambridge: Institute of Terrestrial Ecology.

Harding, P.T., Greene, D.M., Preston, C.D., Arnold, H.R. & Harper, R.J. 1983. Biological Records Centre. *Annu. Rep. Inst. terr. Ecol. 1982*, 44-45.

Heal, O.W. & Perkins, D.F. 1976. IBP studies on montane grassland and moorlands. *Phil. Trans. R. Soc. B*, **274**, 295-314.

Heal, O.W. & Perkins, D.F. 1978. *Production ecology of British moors and montane grasslands.* Berlin: Springer.

Heath, J. & Perring, F.H. 1978. *Biological Records Centre.* Cambridge: Institute of Terrestrial Ecology.

Hill, M.O. 1983. Effects of grazing in Snowdonia. *Annu. Rep. Inst. terr. Ecol. 1982*, 31-32.

Hornung, M. 1984. The impact of upland pasture improvement on solute outputs in surface waters. In: *Agriculture and the environment,* edited by D. Jenkins, 150-154. (ITE symposium no. 13). Cambridge: Institute of Terrestrial Ecology.

Hornung, M., Reynolds, B., Hughes, S., Stevens, P.A. & Hatton, A.A. 1983. Some factors controlling geochemical cycling in an upland grassland. *Annu. Rep. Inst. terr. Ecol. 1982*, 94-98.

Hudson, P.J. 1984. Some effects of sheep management on heather moorlands in northern England. In: *Agriculture and the environment,* edited by D. Jenkins, 143-149. (ITE symposium no. 13). Cambridge: Institute of Terrestrial Ecology.

Hughes, R.E. 1958. Sheep population and environment in Snowdonia (North Wales). *J. Ecol.*, **46**, 169-190.

Hughes, R.E., Dale, J., Lutman, J. & Thomson, A.G. 1975a. Effects of grazing on upland vegetation in Snowdonia. *Annu. Rep. Inst. terr. Ecol. 1974*, 46-50.

Hughes, R.E., Dale, J., Mountford, M.D. & Ellis-Williams, I. 1975b. Studies in sheep populations and environment in the mountains of north-west Wales. II: Contemporary distribution of sheep populations and environment. *J. appl. Ecol.*, **12**, 165-178.

Institute of Terrestrial Ecology. 1978. *Upland land use in England and Wales.* (CCP 111). Cheltenham: Countryside Commission.

Jenkins, D., Watson, A. & Miller, G.R. 1963. Population studies on red grouse *Lagopus lagopus scoticus* (Lath.) in north-east Scotland. *J. Anim. Ecol.*, **32**, 317-376.

Jones, W.D. 1978. A review of some economic aspects of hill and upland farming. In: *The future of upland Britain,* edited by R.B. Tranter, 50-74. (CAS paper no. 2). Reading: Centre for Agricultural Strategy, University of Reading.

Marsh, J. 1984. Recent economic trends in British agriculture. In: *Agriculture and the environment,* edited by D. Jenkins, 28-33. (ITE symposium no. 13). Cambridge: Institute of Terrestrial Ecology.

Miles, J. 1981. *Effect of birch on moorland.* Cambridge: Institute of Terrestrial Ecology.

Miller, G.R. 1979. Quantity and quality of the annual production of shoots and flowers by *Calluna vulgaris* in north-east Scotland. *J. Ecol.*, **67**, 109-129.

Miller, G.R. & Watson, A. 1978. Heather productivity and its relevance to the regulation of red grouse populations. In: *The production ecology of British moorlands and montane grasslands,* edited by O.W. Heal & D.F. Perkins, 277-285. Berlin: Springer.

Miller, G.R., Miles, J. & Heal, O.W. 1984. *Moorland management: a study of Exmoor.* Cambridge: Institute of Terrestrial Ecology.

Mills, S. 1983. French farming: good for people, good for wildlife. *New Scient.*, **100**, 568-571.

Mitchell, B., Staines, B.W. & Welch, D. 1977. *Ecology of red deer: a research review relevant to their management in Scotland.* Cambridge: Institute of Terrestrial Ecology.

Moss, R. & Miller, G.R. 1976. Production, dieback and grazing of heather (*Calluna vulgaris*) in relation to numbers of red grouse (*Lagopus l. scoticus*) and mountain hares (*Lepus timidus*) in north-east Scotland. *J. appl. Ecol.*, **13**, 369-377.

Newton, I., Robson, J.E. & Yalden, D.W. 1981a. Decline of the merlin in the Peak District. *Bird Study*, **28**, 225-234.

Newton, I., Davis, P.E. & Moss, D. 1981b. Distribution and breeding of red kites in relation to land-use in Wales. *J. appl. Ecol.*, **18**, 173-186.

Newton, I., Davis, P.E. & Davis, J.E. 1982. Ravens and buzzards in relation to sheep-farming and forestry in Wales. *J. appl. Ecol.*, **19**, 681-706.

Nicholson, I.A. 1974. Red deer range and problems of carrying capacity in the Scottish highlands. *Mammal Rev.*, **4**, 103-118.

Rawes, M. 1981. Further results of excluding sheep from high-level grasslands in the North Pennines. *J. Ecol.*, **69**, 651-669.

Rawes, M. 1983. Changes in two high altitude blanket bogs after the cessation of sheep grazing. *J. Ecol.*, **71**, 219-235.

Red Deer Commission. 1981. *Red deer management: a practical book for the management of wild red deer in Scotland.* Edinburgh: HMSO.

Smith, R.S. 1982. *The use of land classification in resource assessment and rural planning.* Cambridge: Institute of Terrestrial Ecology.

Staines, B.W., Catt, D.C., Welch, D. & Scott, D. 1982. Red deer and forestry: current work by the Institute of Terrestrial Ecology. *Deer,* **5,** 400-402.

Watson, A. & Moss, R. 1978. Population ecology of red grouse. *Annu. Rep. Inst. terr. Ecol. 1977,* 18-21.

Welch, D. 1981. Diurnal movements by Scottish blackface sheep between improved grassland and a heather hill in north-east Scotland. *J. Zool.,* **194,** 267-271.

Welch, D. & Rawes, M. 1964. The early effects of excluding sheep from high-level grasslands in the northern Pennines. *J. appl. Ecol.,* **1,** 281-300.

The use of remote sensing for monitoring change in agriculture in the uplands and lowlands

B K WYATT
Institute of Terrestrial Ecology, Bangor Research Station

1 Introduction

In assessing the impacts of agriculture upon wildlife and semi-natural habitats, it is necessary to understand, first, the nature of these impacts, and, second, the location and extent of the areas where the effects are felt. The first requirement (how agricultural practices impact upon ecosystems) is considered elsewhere in this symposium volume. The questions of where such conflicts exist or may arise, their degree, extent and duration are equally important if effective measures are to be found for minimizing them, whether through statutory provisions or by voluntary means.

Specific questions which must be answered include the following.

— Where do vulnerable ecosystems and habitats occur?

— Where are agricultural methods being practised which result in conflict with ecological interests?

— Where are changes occurring in agriculture which may affect the situation?

— What is the extent of the effect, locally and nationally? For example, is there localized pressure on a commonly occurring habitat, or is the threat widespread and the habitat rare?

— What are the dynamics of the problem? For example, what is the rate of encroachment of arable farming on permanent grassland?

The range of information needed to answer these questions is considerable. Identification of habitat types demands a knowledge of the basic topography, vegetation cover, pedology, hydrology, etc. In order to evaluate specific agricultural impacts, it is necessary to distinguish patterns of cultivation, often on a field-by-field basis. Further, much of this information must be collected repetitively in order to provide a monitoring capability.

This information is needed at very local scales (eg in assessing potential impacts of agricultural development on a Site of Special Scientific Interest), at broad national scales to evaluate the overall effects of changes in agricultural practices, and at intermediate scales (eg to monitor agricultural impact in a National Park).

In practice, although elements of such an information base exist (eg Coppock 1976; Coleman 1961; Soil Survey of England and Wales 1983; Heath & Perring 1978) and a number of potentially useful sources is described elsewhere in this volume (Ball 1984; Bunce *et al.* 1984), the available information falls short of the requirements identified above.

On the face of it, remote sensing from satellites or aircraft offers an attractive means of collecting much of the necessary information on land cover that would otherwise be so time-consuming and costly to acquire. This paper is an attempt to evaluate its suitability as a technique for mapping and monitoring rural land cover in the UK, to identify inadequacies in existing techniques, and to suggest research needed to minimize these shortcomings.

2 Methodology for obtaining information

2.1 Terminology

Strictly, the term 'remote sensing' covers all methods of data acquisition in which the sensor is not in physical contact with the object under observation. This paper adopts the narrower, and more useful, definition of Reeves *et al.* (1975): 'Observation of the earth's surface in various parts of the electromagnetic spectrum by sensors carried on aerial or space platforms'. A further restriction has been introduced in that the paper covers only those systems which record in digital form. Aerial photography, whose use in agricultural and ecological survey is now routine, is not considered in this review.

2.2 Survey methods

Survey from aircraft in the UK, until recently, has been confined to photographic methods and to infra-red linescan, mainly because of the lack of suitable scanners. Experimental airborne remote sensing campaigns (Williams 1984) have demonstrated their potential for land cover survey applications, but have also highlighted a number of shortcomings. In particular, spatial correction and registration of airborne imagery presents problems, and radiometric correction for the effects of off-nadir viewing needs further study.

Satellite imagery has been more readily available, despite its high capital cost, because the cost of imagery per unit area is modest, and the techniques have been vigorously promoted by national space agencies. Table 1 summarizes the satellite systems from which environmental remotely sensed data are, or will shortly become, available.

Interactions between plants and radiation at visible and near infra-red wave lengths are distinctive (Figure 1). The multispectral scanner (MSS), carried by all the Landsat satellites, exploits this fact, and senses in the 4 bands in this region of the electromagnetic spectrum. Landsats 1-4 have achieved continuity of cover over much of the earth's surface from 1972 to the present time. Consequently, data from the Landsat

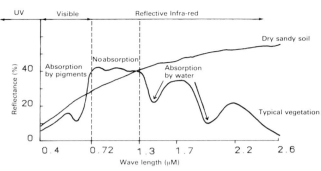

Figure 1. Reflectance and absorption of short-wave solar radiation by bare soil and vegetation (Source: Fenwick & Thompson 1976; Seddon 1976)

programme have been easily the most widely used for vegetation mapping and in studies of vegetation change.

2.3 Image analysis

Remote sensing using conventional photography generates a physical image as the primary product. Although it is possible to analyse photographic images quantitatively, the processes entailed are laborious and inconvenient. A major attraction of data derived from

Table 1. Summary of satellite systems of importance for environmental remote sensing

SATELLITE	SPONSOR	STATUS	LAUNCH	MAIN SENSOR(S)
NIMBUS-7	NASA	IN ORBIT	1978	CZCS/SMMR
HCMM	NASA	NO LONGER OPERATIONAL	1978	HCMR
SEASAT	NASA	NO LONGER OPERATIONAL	1978	SAR SMMR
LANDSAT-1, -2, -3	NASA	NO LONGER OPERATIONAL	1972, 1975, 1978	RBV MSS
LANDSAT-4	NASA	MSS OPERATIONAL TM NOT YET COMMISSIONED	1982	MSS TM
LANDSAT-5	NASA	APPROVED	1984	MSS TM
SPOT-1	FRANCE	APPROVED	1984	MSS
MOS-1	JAPAN	APPROVED	1986	MSS
ERS-1	ESA	APPROVED	1987	RADAR
MAGSAT	NASA	IN ORBIT	1979	MAGNETIC FIELD STRENGTH AND DIRECTION
ERS-2	ESA	PROPOSED	1990	SAR ALTIMETER
SPOT-2	FRANCE	PROPOSED	1988	MSS
GRAVSAT	NASA	PROPOSED	1989	GRAVITY MAGNETIC FIELD
RADARSAT	CANADA	PROPOSED	1990	RADAR
FIREX	USA	PROPOSED	1990s	RADAR
NOAA-7	NOAA	IN ORBIT	1981	TIR
METEOSAT-2	ESA	IN ORBIT	1981	TIR
SHUTTLE EXPTS				
SIR-B	NASA	APPROVED	1984	RADAR

RBV	= Return-beam vidicon		TM	= Thematic mapper
MSS	= Multispectral scanner		HCMM	= Heat capacity mapping mission
TIR	= Thermal infra-red		HCMR	= Heat capacity mapping radiometer
SAR	= Synthetic aperture radar		SMMR	= Scanning multichannel microwave radiometer
CZCS	= Coastal zone colour scanner			

digital recording devices such as scanners and radars is the fact that they are directly available in digital form and readily amenable to analysis using digital computers. The physical image as observed by the sensor is only one (and by no means the most useful) form in which such data can be presented.

Imagery in digital form is readily manipulated by computer, and many software packages and integrated systems are now available for this purpose. Baker (1983) gives a comprehensive description of image analysis processes of relevance for ecological mapping applications, as implemented on one such system. Comparable systems provide similar facilities which differ mainly in the details of the implementation.

3 Monitoring change in land cover

Allan (1981) has given an authoritative review of the principles behind the use of remote sensing for monitoring land use change, and has discussed the needs of land cover monitoring programmes using remotely sensed data. He indicates that, in the case of large area survey, economic considerations dictate a choice between comprehensive coverage from satellite platforms at low resolution (typically 80 m^2) or survey from aircraft at relatively high resolution (perhaps 1 m^2) using sampling methods. These methods are increasingly being used in combination (eg Tomlins 1981; Williams 1984): an aircraft, 'underflying' the satellite, can provide high resolution coverage of selected areas which can then be used to aid interpretation of the satellite image. However, as indicated earlier, literature references to the use of multispectral data for land use survey describe predominantly satellite sources, by far the most common being Landsats 1-3.

As later generations of satellite systems become operational, offering better spatial resolution (eg Landsat Thematic Mapper (30 m^2), SPOT Multispectral Scanner (30-10 m^2)), so the distinction between aircraft and satellite technologies are becoming blurred. Nevertheless, high resolution satellite detectors bring with them problems of analysis, due to the high volumes of data they generate, and in many cases it is likely that some sort of sampling strategy will be employed in routine applications of such imagery for large area survey and monitoring.

Because the spectral response of vegetation is partly a function of phenology, timing of data acquisition is an important consideration when using remotely sensed data for studies of change in land cover. Data should be selected in the first instance to maximize the ability to discriminate the land cover types of interest. For example, if the problem concerns the encroachment of arable farming on areas of permanent pasture, the optimum time of survey is immediately after ploughing, when the difference in spectral response between bare soil and growing vegetation can be

exploited. Successive images should then be acquired so that the vegetation is at similar stages of maturity.

In the case of aircraft based surveys, the timing of the flights must be carefully planned. Time of day is important in order to minimize the effects of different sun angles. A number of images taken at regular intervals may be available, from satellite sources, and, in principle, it is a simple matter to select the most suitable ones.

In practice, cloud cover often seriously limits choice, particularly in temperate latitudes. For example, there were only 3 cloud-free images available for the area of mid-Wales depicted in Plate 8 in the entire period from 1972-83 during which Landsat has been operating. These images were all early summer scenes, so that it has been impossible to study seasonal change, or to use such changes as an aid in classifying ground cover. The problem is less acute in lowland areas of south-eastern Britain, but it seriously restricts the use of satellite methods for routinely monitoring land use change in upland areas (at least until RADAR systems are in regular service, and the use of microwave imagery for identifying vegetation types is better understood).

Given the wide availability of Landsat imagery at reasonable cost, the volume of literature describing its use in vegetation and crop inventory comes as no surprise. Although much of this material is of limited value in advancing understanding of the techniques and use of remote sensing, it does demonstrate collectively that remote sensing is capable of identifying many of the land cover types of interest to the strategic planner. A number of land cover classifications have been suggested for use with remotely sensed data (eg Anderson et al. 1972) (Table 2). These systems tend to be hierarchical in structure. Using the classification techniques already discussed, including multitemporal methods, it is possible to distinguish all Anderson's level 1 classes and most of the level 2 classes with some precision (typically 80-90% pixels are correctly classified for many groups).

It is therefore surprising to note the relative paucity of reports describing the use of multitemporal data for monitoring land cover change, particularly for strategic planning purposes. Now that Landsat imagery has been continuously available over a period of more than 10 years, it is reasonable to suppose the existence of a body of evidence concerning its suitability as a broad-brush aid to environmental monitoring. There are certainly examples of such applications in the literature. On the continental scale, the success of the Large Area Crop Inventory Experiment (MacDonald 1979) in monitoring crop growth and predicting yields has already been remarked. Satellite data have been used successfully to monitor arid land conditions in several regions (eg Maxwell et al. 1980; Robinove et al. 1981). Instances of the use of multitemporal

Table 2. Land use and land cover classification system for use with
remote sensing data
(Source: Anderson *et al.* 1972)

LEVEL 1	LEVEL 2
1 Urban or built-up land	11 Residential
	12 Commercial and services
	13 Industrial
	14 Transportation, communications and utilities
	15 Industrial and commercial complexes
	16 Mixed
	17 Other
2 Agricultural land	21 Cropland and pasture
	22 Orchards, groves, vineyards, nurseries and ornamental horticultural areas
	23 Confined feeding operations
	24 Other
3 Rangeland	31 Herbaceous range
	32 Shrub-brushland range
	33 Mixed
4 Forest land	41 Deciduous
	42 Evergreen
	43 Mixed
5 Water	51 Streams and canals
	52 Lakes
	53 Reservoirs
	54 Bays and estuaries
6 Wetland	61 Forest
	62 Non-forested
7 Barren land	71 Dry salt flats
	72 Beaches
	73 Sandy areas other than beaches
	74 Bare exposed rock
	75 Strip mines, quarries, and gravel pits
	76 Transitional areas
	77 Mixed
8 Tundra	81 Shrub and brush tundra
	82 Herbaceous tundra
	83 Bare ground tundra
	84 Wet tundra
	85 Mixed
9 Perennial snow or ice	91 Perennial snowfields
	92 Glaciers

remotely sensed imagery to monitor urban encroachment and urban change abound (eg Todd 1977; Angelici *et al.* 1977; Stauffer & McKinney 1978; Stove *et al.* 1980; Toll *et al.* 1980). Elsewhere, there are examples of monitoring programmes for agriculture (eg Loveland & Johnson 1983) and forestry (eg Smith 1979; Nelson 1982, 1983), but comparatively few instances in which the focus is on natural or semi-natural habitats. In the UK, there is remarkably little relevant published material. The Department of Agriculture and Fisheries for Scotland has commissioned a study to evaluate the use of remote sensing in compiling a national inventory of bracken (Grampian Regional Council 1982), and NERC is funding a number of programmes involving vegetation mapping, including an evaluation of the use of Landsat imagery for monitoring the drainage of wetlands and agricultural encroachment (J R Baker pers. comm.).

The reasons for the comparatively slow adoption of remote sensing as a tool for monitoring land use change are complex. There are a number of technical problems (see below). There have also been the educational and promotional difficulties which are often associated with the introduction of any new methodology, but which have, perhaps, been exacerbated by a tendency to 'over-sell' satellite remote sensing in its early days, earning for it the unjust reputation of a technique in search of an application.

An important consideration is that remote sensing alone can provide, at best, only a superficial analysis of the ecological consequences of changes in land use. In conjunction with other data sets recording topological, pedological, hydrological and biological variables, for example, the potentials of remotely sensed data are much enhanced. NERC is in a strong position to draw upon the resources of its Institutes, the university research it finances and its in-house cartographic expertise (Jackson 1981) to construct such geographic information systems.

ITE, at its Bangor Research Station, has recently embarked on a programme of work to assess the contribution of remote sensing, used in conjunction with such data sources, for ecological research and surveillance. The focus of the work is the characterization of vegetation cover in upland areas of Wales, using Landsat and supplementary information from NERC digital cartographic sources, from existing vegetation maps, from aerial photographs, airborne multispectral data and ground survey. After development of suitable land cover classification procedures, the programme will use Landsat imagery from 1975-83 to investigate changes in upland land use, and, in particular, changes due to the encroachment of forestry and agriculture upon natural and semi-natural habitats. The methodology is being developed in a test area, 20 km x 20 km, east of Dolgellau, with the ultimate aim of extending the system to give a comprehensive land cover monitoring capability for the whole of Wales.

The programme is still at a relatively early stage, but already a number of general principles are becoming apparent. The importance of access to accurate ground truth records cannot be over-emphasized. They are required for training purposes and to evaluate the results of the classifications. They should include examples of the entire range of cover types of interest, and should be, as far as possible, contemporary with the scenes being used to develop the classification procedures. In the case of the ITE project, with its emphasis on monitoring potential, it is important to be able to establish and verify a base-line. We have been fortunate in establishing this base-line as long ago as 1973, when extensive aerial photographic cover, together with some ground survey results, was available to assist interpretation of an early cloud-free Landsat scene.

Areas of natural vegetation are much less easy to characterize unambiguously from satellite imagery than is the case with agricultural land. Natural vegetation is less homogeneous than crops or agricultural grassland; physical boundaries are usually less distinct; spectral response tends to be more variable; and topographic variables such as slope and aspect tend to be more extreme, at least in upland areas, leading to areas of apparent contrast which may have little to do with the vegetation cover.

It has been possible to construct maps of broad structural vegetation types, such as those depicted in Plate 8a. The vegetation classes in this map appear to match well with ground observations, and a detailed evaluation against aerial photographic evidence is now in progress. While such a map providing synoptic cover over the whole of a region such as Wales would certainly be better than anything presently available, its ability to distinguish land cover types is too crude for most ecological and conservation applications. It is therefore clear that considerably more work is required on improving our ability to recognize and distinguish important natural vegetation communities from remotely sensed data.

In the case of land used for agriculture and forestry, classification problems are less acute. Plate 8b demonstrates the use of multitemporal imagery to identify areas of forest change in the 20 km x 20 km survey area. Further field work is necessary to identify the precise nature of the changes that are recorded. For example, an apparent increase in forest cover may be the result of canopy closure, rather than new planting. Similarly, reduction in cover may be the result of either thinning or felling. By counting pixels in various classes, it is possible to make a quantitative estimate of the rate of change. For example, in the case of this particular scene, there was an apparent increase of 1072 ha (2.7%) of mature forest canopy during the period 1975-82. This estimate is currently being compared with Forestry Commission records and with the evidence of field survey and aerial photography.

4 Summary of future research needs

4.1 Spatial resolution

Early generation Landsat imagery has often been criticized for its relatively poor spatial resolution. Leaving aside the question of how to measure the spatial resolution of a digital sensor, it is, of course, self-evident that Landsat MSS imagery is much inferior in this respect to conventional aerial photographs.

However, for purposes of large area survey, the ability to record an integrated synoptic picture is important and, except when individual vegetation stands are of interest, poor spatial resolution may well be less of a constraint than has been suggested in the past. Sensors with improved spatial resolution are already available. Few people can fail to be impressed with the quality of the published imagery from the Landsat

Thematic Mapper (Townshend et al. 1983), and the French SPOT satellite offers the prospect of even better spatial resolution. Nevertheless, as Forshaw et al. (1983) point out, for purposes of ground cover classification, improved spatial resolution can be a mixed blessing as within-class variability is substantially increased. The imagery records real physical differences which are superimposed on the variation due to differences in cover type. For synoptic mapping purposes, the smoothing effect of low resolution sensors may prove, in retrospect, to have been no bad thing! If Thematic Mapper data and other high resolution sources are to be used for these applications (as inevitably they will be), then it is imperative that more sophisticated classification algorithms are developed to allow the data to be fully exploited.

4.2 Radiometric resolution

Much of the work on distinguishing and classifying land cover types has hitherto been based on empirical analysis and manipulation of multispectral imagery. The powers of discrimination of existing sensors have largely been limited by the choice of bands. New sensors such as the Thematic Mapper, which records in 7 bands, promise considerable improvement in species discrimination and in vegetation health studies. There is an urgent need for a programme of work using ground-based radiometers, under carefully controlled conditions, (i) to investigate the detailed reflectance characteristics of the various vegetation canopies of interest for wide area mapping, and (ii) to monitor these characteristics under various conditions of illumination. This programme is required in order to understand better the relationships between vegetation community composition and spectral response. Such a programme will also furnish useful information for the design of future sensors.

4.3 Another area where information is sparse, and potential benefits are great, is in the use of RADAR imagery for vegetation mapping. RADAR remote sensing offers the prospect of an all-weather monitoring system, capable of returning detailed information on surface texture which, allied with multispectral imagery, could greatly enhance our ability to classify land cover types.

4.4 Extrapolation in space and time

Large area mapping and multitemporal analysis make the basic assumption that it is possible to apply statistics from training sets in one scene or in one portion of a scene to other images. This assumption is not entirely valid. Large area mosaics composed of several Landsat scenes inevitably exhibit perceptible differences in contrast across the composite image (Merson 1983). Neighbouring scenes are not necessarily imaged on the same day; the problem is even more acute in multitemporal studies. The effects of different sun angle on plane surfaces are easily corrected. The effect of topography, and, in particular, differences in slope, can only be dealt with satisfactorily if terrain data are available in digital form. This is rarely the case. Atmospheric conditions also affect image quality and, until procedures have been devised which are capable of routine systematic correction for these variables, it is not possible to envisage the regular use of automatic classification of remotely sensed imagery for land cover monitoring. However, remote sensing, in combination with other relevant data sources and in the hands of informed and experienced operators, does offer the prospect of a cost-effective surveillance and monitoring capability that could not be satisfied by other means.

5 Summary

The paper reviews the use of digital remotely sensed data from air and space for land cover survey and for monitoring change in land cover. In particular, interactions between agriculture and areas of importance for wildlife and conservation are considered.

The paper outlines the techniques involved, including the characteristics of the more commonly encountered sensors and platforms, and reviews existing and future sources of remotely sensed imagery. Data analysis procedures, including methods of correction, enhancement and examination of digital imagery, are described.

The preparation of land cover maps from remotely sensed data is reviewed, and examples of the use of remote sensing to monitor the change in type and extent of cultivated areas are presented. The suitability of the method for deriving quantitative estimates of land cover and rates of change at synoptic scales is demonstrated, and the value of these techniques for assessing the ecological impacts of agriculture is indicated.

Limitations in the data and in existing analytical techniques for these purposes are noted, and the need for further research in the following areas is suggested.

i. Understanding the mechanisms which determine the characteristics of integrated radiance signals derived from a wide range of land cover types and, in particular, from complex natural vegetation communities.

ii. Investigating the effects of seasonal change on the reflectance characteristics of various land cover types to improve powers of discrimination.

iii. Solution of the problem of classifying structural vegetation types with non-uniform reflectance characteristics. This problem is exacerbated with increasing spatial resolution.

iv. Development of procedures to correct imagery for variation in experimental conditions (eg differences in irradiance levels, look angle, sensor

characteristics) to facilitate extrapolation of the results of image classification both in space and time.

6 References

Allan, J.A. 1981. Remote sensing of temporal changes in land cover. In: *Plants and the daylight spectrum,* edited by H. Smith, 115-128. London: Academic Press.

Anderson, J.R., Hardy, E.E. & Roach, J.T. 1972. A land-use classification system for use with remote-sensor data. *Circ. U.S. geol. Surv.,* no. 671, 1-16.

Angelici, G.L., Bryant, N.A. & Friedman, S.Z. 1977. Techniques for land-use change detection using Landsat imagery. *Am. Soc. Photogramm. Annu. Meet. Pap. Proc.,* 217-228.

Baker, J.R. 1983. Analysis of remotely sensed data on the NERC I²S system. In: *Ecological mapping from ground, air and space,* edited by R.M. Fuller, 125-133. (ITE symposium no. 10). Cambridge: Institute of Terrestrial Ecology.

Ball, D.F. 1984. Studies by ITE on the impact of agriculture on wildlife and semi-natural habitats in the uplands. In: *Agriculture and the environment,* edited by D. Jenkins, 155-162. (ITE symposium no. 13). Cambridge: Institute of Terrestrial Ecology.

Bunce, R.G.H., Tranter, R.B., Thompson, A.M.M., Mitchell, C.P. & Barr, C.J. 1984. Models for predicting changes in rural land use in Great Britain. In: *Agriculture and the environment,* edited by D. Jenkins, 37-44. (ITE symposium no. 13). Cambridge: Institute of Terrestrial Ecology.

Coleman, A. 1961. The second land use survey: progress and prospect. *Geogr. J., 127,* 168-186.

Coppock, J.T. 1976. *An agricultural atlas of England and Wales.* London: Faber & Faber.

Fenwick, I.M. & Thompson, R.D. 1976. Applications of remote sensing in pedology and hydrology. In: *UN/FAO Training Seminar on the Applications of Remote Sensing for Natural Resources Survey, Planning and Development,* Collected Papers, Vol. 2. Reading: Dept of Geography, University of Reading.

Forshaw, M.R.B., Haskell, A., Miller, P.F., Stanley, D.J. & Townshend, J.R.G. 1983. Spatial resolution of remotely-sensed imagery. A review paper. *Int. J. remote Sens.,* **4,** 497-520.

Grampian Regional Council, 1982. *Remote sensing and resource planning in Scotland. Report of a Working Party.* Aberdeen: Grampian Regional Council.

Heath, J. & Perring, F.H. 1978. *Biological Records Centre.* Cambridge: Institute of Terrestrial Ecology.

Jackson, M.J. 1981. Automated cartography at the Experimental Cartography Unit, NERC. In: *Computers in cartography,* edited by D. Rhind & T. Adams, 132-142. (British Cartographic Society special publication no. 2). London: British Cartographic Society.

Loveland, T.R. & Johnson, G.E. 1983. The role of remotely sensed and other spatial data for predictive modelling: the Umatilla, Oregon, example. *Photogramm. Eng. & remote Sens.,* **49,** 1183-1192.

MacDonald, R.B. 1979. *A technical description of the Large Area Crop Inventory Experiment.* (Proc. Techn. Sess, vols 1 and 11. JSC 16015). Houston, Texas: National Aeronautics and Space Administration.

Maxwell, E.L., Aherron, R.M., Fitz, D., Gross, G., Grunblatt, J. & Morse, A. 1980. *Monitoring drought impact from Landsat.* Fort Collins: Earth Resources Department, Colorado State University.

Merson, R.H. 1983. A composite Landsat image of the United Kingdom. *Int. J. remote Sens.,* **4,** 521-527.

Nelson, R.F. 1982. *Detecting forest canopy change using Landsat.* (NASA/TM 83918). Greenbelt, Md: Goddard Space Flight Center.

Nelson, R.F. 1983. Detecting forest canopy change due to insect activity using Landsat MSS. *Photogramm. Eng. & remote Sens.,* **49,** 1303-1314.

Reeves, R.G., Anson, A. & Landen, D. eds. 1975. *Manual of remote sensing.* Falls Church, Va: American Society of Photogrammetry.

Robinove, C.J., Chavez, P.S. Jr., Gehring, D. & Holmgren, R. 1981. Arid land monitoring using Landsat albedo difference images. *Remote Sens. Environ.,* **11,** 133-156.

Seddon, B. 1976. Applications of remote sensing in ecology, crops and land use. In: *UN/FAO Training Seminar on the Applications of Remote Sensing for Natural Resources Survey, Planning and Development,* Collected Papers, Vol. 1. Reading: Dept of Geography, University of Reading.

Smith, G.S. 1979. Sampling techniques to monitor forest area change. *Proc. Symp. Remote Sens. Environ., 13th,* Ann Arbor, Michigan, 1409-1418.

Soil Survey of England and Wales. 1983. *1:250 000 scale soil map of England and Wales.* Rothamsted: Soil Survey of England and Wales.

Stauffer, M. & McKinney, R. 1978. *Landsat image differencing as an automated land cover change detection technique.* (Computer Sciences Corporation report CSC/TM-78/6215). Greenbelt, Md: Goddard Space Flight Center.

Stove, G.C., Birnie, R.V., Cairns, J.G. & Ritchie, P.F.S. 1980. *Land use survey of Buchan based on satellite remote sensing.* Aberdeen: Macaulay Institute for Soil Research.

Todd, W.J. 1977. Urban and regional land use change detected by using Landsat data. *J. Res. US Geol. Surv.,* **5,** 529-534.

Toll, D.L., Royal, J.A. & Davis, J.B. 1980. *Urban area update procedures using Landsat data.* (RS/E/1-17). New York: American Society of Photogrammetry.

Tomlins, G.F. 1981. Canadian experience in wetland monitoring by satellite. In: *Plants and the daylight spectrum,* edited by H. Smith, 101-113. London: Academic Press.

Townshend, J.R.G., Gayler, J.R. & Hardy, J.R. 1983. Preliminary analysis of Landsat-4 Thematic Mapper products. *Int. J. remote Sens.,* **4,** 817-828.

Williams, D. 1984. An overview of the NERC airborne Thematic Mapper Campaign. *Int. J. remote Sens.,* **5,** 631-634.

Wildlife as disease carriers

H V THOMPSON
Cantab Group Ltd, Rose Cottage, Lower Farm Road, Effingham, Leatherhead

1 Introduction

Wild mammals and birds, to which this paper is confined, have many diseases and provide reservoirs of infection which may be passed on to domestic animals and man. Since I reviewed the subject some years ago (Thompson 1961), there have been major agricultural changes, even in our stable and settled conditions, and a quickening interest in epizootics. Because of its geographic isolation, Britain is relatively free from disease, even compared with mainland Europe, and this situation can lead to a complacent attitude that is all too easily shattered when an infected animal slips through quarantine and an alarm is raised.

2 Viruses

Rabies provided alarm in 1969, when a rabid dog was at liberty on a common in the Camberley area of Surrey for some 50 minutes, after it had bitten its owner. The dog had been imported from Germany and there were fears (fortunately groundless) that British wild mammals might have become infected. Starting from Poland in the 1940s, rabies in wildlife, especially foxes, has spread across central and western European states and eastwards into the USSR (Steck 1982). Other wild mammals and domestic mammals, particularly cats, have become infected, but there have been few human cases. In the USSR, wolves and wolf-dog hybrids may be rabid and cause concern, as in Kazakhstan, because of attacks on man (Cherkasskiy 1983). The 1969 incident led to increased research on fox biology, both in state laboratories and in universities, to an official Inquiry (MAFF 1971) and a tightening-up of quarantine regulations, with severe penalties for offenders.

Myxomatosis is a disease limited almost entirely to rabbits, and occasionally hares, but is mentioned here because of the immense effect of rabbits on habitats and on agriculture and forestry. The introduction of the disease to Britain in 1953 and its subsequent spread in 1954-55 greatly affected the natural scene and encouraged the cultivation of downland and some former upland grazings. It also led to an expansion of research on the disease, the effects of rabbits on vegetation, rabbit biology, behaviour and control (Fenner & Ratcliffe 1965; Fenner & Myers 1978; Ross 1982).

Foot-and-mouth disease poses problems in many parts of the world, and the involvement of wild animals in its epizootiology is little understood. Wild birds are often suspected of carrying this and other diseases and the subject has been reviewed by Keymer (1958), and by McDiarmid (1962). Starlings, for example, have often been suspected, on circumstantial grounds, of being mechanical carriers of foot-and-mouth disease, but Murton (1964), Thearle (1968), Snow (1968), and Feare (1980) were unable to find convincing evidence.

Newcastle disease, or fowl pest, puts the national poultry flock at risk, and there is a need for more research on wild birds in this context and, especially, on the hazard posed by the trade in captive birds which come from all over the world, but particularly alarmingly from some African countries and the Far East. Ashton (in press) has drawn attention to the dangers of spreading this disease, and also psittacosis, influenza viruses and others. On 6 February 1984, the UK Government banned the import of all cage birds because of an outbreak of Newcastle disease at quarantine stations in north London and Essex.

Thousands of budgerigars, canaries and parrots were slaughtered as a precautionary measure (Anon 1984). Subsequently, a domestic outbreak of the disease, the first large outbreak since 1970, resulted in the slaughter of 250 000 poultry in Shropshire and Yorkshire.

Louping-ill, an infective paralytic disease of sheep in northern Britain, transmitted by the sheep tick, has also been found in red grouse which can act as an amplifier host for the virus (Reid *et al.* 1978; Duncan 1983). The breeding of grouse is affected in high tick areas, and more research is needed.

3 Bacteria
Bovine tuberculosis, a disease of both cattle and man, has only recently (Muirhead *et al.* 1974) been found to involve a wild mammal, the badger, in parts of Britain. In 1934, it was estimated that 40% of dairy cows were infected with TB and total eradication was planned. Using the tuberculin test and a policy of slaughtering reactor cattle, the incidence was reduced to one fifth of 1% by 1961. The incidence of reactors was much higher in south-west England than elsewhere, and it was quite by accident that the badger was found to be infected. As a result, badgers found to be infected, and those exposed to infection, were killed in areas where cattle reactors were disclosed, but the disease persists and an extensive programme of research, involving biologists, veterinarians and ethologists is in progress (Zuckerman 1980; Wilesmith *et al.* 1982, Little *et al.* 1982a, b). The prevalence of TB in wild badgers *now* is being studied and, to discover how they contaminate pasture and how cattle may be infected, other work including observations on cattle/ badger behaviour is being done. The immune status of badgers is being studied and the possibility of managing badger populations so as to reduce or eliminate cross-infection with cattle must be considered (Thompson 1982).

Salmonellae have been isolated from many living animals and are an important cause of food poisoning in man and disease in domestic animals. The commonest of all salmonellae, *S. typhimurium*, is common in wild birds (Taylor 1969), although Feare (1980) discounts its importance in relation to starlings. Among mammals, some rodents, especially brown rats and mice, are very susceptible to salmonella infection, and isolations have been made from the fox and hedgehog. The serotype *S. enteritidis* var. *danysz* is highly pathogenic to brown rats and was at one time misguidedly used for rodent control, occasionally resulting in infection in domestic animals and man.

Leptospirosis is infection with spirochaetes of the genus *Leptospira*, and causes jaundice in dogs, cattle and pigs and Weil's disease in man. Recent studies (Salt & Little 1977; Hathaway *et al.* 1983a, b, c) indicate the extent to which brown rats, field voles, bank voles, wood mice, grey squirrels, hedgehogs, badgers, mink and foxes are infected. The emergence of the Australis serogroup as a cause of disease in domestic animals and the discovery of a substantial wildlife reservoir are potentially very important.

4 Rickettsia
Q fever was first described in Brisbane in 1935 as a disease of unknown etiology among abattoir workers. The 'Q' indicates Query (Baca & Paretsky 1983). The disease is not of direct agricultural importance but is a public health concern, particularly in relation to the obstetrics of cattle, sheep and goats, since a survey indicated that 28% of veterinary surgeons in northwest England had a significant level of Q fever antibodies. The causal organism, *Coxiella burnetii*, elicits no symptoms in domestic or wild mammals, although it is widespread. In Europe, the organism has been found in the hedgehog, brown rat and house mouse, but has not yet been isolated from wild mammals in Britain (Little 1983).

Diseases enzootic in wildlife may result in high epizootic mortality at times, but seldom effectively control the wild species. The existence of reservoirs of disease calls for strict precautions and prompt treatment where the infection of man and domestic stock is concerned. The need for much more research into the ecology of diseases in wildlife is evident.

5 Summary
The pressure of increasing human populations stimulates agricultural development, leading to loss of semi-natural habitats and often increased contact between man and wildlife, which may result in the spread of infections.

Geographic isolation has resulted in Britain being relatively free from disease, and this should be maintained by strict quarantine. Specific diseases are discussed, notably rabies in foxes, bovine tuberculosis in badgers, and myxomatosis in rabbits, and reference is made to others such as foot-and-mouth disease, salmonellosis, leptospirosis, psittacosis, Q fever and louping-ill. There is a need for much more collaborative research on infections in wild mammals and birds, by ecologists, veterinarians and agriculturalists. Research should include the optimum use of culled animals for the study of viruses, bacteria, protozoa, ecto- and endo-parasites, mycoses and neoplasms.

5.1 Priority points for new research
5.1.1 The fullest use of material from ecological studies and control programmes (eg of badgers, rabbits, rats, coypu, deer).

5.1.2 More research on infections in wild birds, eg using material obtained when bird ringing.

5.1.3 Further studies of leptospirosis in wildlife, particularly voles, and possible infection of domestic stock.

5.1.4 Assessment of disease risks posed by the trade in captive birds (there is a danger of importing non-indigenous pathogens; over 300 000 birds were imported in 1983).

5.1.5 Research on Q fever, which is of some public health importance, is necessary. The agent, *Coxiella burnetii*, is present in sheep and cattle in Britain but has not yet been isolated from British wild mammals.

6 References

Anon. 1984. *Cage bird imports banned.* The Times, 7 February.

Ashton, W.L.G. In press. The risks and problems connected with the import and export of captive birds. *Br. vet. J.*

Baca, O.G. & Paretsky, D. 1983. Q fever and *Coxiella burnetii*: a model for host-parasite interactions. *Microbiol. Rev.*, **47,** 127-149.

Cherkasskiy, B.L. 1983. The wolf in the epidemiology of rabies. *Rabies Bull. Europe* 7/3.

Duncan, J. 1983. Sheep tick project. *Annu. Rev. Game Conservancy, 1983,* no. 14, 69-71.

Feare, C.J. 1980. The economics of starling damage. In: *Bird problems in agriculture,* edited by E.N. Wright, I.R. Inglis & C.J. Feare, 39-55. (Monograph no. 23). Croydon: British Crop Protection Council.

Fenner, F. & Myers, K. 1978. Myxoma virus and myxomatosis in retrospect: the first quarter century of a new disease. In: *Viruses and environment,* edited by E. Kurstak & K. Maramorosch, 539-570. New York; London: Academic Press.

Fenner, F. & Ratcliffe, F.N. 1965. *Myxomatosis.* Cambridge: Cambridge University Press.

Hathaway, S.C., Little, T.W.A., Headlam, S.A. & Stevens, A.E. 1983a. Infection of free-living carnivores with leptospires of the Australis serogroup. *Vet. Rec.*, **113,** 233-235.

Hathaway, S.C., Little, T.W.A. & Stevens, A.E. 1983b. Identification of a reservoir of *Leptospira interrogans* Serovar muenchen in voles (*Microtus agrestis* and *Clethrionomys glareolus*) in England. *Zentralbl. Bakteriol. Mikrobiol. Hyg., 1 Abt. Orig. A,* **254,** 123-128.

Hathaway, S.C., Little, T.W.A., Stevens, A.E., Ellis, W.A. & Morgan, J. 1983c. Serovar identification of leptospires of the Australis serogroup isolated from free-living and domestic species in the United Kingdom. *Res. vet. Sci.*, **35,** 64-68.

Keymer, I.F. 1958. A survey and review of the causes of mortality in British birds and the significance of wild birds as disseminators of disease. *Vet. Rec.*, **70,** 713-720, 736-739.

Little, T.W.A. 1983. Q fever—an enigma. *Br. vet. J.*, **139,** 277-283.

Little, T.W.A., Swan, C., Thompson, H.V. & Wilesmith, J.W. 1982a. Bovine tuberculosis in domestic and wild mammals in an area of Dorset. II. The badger population, its ecology and tuberculosis status. *J. Hyg., Camb.*, **89,** 211-224.

Little, T.W.A., Swan, C., Thompson, H.V. & Wilesmith, J.W. 1982b. Bovine tuberculosis in domestic and wild mammals in an area of Dorset. III. The prevalence of tuberculosis in mammals other than badgers and cattle. *J. Hyg., Camb.*, **89,** 225-234.

McDiarmid, A. 1962. Diseases of free-living wild animals. *FAO agric. Stud.*, no. 57.

Ministry of Agriculture, Fisheries and Food. 1971. *Final report of the Committee of Inquiry on Rabies.* (Cmnd 4696). London: HMSO.

Muirhead, R.H., Gallagher, J & Burn, K.J. 1974. Tuberculosis in wild badgers in Gloucestershire: epidemiology. *Vet. Rec.*, **95,** 552-555.

Murton, R.K. 1964. Do birds transmit foot and mouth disease? *Ibis,* **106,** 289-298.

Reid, H.W., Duncan, J.S., Phillips, J.D.P., Moss, R. & Watson, A. 1978. Studies on louping-ill virus (Flavivirus group) in wild red grouse (*Lagopus lagopus scoticus*). *J. Hyg., Camb.*, **81,** 321-329.

Ross, J. 1982. Myxomatosis: the natural evolution of the disease. In: *Animal disease in relation to animal conservation,* edited by M.A. Edwards & U. McDonnell, 77-95. (Symp. Zool. Soc. Lond. no. 50). London: Academic Press.

Salt, G.F.H. & Little, T.W.A. 1977. Leptospires isolated from wild mammals caught in the south west of England. *Res. vet. Sci.*, **22,** 126-127.

Snow, D.W. 1968. Birds and the 1967-68 foot-and-mouth epidemic. *Bird Study,* **15,** 184-190.

Steck, F. 1982. Rabies in wildlife. In: *Animal disease in relation to animal conservation,* edited by M.A. Edwards & U. McDonnell, 57-75. (Symp. Zool. Soc. Lond. no. 50). London: Academic Press.

Taylor, J. 1969. Salmonella in wild animals. In: *Diseases in free-living wild animals,* edited by A. McDiarmid, 51-73. (Symp. Zool. Soc. Lond. no. 24). London: Academic Press.

Thearle, R.J.P. 1968. Urban bird problems. In: *The problems of birds as pests,* edited by R.K. Murton & E.N. Wright, 181-191. (Symp. Inst. Biol. no. 17). London: Academic Press.

Thompson, H.V. 1961. Ecology of diseases in wild mammals and birds. *Vet. Rec.*, **73,** 1334-1337.

Thompson, H.V. 1982. General discussion. In: *Animal disease in relation to animal conservation,* edited by M.A. Edwards & U. McDonnell, 298-299. (Symp. Zool. Soc. Lond. no. 50). London: Academic Press.

Wilesmith, J.W., Little, T.W.A., Thompson, H.V. & Swan, C. 1982. Bovine tuberculosis in domestic and wild mammals in an area of Dorset. I. Tuberculosis in cattle. *J. Hyg., Camb.*, **89,** 195-210.

Zuckerman, Lord. 1980. *Badgers, cattle and tuberculosis. (Report to Minister of Agriculture, Fisheries and Food).* London: HMSO.

A questionnaire survey of farmers' opinions and actions towards wildlife on farmlands

D W MACDONALD
Department of Zoology, University of Oxford

1 Introduction

There can be no doubt that much modern agricultural practice can be detrimental to the survival of wild animals and plants. Equally, there are wild species which can damage agricultural interests. Opinion differs about the extent to which these facts throw the farmer and conservationist into irreconcilable dispute (Mabey 1980; Mellanby 1981; Shoard 1980). The results of our 6-year project on aspects of conservation and farmland convince us that, although imperilled by economic strictures, there is much in common between farmers and wildlife conservers. Most important, minor adjustments of farmland management can cost the farmer little, while benefiting wildlife considerably. Identifying these adjustments, and quantifying their advantages and disadvantages is a high priority. Less than 0.5% of England and Wales is devoted to nature sanctuaries, while 78% (about 12M ha) is farmed. The cumulative benefit to wildlife of numerous, even if small, conservation-oriented changes in farm practice could be great.

The aim of this paper is to sketch a profile of wildlife on farmland, and so to highlight problems which might be resolved by future research. Although all the ingredients of the farmland ecosystem are dependent, I emphasize here the need for research on the impact of agriculture on wild mammals. The term 'wildlife management' is sometimes mistakenly taken as a euphemism for the killing of pest species. A better usage embraces much more, ranging from the conservation of fauna and flora, through the ranching of game, to the control of disease among its vectors (Macdonald 1981). The conservation of each of the 60 or so terrestrial species of British mammal could benefit from a better understanding of the relationships between agriculture and wildlife, as could the control of the 2 dozen or so supposed pests amongst them. The science of wildlife management in the British Isles must grow if it is to shoulder the task of integrating the necessities of agriculture with the desire for a diverse ecosystem and abundant flora and fauna.

At Oxford, we are trying to develop studies according to 4 stages:

i. to establish the farmer's view of wildlife and non-agricultural land on his farm (questionnaire surveys and conversation), and thereby to identify useful topics for investigation;

ii. to quantify the elements of these topics (by further questionnaires and field work), and thereby to develop hypotheses about the consequences of management practice upon wildlife and agriculture;

iii. to gather the data (by field work) necessary to test the hypotheses;

iv. to inform the farmer and countryman of the results, thereby influencing their opinions and/or management practices.

As an example of this sequence of stages, we sought farmers' opinions on the merits and demerits of retaining hedgerows and managing them according to various regimes; we then quantified the pattern of hedgerow management employed by each farmer; and, third, we studied the numbers of species and individuals of birds which nested in hedgerows under different regimes. The aim was to provide the farmer with straightforward, numerical advice on the likely consequences for hedgerow birds of his hedgerow management programme. Other examples include the impact of farm practice upon badgers and of hedgerow management on small mammal populations, and the impact of field sports on farmland habitat. These results will be published elsewhere. This paper briefly reviews farmers' attitudes and actions towards (i) non-agricultural land and (ii) wild mammals and birds as pests and as assets. It analyses questionnaire data for 2 predatory mammals, the Eurasian badger and the red fox, and discusses some questions which arise in relation to integrating management of wildlife with agriculture.

2 Methods

Ten regions were selected as embracing the major lowland agricultural landscapes of England (with reference to Coppock's (1976) agricultural atlas). From these regions, 867 farmers (Sample A) filled in an initial questionnaire which included 130 questions relevant to diverse aspects of wildlife on their farms. A further 101 'midland' farmers from Oxfordshire, Buckinghamshire, Northamptonshire and Warwickshire subsequently completed a more comprehensive questionnaire involving 236 questions. The questions put to Samples A and B differed in 2 main respects: first, those put to Sample B were partly generated by the answers from Sample A; second, the questions put to Sample A often involved the selection of options (eg tick which of the following . . .). Sample B emphasized questions where the respondent was required to be forthcoming (eg list the factors which you believe are most relevant to . . .). Both types of question can have their biases, some of which are reduced, or at least identified, by comparison of the 2 approaches. Farmers who are prepared to complete questionnaires may differ from those who decline to do so, and it is impossible to control completely for this difference; however, we could detect no obvious bias of this sort.

3 Results

Farmers contributing to the survey (Sample A) occupied farms varying in size from 1.7 to 4166.7 ha, with a mean of 148.6 ha. Overall, 55% of farms were under 100 ha and just over one third were between 100 and 300 ha. Almost half of the respondents farmed 'heavy' land, and the average farm (which, of course, varied regionally) was dominated by grass ley (41.2% of the farm area) and cereals (36.0%). Woodland comprised an average of 2.7% of the agrarian landscape (reaching a maximum amongst our regions of 6.4% in Sussex). Over two-thirds of the respondents were owner-occupiers. Their declared interest and attitudes covered every shade of opinion on a multitude of topics ranging from field sports to feral cats.

3.1 Habitat

Farmers were asked to state whether they had removed any hedgerows in the previous decade (1970-80), and, if so, what length. Just under half (46.8%) had removed hedgerows (of which only 14.5% had replaced any with wire). The average farmer had removed 460 m of hedges (ie approx 3 m/ha), and, while the slight majority had not grubbed out any hedges, over half of the remainder (25.4% of the total) had removed up to 500 m. These results were broadly similar to less detailed information for the same farms over the last 2 decades, but only 10.4% of farmers stated that they had plans to remove more hedgerows. Of farmers who had removed hedgerows in the previous decade, 87.2% had done so to increase efficiency (over half had removed hedges which were not stock-proof, while one third had been influenced by fears of invasions of weeds and other pests from the reservoir in the hedge).

The farmers were asked about all the other categories of non-agricultural enclaves on their farms, for example shelter belts, field corner spinneys, scrub and marsh. Two-thirds (63.4%) of respondents had at least one shelter belt or covert on their land. Although less clear-cut than with hedgerows, their answers were evidence of a continued, if gradual, attrition of this form of cover over the last 2 decades. Some answers were difficult to quantify due to mixed practices (destroying one part of a covert, but encouraging the remainder). However, about 6% had removed at least some coverts, of which as many as half may have removed all their coverts. Taking 105 respondents from Oxfordshire as an example, an estimated one covert had been lost per 100 km² of farmland during the last 20 years. There was a tendency for losses in each of the 7 categories of non-agricultural land considered.

3.2 Wildlife
3.2.1 Pests

Questions were posed to explore the farmers' attitudes to various vertebrates. Farmers in Sample A were asked whether they suffered significant damage from each of several species on a list, and whether they attempted control of each. Questions concerning control are inevitably confounded by the murky matter of prophylaxes. For example, 79.2% of respondents attempted to control rats, while only 55.9% expressed the view that they suffered significant rat damage. We phrased the questions in this way to reveal the 23.3% who presumably believe that the reason they suffer insignificant rat damage is that they exert pre-emptive control.

Rabbits, rats and moles were, in descending order, the most commonly cited causes of damage, being also

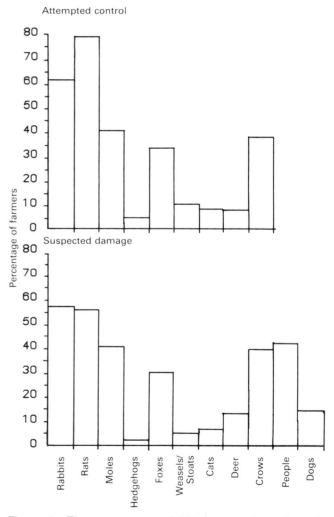

Figure 1. The percentage of 803 farmers from Sample A who expressed the opinion that they suffered 'significant damage' through the activities of each of the species shown, and the percentage of farms on which attempts were made to control each species. For comparison, the percentages of farmers complaining about dogs and people are shown. The results for cats do not distinguish between barn and more feral cats

the most commonly controlled species (but in the order rats, rabbits and moles) (see Figure 1). Of wild species, crows were thought to cause nuisance to just under 40% of farmers, and foxes to 30.2%. Most farmers who believed that they suffered significant damage from foxes also tried to control them (32.6% of the 803 people who answered this question). Deer were cited as causing problems to 13% of farmers, varying widely on a regional basis to a peak of 40.8% in Dorset. Naturally, there was considerable regional variation in the results concerning wild species (and domestic ones too, with Warwickshire recording the highest rate of complaints against each of cats, dogs and careless people).

Respondents belonging to Sample B were asked to complete a table, spontaneously naming up to 6 vertebrate pests and ranking them in order of importance on their farms. Other information required for this table included the types and effectiveness of control employed against each species. Of the 101 respondents, 84 completed this table (amongst the remaining 17 were those daunted by the task, and others who considered that they had no significant pests). Some of the results are summarized on Table 1, which lists the 24 nominations for pest species. Table 1 presents separately the percentage of respondents who ranked each species (i) as their most important pest, and (ii) anywhere on their list of up to 6. Comparison of the 2 columns shows, for instance, that crows were cited as a pest by a large proportion (41.7%) of farmers, but of paramount importance by a smaller proportion (9.5%). The 6 most widely cited vertebrate pests (in descending order of frequency, but not necessarily gravity) were rabbits, pigeons, crows, foxes, rats and rooks. Although they stem from quite different questions, the results from Samples A and B were similar for some species (eg crows were regarded as pests by 39.5% in Sample A and 41.7% in Sample B). Where the answers differed between samples, this could be explained by regional differences in the abundance of candidate pests and in agriculture, and by the different techniques of questioning (the technique of ticking options has the merit of jogging the farmer's memory, and the demerit of putting ideas into his head, whereas the technique of requiring spontaneous answers has roughly opposite attributes).

3.2.2 Resources

It would be wrong to conclude from the list of species viewed as pests that farmers expressed generally antagonistic views towards wildlife. On the contrary, only 3.7% expressed disinterest in the wildlife on their land, whereas 40.2% professed to be very interested, and 61.4% of 832 respondents stated that they believed that the responsibility for conservation of wildlife and the countryside lies primarily with their profession. Although only 10.5% had ever sought advice on nature on their land, 47% would welcome this advice if (and the proviso was spontaneously voiced) it were couched in economically sensible

Table 1. The categories of significant pest listed spontaneously by 84 respondents in Sample B from the midlands. Each farmer ranked the pests he nominated in order of descending importance (1-6). The Table shows (i) the percentage of farmers who listed given 'pests' as their first choice, and (ii) the percentage who mentioned each category anywhere on their list. The categories listed are as given by the farmers and it is not clear whether respondents who named crows were being specific or generic. (The total for the left column does not add up to 100% due to the exclusion of 2 farmers who nominated dogs and people, although the question concerned wildlife)

Species	Major pest	Pest
Rats	14·2	31·0
Mice	1·2	10·7
Squirrels	1·2	3·6
Rabbits	20·2	46·4
Hares	0·0	1·2
Moles	2·4	4·8
Foxes	14·3	33·3
Badgers	1·2	4·8
Stoats/Weasels	0·0	4·8
Feral cats	1·2	2·4
Deer	1·2	3·6
Birds (unspec)	0·0	2·4
Pigeons	15·5	42·9
Doves	1·2	6·0
Starlings	4·8	9·5
Sparrows	0·0	7·1
Crows	9·5	41·7
Rooks	6·0	28·6
Jackdaws	1·2	2·4
Magpies	2·4	15·5
Jays	0·0	1·2
Seagulls	0·0	3·6
Canada geese	0·0	1·2
Pheasants	0·0	1·2

terms. From spontaneous comments in both Samples A and B, it was clear that many farmers enjoyed seeing hedgerow birds, butterflies and wild flowers on their land, and took the abundance of these as indicators of the well-being of wildlife on their farms.

We asked the farmers which of a selection of outdoor hobbies they pursued. Over one third engaged, at least occasionally, in each of the following (in descending order of popularity): shooting, country walks, country drives, visiting nature reserves, and fox hunting. For 678 farmers who professed some interest in wildlife, that interest stemmed principally (but not exclusively) from enjoyment of field sports in 60.3% of cases, and principally from other motives in 39.7% of cases. When the respondents ranked their concerns for wildlife on their farm, their leading priorities were for the balance of nature and aesthetics.

Some farmers stated that their interests in nature had some influence on their management of their farms. For example, among farmers in Sample A who were asked which considerations had influenced their decision to retain certain hedgerows, over half ticked options concerning benefits to wildlife, aesthetics of the landscape and field sports. When asked to rank the various considerations, a total of 13.1% put one or other of these non-agronomic reasons first (the majority ranked being stock-proof as a hedgerow's main asset). In this sample, 8% answered that their principal reason for retaining hedgerows was simply that they had no reason to remove them.

3.2.3 The Eurasian badger

Main badger setts were known on 45 of 101 midland farms, and badgers travelled at least 92 farms (we described to the farmers the characteristics of main setts). On over half of these they were not regarded as even minor pests; 50 farmers welcomed the badgers' presence, 11 ignored them, whereas 27 regarded them as a 'slight nuisance' and 2 as a 'considerable nuisance'. Sixteen farmers stated that badgers were a nuisance through problems which recurred annually, while the remainder said that the problems were more sporadic.

We asked each of the 92 farmers to indicate which of 7 categories of nuisance they believed they had suffered from badgers (and to list any additional categories). Table 2 presents the results separately for the period of occupancy of the farm and for the previous 12 months. The most common causes of complaint were trampling and rolling of crops and tunnels collapsing under vehicles. Examples of the 8 'other' categories of nuisance listed spontaneously were spoil heaps blocking ditches (2 cases), damaged fences (2) and drains (1), and chewing lambs' tails (1). Farmers were asked to estimate the cost for the previous 12 months in time and money of damage by badgers. Only 3 estimated their financial losses (£5, £200, £600). Three respondents had lost 1 day and one had lost 2 days; we interpreted the other 97% of replies to indicate that losses in time and money were judged inconsequential.

Table 2. The percentage of farmers in Sample B who listed each of several categories of nuisance which they believed badgers had caused them. The answers distinguish between those who stated that they had suffered the damage during the preceding 12 months and those who had done so at any time during their occupancy of their farm

	% replies	
	Ever	Last year
Vehicles fall in tunnels	16·8	6·9
Crops trampled	23·9	5·9
Crops eaten	2·0	0·0
Sett inconvenient site	8·9	5·0
Lose game egg/chick	5·9	3·0
Lose penned game	1·0	0·0
Lose farm stock	6·9	2·0
Other	7·9	4·0

Only 7 of the 101 farmers stated that they felt compelled to take some action to reduce badger nuisance (eg one had grubbed up a hedge in order to dislodge the badgers from their sett). These 7 were asked to list spontaneously, and to rank, up to 3

problems which had prompted their actions. The most important reasons were inconvenient sett, crop damage, lamb killing and tunnels posing a hazard to machinery (secondary factors were given as gamebird losses, offering refuge to foxes and the risk of TB).

Longer commentaries given by some farmers (on the questionnaire and in conversation) emphasized the badger's inadvertent involvement with other farmland 'pest' issues, for example due to cohabitation with rabbits and foxes. Nine and 10 farmers had felt it necessary to gas badger setts in the course of attempted rabbit and fox control, respectively. Similarly, 16 farmers stated that they set snares for foxes (67 never did so and 18 gave no answer), and 2 of these had caught badgers inadvertently. In answering these questions (in 1982), the badger's legal status was doubtless in some farmers' minds and therefore the figures are probably minimum estimates.

Badgers are also affected by fox hunting in that setts were 'stopped' on hunting days (modally, 4-6 times per season) on 29 of the 45 farms where their locations were known (82.2% of farms were hunted). Some effects of 'stopping' on badgers were therefore investigated in a field study and will be reported elsewhere.

Opinion towards badgers seemed to have been hardened by the developing controversy concerning their role in the epidemiology of bovine tuberculosis. Almost half the respondents (44.3%) stated that they had read technical material on this topic; their major sources were the farming press and MAFF/ADAS material. Of the 27 who could remember where they had acquired 'technical' information about 'badgers and TB', none cited a natural history or conservation-oriented source.

Badgers were inevitably and coincidentally involved in many agricultural practices (eg hedgerow removal affecting setts, crop rotation affecting foraging areas). Some 14% of respondents had main setts in cultivated land. Almost half of these farmers ploughed around these setts, whereas the remainder ploughed over them. We made a preliminary study of the behaviour of badgers at setts which were routinely ploughed over, and found that the holes were re-opened and the badgers continued in occupancy.

3.2.4 Red fox

Just under three-quarters of respondents were of the opinion that foxes needed to be controlled in towns, and 90% in the countryside. Of the 750 farmers who thought that there were reasons for attempting control of foxes, they ticked the following (in descending order): depredations on stock (67.8%), 'too many' (65.2%), spread disease (45.8%) and kill game (44.5%). It is important to note, as in Section 3.2.3, that these figures describe the farmers' opinions, and not necessarily any real need for fox control (or necessarily that they attempt control: 44.4% of Sample B respondents attempted control, of whom half did so as a matter of annual routine, and half only in response to sporadic damage). For example, it is unlikely that even one of the farmers who completed the questionnaire had ever lost stock to a disease transmitted by a fox. The candidate reasons for control presented to these farmers were selected after numerous conversations to assess the categories of motive which best summarized farmers' views. Thus, although as a motive for control 'too many' is uninterpretable, it is nevertheless included as it was so popular with farmers. In practice, conversation often revealed that 'too many' simply meant that the speaker had seen a fox recently. Sample B respondents spontaneously listed (in order of importance) their reasons for attempting fox control. Of the 20 reasons given, the 3 most commonly stated as most important (in descending frequency) were (i) kill game, (ii) kill lambs and (iii) need to 'keep numbers low'. Seventy per cent of Sample B farmers believed that they had suffered fox damage during their occupancy of their farm (39.2% during the previous 12 months). Paradoxically, of course, the interest in game which apparently heightens their appreciation of wildlife in general also estranges many farmers from predators in particular.

The loss of stock most commonly and vehemently linked with foxes was of lambs. Some 45.5% of the 820 respondents kept sheep, and amongst them the average flock numbered 368. Some 54% of those with sheep believed they had been victims of lamb-worrying at some time. Of 210 people who listed their evidence, 38.4% stated they had seen the fox attack. Indirect evidence of foxes causing lamb losses was that foxes were seen in the flock (82.9%), mauled carcases were found (80.0%) and lambs were found at earths (45.7%). None of the circumstantial evidence permits cases of scavenging and killing to be separated. The numbers of lambs thought to be lost to foxes on our census farms over 3 years are given in Table 3.

Table 3. The percentage of sheep farmers who believed that they lost given numbers of lambs to foxes during the 3 seasons 1976-78. The evidence quoted in support of the conclusion that foxes had killed these lambs was partly equivocal (see text)

Numbers of lambs said to have been killed	% farms reporting given losses		
	1976	1977	1978
0	73·6	71·3	62·1
1–5	13·8	15·8	19·1
6–10	8·4	8·0	6·0
11–15	2·3	1·5	2·0
16–20	2·1	1·3	1·8
>20	1·8	2·0	2·3
Number of farms	383	390	398

In recent years, a new factor has entered the rural view of foxes, namely their potential as a resource for the fur harvest. Figure 2 shows how the price soared in the late 1970s. Despite the mounting numbers of fox skins traded, there are no data from which to judge the extent to which more foxes were killed in this period. Only 9.9% of respondents believed that the pelts of foxes killed on their land were sold, although one third knew of other farms from which fox skins were sold. If fox skins are sold from 10% of farms, this trade would involve over 15 500 properties in England. Irrespective of their opinions on killing foxes for other reasons, over three-quarters of respondents stated that they disapproved of foxes being killed for their pelts.

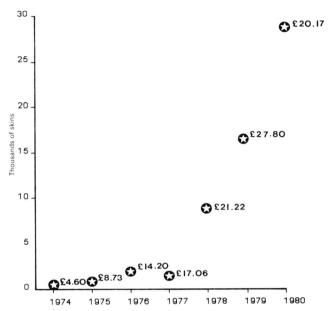

Figure 2. Documenting the harvest of foxes for their pelts is difficult in the United Kingdom as no statutory records are kept. However, the Figure shows the numbers of fox skins originating from the British Isles traded by the major auctioneers in London during the late 1970s, together with the mean annual prices at auction (Source: Macdonald & Carr 1981)

4 Discussion

Part of the foregoing profile of wildlife on lowland farms stems from farmers' statements of opinion, and not necessarily from fact. These opinions were a deliberate starting point for 2 reasons. First, if prejudice can be sifted from insight, the ideas of people close to the land are of paramount importance in focusing attention on real problems between agriculture and wildlife. Second, it is what people believe to be the case that influences their actions; the task of wildlife management is not only to unearth the facts, but to convince farmers of their veracity. For example, the belief that foxes currently pose a disease threat in the UK represents a failure of communication.

The cases of the fox and badger illustrate different problems. That of the badger is more straightforward: the spread of cereal farming and enlargement of fields have not only reduced the carrying capacity of some farmland for badgers, but have thrown the survivors into the role of nuisances. A sett once situated unobtrusively in a hedge beside pasture now finds itself in the middle of a field with corn to be trampled on every side. At the start of our survey, it seemed that farmers' attitudes were hardening nation-wide towards badgers, due to spin-off from publicity about TB in the south-west of England. This prompted questions about the extent to which badgers were a nuisance to farmers, aside from the complex and unresolved TB issue. The results above indicate that, in the midlands, the answer is that badgers generally cause little or no inconvenience to farmers. The losses incurred due to trampling cereals are measurable but small in comparison to the disadvantages of reducing them. In areas where maize is an important crop, damage by badgers may be more serious (Lafontaine 1983).

The situation of the fox is greatly complicated by its several different and conflicting attributes: the same species is regarded as an unwelcome predator of poultry, lambs and game, and a welcome one upon rodents and rabbits. To some it is a resource for pelts, to others a joy to behold, and to yet others a quarry for sporting pursuit. Neighbouring farmers may regard the fox in very different ways, and thereby negate each other's attempts at management, whether well founded or not. Few species could better illustrate the complexity of mammal management: the fox's 'pest' status is inadequately documented, the consequences of control on either its populations or on the damage it may cause are not understood, and the values involved in decision-making are divergent and often confused. The result (above) that more farmers believe that foxes should be controlled than have ever suffered damage themselves, and that half of those who had ever suffered damage did so in the 12 months preceding the survey may indicate that the fox's reputation as a pest is enhanced by notoriety and by long memories. If predator control is to be part of wildlife management on farmland, then there is a need to understand its consequences.

Research is needed so that predator (and other pest) control schemes can be evaluated on (amongst other criteria) a precise understanding of their likely consequences. For example, it is conceivable that the effects on game yields of killing predators might vary greatly, depending on the size of the block over which attempted control was exerted. In that case, circumstances would determine whether such attempted control was desirable or worse than useless (worse because each aspect of management has costs as well as possible benefits). It is particularly important, and often difficult in practice, to evaluate supposedly prophylactic control: in many cases, the view is strongly held, and weakly sustained, that problems have been pre-empted by anticipatory control.

It is impossible completely to disentangle the control versus conservation facets of the relationship between agriculture and wild mammals, not just because the same species play different roles on different farms, but merely because all at least partly depend on the same 'non-productive' habitats. Conserving mammals, and the rest of nature, boils down to habitat management; the calibrating effects of pest control and other influences are inevitably secondary. On the supposition that farmers who participate in field sports preserve more non-agricultural habitat, it is therefore argued that non-game species benefit from field sports. This argument excludes most predatory species. Clearly, it is important to assess the impact of game management on non-target species, but only as part of the wider issue of how habitat management, by sporting and non-sporting farmer alike, influences wildlife. Just as it is unsatisfactory to attempt control of a pest with inadequate predictions of the consequences, so it is to espouse the cause of laid-hedges or islands of scrub without knowing their role. For example, the impact of modern agriculture on many species of small mammals harboured in hedgerows is almost unknown.

The results presented in Section 3.1 indicate a continuing loss of some farmland habitats, and highlight not only an overwhelming need for monitoring these changes, but also the prevailing ignorance of their consequences. Many of these trends were apparent 30 years ago (Pollard et al. 1974), but have attracted little recent research. This is not because all the relevant questions have been resolved already; simple questions remain unanswered. Which species use hedgerows, and which are entirely dependent on these natural enclaves for food and shelter? What is the minimum area and structure of non-agricultural habitats required to sustain given species or communities on farmland (see Helliwell 1976), and what precisely are the habitat characteristics needed for their continued survival? To what extent do hedgerows serve as conduits for dispersal and gene flow in small mammal populations, and what is the effect of, say, the size of spinneys on their fauna and flora? The answers to each of these questions need to be separated for potential pests versus other species, and they need to be effectively communicated to farmers. Recent studies of farmland birds, such as Arnold (1983), Rands (1982) and O'Connor (1984), illustrate the intricate relationship between farmland and fauna. Barnes and Tapper (1983) show how one mammal, the brown hare, has been affected by modern agriculture, while Newton et al. (1977) and Macdonald et al. (1981) illustrate how variations in the farmland landscape may affect numbers of 2 predatory species.

The future of wildlife on British farmland may largely be as an incidental victim or beneficiary of the EEC's Common Agricultural Policy and the world economy, but awareness of the power of economics should not blind us to the practical potential of informed wildlife management; with ecological knowledge, land management can integrate better the requirements of agriculture, conservation and recreation. One elegant illustration is Potts's (1984) discovery that partridges are an inadvertent victim of some cereal fungicides with unexpected, unscreened and unnecessary insecticidal properties.

There is hardly a species of mammal in the British Isles, putative pest or otherwise, whose ecology is understood sufficiently to make the best of its conservation. With more information, decisions could better be taken along the diverging roads of agricultural desert and wilderness. Of course, biological and agronomic data, the 'market forces' of conservation, need not be the sole bases for decision, to the exclusion of values such as beauty, sentiment and enjoyment. It is the balance of these virtues merged with sound information which will determine whether farmers tend to be benevolent custodians of the countryside, and it is the responsibility of biologists to make sure the information is available and adequate.

5 Summary
The behaviour and opinions of farmers are important ingredients of any consideration of wildlife management on farmland. Questionnaire surveys were employed to explore farmers' actions and attitudes. The results indicate a continuing attrition of agriculturally unproductive habitats on farmland, and a widespread loss of hedgerow. However, the respondents professed interest in wildlife on their properties and concern for its conservation. The majority stated that this conservation was their responsibility. Attitudes towards badgers and foxes are taken as examples which reveal some of the problems of integrating wildlife with modern agriculture. It is concluded that, amongst priorities for research, it is especially important to quantify the consequences (for wildlife and agronomics) of various land management practices, so providing the farmer and conserver with predictions of the merits and demerits of different courses of action.

6 References
Arnold, G.W. 1983. The influence of ditch and hedgerow structure, length of hedgerows, and area of woodland and garden on bird numbers in farmland. *J. appl. Ecol.*, **20**, 731-750.

Barnes, R. & Tapper, S. 1983. Why we have fewer hares. *Annu. Rev. Game Conservancy, 1982*, no. 14, 51-61.

Coppock, J.T. 1976. *An agricultural atlas of England and Wales.* London: Faber & Faber.

Helliwell, D.R. 1976. The effects of size and isolation on the conservation value of wooded sites in Britain. *J. Biogeogr.*, **3**, 407-416.

Lafontaine, L. 1983. Blaireaux. *Penn Bed*, **113**, 81-128.

Mabey, R. 1980. *The common ground: a place for nature in Britain's future?* London: Hutchinson.

Macdonald, D.W. 1981. Wildlife management. In: *The Oxford companion to animal behaviour*, edited by D.J. McFarland, 600-608. Oxford: Oxford University Press.

Macdonald, D.W. & Carr, G.M. 1981. Foxes beware: you are back in fashion. *New Scient.*, **89**, 9-11.

Macdonald, D.W., Bunce, R. & Bacon, P.J. 1981. Fox populations, habitat characterisation and rabies control. *J. Biogeogr.*, **8**, 145-151.

Mellanby, K. 1981. *Farming and wildlife.* (New naturalist no. 67). London: Collins.

Newton, I., Marquiss, M., Weir, D.N. & Moss, D. 1977. Spacing of sparrowhawk nesting territories. *J. Anim. Ecol.*, **46**, 425-441.

O'Connor, R.J. 1984. The importance of hedges to songbirds. In: *Agriculture and the environment*, edited by D. Jenkins, 117-123. (ITE symposium no. 13). Cambridge: Institute of Terrestrial Ecology.

Pollard, E., Hooper, M.D. & Moore, N.W. 1974. *Hedges.* (New naturalist no. 58). London: Collins.

Potts, G.R. 1984. Monitoring changes in the cereal ecosystem. In: *Agriculture and the environment*, edited by D. Jenkins, 128-134. (ITE symposium no. 13). Cambridge: Institute of Terrestrial Ecology.

Rands, M.R.W. 1982. *The influence of habitat quality on the population ecology of partridges.* DPhil thesis, University of Oxford.

Shoard, M. 1980. *The theft of the countryside.* London: Temple Smith.

Ministry of Agriculture, Fisheries and Food (MAFF) interests in the results of ecological research on wildlife and the countryside

J M WAY
Ministry of Agriculture, Fisheries and Food, London

1 Introduction
The Ministry of Agriculture, Fisheries and Food (MAFF) has always been aware of the need to pursue a policy of food production which takes into account the importance of conserving wildlife and other aspects of the countryside. Since 1968, economic pressures and acceleration of changes in agricultural technology have caused successive Governments to enact legislation making conservation an integral and important part of

MAFF's responsibility. Most recently, the obligations of MAFF Ministers under the general provisions of Section 11 of the Countryside Act 1968 (HMSO 1968) have been specified more precisely in Section 41 of the Wildlife and Countryside Act 1981 (WCA) (HMSO 1981), so that MAFF now has a statutory role in giving advice on the conservation of the countryside to persons carrying on agricultural businesses. It is in this field of advice that MAFF's interest in ecological research on wildlife and the countryside is most widely to be found. In the discussion that follows, these interests are explored in relation to a number of the more important activities where agriculture and conservation tend to conflict, and where ecological research is especially needed to help resolve the problems that then arise. In the final section, emphasis is given to the importance of transferring the results of research into good practices that, as far as possible, will bring agriculture and conservation into harmony.

2 Land use

Agricultural land is recognized as a valuable and finite national resource, and the policy for its protection is described in DOE Circular 75/76 (HMSO 1976a): 'To ensure that, as far as possible, land of higher quality should not be taken [for development] where land of a lower quality is available, and that the amount of land taken is no greater than is reasonably required for carrying out the development in accordance with proper standards'.

Happily, agriculture and wildlife conservation are rarely in conflict over the allocation of higher quality land to agricultural production, except in 2 instances. The first concerns the improvement or reclamation of *potentially* high quality land which for one reason or another is also of wildlife interest. The second involves the problem (encapsulated in DOE Circular 75/76) where decisions have to be made concerning, for instance, the alternative routes for a motorway where one line will take high quality agricultural land and lead to severance of farms, and another will destroy a Site of Special Scientific Interest (SSSI). In the first instance, there is a direct conflict of interest, whilst in the second the agricultural and wildlife interests are not usually deciding factors but are certainly important contributory ones. In both instances, the ecological advice provided by the wildlife conservation parties is of interest to MAFF, and the quality of this advice depends upon the ecological research upon which it is based.

Within this field, there is a need in MAFF, as in the other agencies concerned with countryside planning, for a sound ecological data base at a scale that is readily relatable to a particular piece of ground. For example, if interest is centred on a particular herb-rich meadow, it will be necessary to know if that field is exceptional in the context of its immediate surroundings, of the neighbourhood, county or region (or grid square or some other parameter), and if it is a special site in the national context. It will be necessary to know whether, if steps are taken to avoid development on that site, development on an alternative site will affect another feature of interest.

Additionally, there is scepticism in some quarters about the repeated occurrence of such phrases as 'one of the last remaining sites where such and such occurs' referring to the same animal, assemblage of plants or other feature. Conservation bodies may be asked to be more precise, and the agencies themselves may want to confirm the validity of such statements. Sufficient information already exists for such a data base to be organized, and discussions about the means of producing it have been continuing for several years.

3 Mineral extraction and land reclamation

The difference between mineral extraction and other forms of development is that minerals can only be worked where they are found. Nevertheless, MAFF will always seek to ensure that good quality land is not used if alternative sites of lower quality are available, and that agricultural land is effectively restored to agricultural use after minerals have been extracted.

In the first instance, MAFF may find itself in conflict with conservation interests in the same way as for other development matters, because the alternative sites of lower agricultural quality favoured by the Ministry may be of high conservation value. There will thus be the same interest as before in the quality of ecological evidence brought forward to support the conservation case.

In the second instance, the restoration of land for agriculture follows the same ecological principles as reclamation of such sites for other purposes (Bradshaw & Chadwick 1980), and matters such as soil structure, drainage, nutrient levels and seeding are of primary concern. Once the decision has been made that a site should be restored to agriculture, the procedures for doing so are well established, although there may be a continuing need for research on the agricultural aspects.

4 River, coast and field engineering

Under Section 90 of the Land Drainage Act 1976 (HMSO 1976b), the Minister of Agriculture may make grants to Water Authorities for construction of new drainage works, and for improvement of existing works, including flood and coastal protection barriers; under Section 91, grants may be made to Drainage Authorities. In Section 48 of the WCA, both Water and Drainage Authorities, together with relevant Ministers, are instructed to 'further' conservation objectives, insofar as this is consistent with the purposes of the Water and Land Drainage Acts, and with exceptions for emergencies. It is a necessary part of the MAFF agreement to grant that this furthering of conservation can be shown to have been done.

Responsibilities of MAFF in field engineering (usually drainage) arise in general from the overall duty in the Agriculture (Miscellaneous Provisions) Act 1944 (HMSO 1944) to give advice, and specifically from the provisions for giving grant-aid under various enactments, for example Section 29 of the Agriculture Act 1970 (HMSO 1970), relating to farm capital grants.

Field engineering, by its nature, is site-specific and a vital element in productive agriculture (Agricultural Advisory Council 1970). At the same time, it is clearly recognized that drainage of a particular field may affect neighbouring land, both above and below, and the drainage water from it may affect receiving ditches and watercourses. There are not often opportunities for ecological research in respect of drainage of individual sites in the lowlands. Exceptions arise in special cases where the cumulative effect of a number of schemes may have much wider ecological consequences, or where the site itself is of conservation interest. In these cases, the research is likely to be specific to the site.

In the uplands, the situation is different, and research with wider application (eg on peat hydrology) may be appropriate. Thus, a recent review of the implications of moor gripping (Stewart & Lance 1983) is of interest, although the practice of gripping is not now widely undertaken for agricultural purposes in England and Wales.

Research by the Agricultural Development and Advisory Service (ADAS) into the practice of drainage is done both by the specialist Field Drainage Experimental Unit, and by Regional staff. Drainage, with subsequent improvement, has become one of the most important areas of conflict, and one where there is still a great deal to be learned on both the agricultural and the wildlife conservation sides about the effects on the environment. Continuing discussions are needed between ADAS, the Nature Conservancy Council (NCC), and other organizations concerned with the environment, to identify areas where further research is required. Examples include: leaching or runoff of fertilizers, sulphide generation in peat soils, frequency of control of aquatic vegetation, and channel design. The emphasis must be on problems that can be studied with an expectation of usable results. The value of research on water table management, for instance, is debatable, because there is usually little opportunity for compromise between the water levels that are known to be required for productive agriculture, and those known to be favourable to wildlife.

5 Pest control
5.1 Environmental effects of pesticides
The concern of MAFF about the environmental effects of pesticides stems from its advisory role, from its responsibilities for pesticide registration and control, including the Pesticides Safety Precautions Scheme and the Agriculture Chemicals Approval Scheme, and from recommendations such as those made by the Royal Commission on Environmental Pollution (1979) in its Seventh Report. There are concerns both for agriculture and for the environment from the use of pesticides. Because agriculture and the environment are interdependent it is not worthwhile trying to separate them. Thus, agricultural consequences such as the potential of pesticides to bring about changes in agricultural practices (eg direct drilling), the potential of

weeds, pests, and diseases to exploit changes in practice (eg the emergence of barren brome as a serious weed associated with the development of winter barley), and the potential of insects and fungi (principally) to become resistant to individual chemicals, all have implications for the environment.

Bunyan and Stanley (1983) have recently reviewed the evidence for direct and indirect costs (effects) of the agricultural use of pesticides, and conclude that there is very little *evidence* that the survival of individual species is threatened by the direct effects. They record that, where direct effects have been identified in the past, action has been taken to rectify the position (Wilson 1969), and that this situation is likely to continue. They point (as have many authors before) to the difficulty of measuring, or even identifying, indirect effects. Yet, there should not be any doubt that some 35 years of spray drift of herbicides and insecticides from ground and aerial spraying have had an effect on the flora and insect fauna of field margins. The Game Conservancy's *Partridge Survival Project* is an example where indirect effects have been demonstrated, and one of the few that have been carried out over a long period of time (Game Conservancy 1982); in this work, the decline of the partridge population is an indirect effect in that it is the foodplants and prey organisms that are affected by pesticides (but not actually at risk in terms of their survival), and not the partridge directly.

Other examples could be given, and the fact that discussion on them is not pursued further here is no indication of the lack of importance, or of the priority, that should be attached to the ecological study of the indirect effects of pesticides on the fauna and flora, and especially of herbicides on the flora. It should be further emphasized that indirect effects of pesticides occur both in space and in time. Thus, because of their efficiency and ease of application, very large areas can be treated, which may be greater than many organisms can cross between one remnant of favourable habitat and the next; additionally, effects in nature are rarely manifested suddenly, so that observations and measurements need to be continued over a number of years. The Common Birds Census of the British Trust for Ornithology is a good example of a long-term monitoring exercise that is now producing scientific results of great interest, because of the length of time over which the data have been collected.

Research at MAFF's Tolworth Laboratory (see, eg, Stanley & Hardy 1984) concerns the ecological effects of pesticides, including the analysis of residues of pesticides for monitoring their occurrence in wildlife and the investigation of specific wildlife incidents. This work not only contributes to the safer use of pesticides, but also has an ecological advantage in that it sometimes provides an insight into relationships between organisms, and between organisms and their environment. It is extended into the field as part of the project at the Boxworth Experimental Husbandry Farm (EHF) in Cambridgeshire, where the objectives, in a joint study with other organizations, are to evaluate the economic and ecological effects of pesticides and farming practices on the pests, diseases, weeds and wildlife of intensively grown cereal crops. Work at the Harpenden Laboratory concerns the registration and control of pesticides, and their efficacy in use.

In summary, there is a continuing need for ecological research on the long-term indirect effects of pesticides on the environment, and on individual species of wild plants and animals, the results of which will be of concern to MAFF.

5.2 Management of vertebrate pests

Many vertebrate animals are protected under Part 1 of the WCA 1981. Authority to issue licences to take protected animals, or to use otherwise prohibited methods of control, as defined under Part 1 of the Act, in order to prevent damage to crops or for other special purposes, is vested in MAFF. Badgers and brent geese, among other species, are of special interest at the present time. The discovery that the occurrence of TB in cattle is sometimes linked with TB in badgers has stimulated the study by MAFF of badger ecology in relation to the occurrence of this disease. The information gained has contributed greatly to the speed and efficiency of badger control operations, but the longer term main objective is to establish the factors contributing to cross-infection between badgers and cattle, in the hope that these factors may prove susceptible to management.

There is also a need to know more about the ecology of brent geese in Britain, at their Arctic breeding grounds, and during their migrations. In the UK, there is particular interest in the apparent change of behaviour which brings them inland to feed early in the season, even when marine food species (principally eelgrass) are available. From the point of view of preventing damage to crops, there is interest in determining whether shooting to kill (a licensable act) is a necessary adjunct to the use of other scaring techniques, recognizing that whatever scaring methods are used the birds have to go somewhere. This raises the whole question of acceptable alternative feeding and roosting grounds, and the management that such areas require to make them attractive. The problem of brent geese also raises the more general question of the status of species of conservation interest that may also, as a result of population or behavioural changes, become agricultural pests. With brent geese, the maximum world population is limited by events at the breeding grounds in the Arctic; but at a population lower than the maximum they are becoming a pest, and at a lower population again the species may be endangered. The point of interest is to establish (if possible) the population level around which the species should be maintained in order to ensure its survival, without reaching the threshold

where it becomes a pest. The philosophical point is whether local populations of species such as the brent goose should be protected, even though they have reached pest status.

MAFF also carries out ecological research in relation to damage control on a number of non-protected species. Work on rabbits, wood pigeons, and rodents of commercial importance represents continuing efforts to control the damage caused by species which have been pests for a very long time, and about which much is known, whilst work on the coypu concerns the policy to contain, and if possible eliminate, an exotic pest species.

6 Various agricultural practices

There are a large number of other agricultural practices, besides those already mentioned, that may have effects on wildlife and for which research is required. Some of these, together with the essentially practical research being undertaken by ADAS aimed at resolving the choices between management options, are outlined below.

6.1 Hedges and trees

The establishment and management of hedges, and the planting and protection of trees have agricultural benefits from stock containment and shelter, and wildlife benefits from increased or improved habitat.

6.2 Grassland management

A very wide range of investigations into agricultural grasslands is done by ADAS. In the lowlands, wildlife conservation interest arises mainly from work on the effects of management of unimproved areas. Although most work by ADAS is for agricultural purposes, there is an increasing emphasis on conservation. In the particular case of the Somerset Moors, joint work by ADAS and NCC is proposed to try to resolve some of the problems, such as levels of nitrogen input, where it may be possible to reach a compromise between farming and conservation.

In the uplands, where there are more extensive proposals for grassland improvement, and where stocking densities are a matter of concern, there is also much research by ADAS. The emphasis is again on agricultural purposes, but the effects on conservation of such matters as heather and bracken management, drainage, liming and fertilizer application are of increasing concern, especially in SSSIs.

6.3 Soils and fertilizers

Soils and fertilizers are basic areas of field research in ADAS, and there is a continuing and varied range of projects, many of more than purely agricultural interest. The knowledge of soils and their characteristics is fundamental to land management; this fact has been appreciated by man since very early times, and has, for instance, often determined the otherwise illogical shapes of many farmland fields. Research on fertilizers is ultimately bound up with soils, crops, and natural inputs of plant nutrients from fixation and organic breakdown. It is a popular concept in conservation ecology that plant diversity and wildlife value are associated with soils of low nutrient status, and are incompatible with productive agriculture which depends on high nutrient status. This concept needs further examination, both in terms of the levels of nutrients (and which nutrients) that are associated with plant diversity, and in terms of input levels to provide the best financial returns from crop production. Research into these and allied fields of considerable ecological interest will continue to be done by ADAS.

6.4 Heather and grass burning

MAFF has the responsibility for the licensing of heather and grass burning (MAFF 1983) during the prohibited period (31 March-1 November in the lowlands; 15 April-1 October in the uplands). Licences may be granted under certain circumstances: in practice, when there are no conservation objections, and where there are over-riding needs to burn and it has been impossible (usually because of the weather) to do so at other times when licences are not required. Insofar as there is general presumption against the granting of these licences on risk and conservation grounds (involving consultation with NCC), there may be a need for further research on the effects of late spring and summer burns to help NCC in deciding upon its advice in particular cases. In this context, the topic of fire as a management tool (Green 1983) is of considerable interest, and is one on which more research is needed, particularly from the point of view of effects on vegetation and on nutrients in the soil.

6.5 Management of non-crop land

Non-crop land, including derelict land and the restoration of mineral workings, is the subject of a significant and increasing amount of research by ADAS. There is particular interest in non-crop areas in the ADAS involvement in projects on the Countryside Commission's Demonstration Farms, where the application of ecological principles and techniques is essential to demonstrate the integration of agriculture, wildlife conservation and landscape. Wildlife surveys on other farmlands, mainly concentrating on non-crop areas, are planned or in progress, including participation in the Mammal Society's Small Mammal Survey by members of the Wildlife and Storage Biology Discipline. More generally, land use monitoring, evaluation and change are studied by the ADAS Resource Planning Group.

7 Sites of Special Scientific Interest (SSSI)

The notification of a SSSI goes through a number of stages where MAFF may be consulted, or may wish to consult. These stages fall naturally into procedures before notification takes place, and those that take place afterwards. Before notification, when the boundaries and details of a proposed site have been made known to it, MAFF will need to assess the potential effect on agriculture, particularly where there is likely to be interference with farm improvements and/or grant-aidable schemes. Where there is an effect, MAFF will assess it and enter into discussions with NCC over the scientific basis for notification, and other relevant matters including the line of the SSSI boundary. It is during these discussions that MAFF needs to have detailed scientific information about the ecological characteristics of the site, so that it can understand and be assured of the conservation value, and be able to substantiate it to those who look to the Ministry for advice. Again, it is clear, as in the discussion under land use, that there is a continuing need for research, both in the field and in the laboratory, into patterns, inter-relationships (national and international), and processes of wildlife ecology, as they affect the criteria (Ratcliffe 1977) for the identification and notification of SSSIs.

Following notification, a different set of requirements arises, concerning the ways in which the land in question can be economically managed as part of the farm holding, and, in some cases, whether the farm business itself, to which the land may make an essential contribution, can continue at the same level as before. Very often, where productive land is concerned, the effects of enforcement of the 'potentially damaging operations' specified in the notification may place constraints, which need to be evaluated, on the historic management of the land (eg in terms of current fertilizer levels, stocking rates), on changes in farming practice (eg from hay to silage), or on improvement (eg to drain and re-seed). Because it is an essential part of the SSSI concept that responsibility for management of the land remains with the owner or occupier, and because he is entitled to a return from his investment, there are economic pressures to minimize the effect that managing for conservation may have on the income obtainable from productive agricultural land. There is scope here for ecological research on the economic management of the types of land in question (almost always grassland in one form or another), to sustain their agricultural contribution and retain or improve the wildlife value. The sorts of topics of immediate concern include effects of major nutrient levels individually or in combination; consequences of drainage discussed earlier in this paper; the palatability and nutritional value to stock of wild species; the habitat requirements of ground nesting birds in terms of vegetation structure, and whether the tussocky or hummocky conditions that often suit such birds can still provide a useful agricultural return. Questions like these recur continually. In some instances, sufficient may be known to answer the practical question, but, if so, the answer may not be widely enough known, so that there is a problem of communication.

Most often, the conservation management prescription will be for traditional or even old-fashioned farming practices to be undertaken. When these practices conflict with the economic development of the land, management agreements are entered into which still involve the occupier in managing it, but in such a way as to conserve the wildlife interest. Either way, there is a continuing need for the results of ecological research into practical aspects of management.

There remain the management problems of agriculturally unproductive land within SSSIs on farms, for which, nevertheless, the farmer may find himself responsible. Scrub encroachment into herb-rich chalk grassland remnants on steep slopes comes immediately to mind, but, more generally, there may be requirements by NCC for particular forms of management of hedge and field boundaries, ditches, or farm roads, where it is argued that, although these features may not have been important in the choice of the site, their management should now be directed to conservation objectives in the interest of maintaining the 'integrity of the site'.

8 Converting research results into practical advice

The obligation on MAFF to 'have regard to' conserving the natural beauty and amenity of the countryside in the Countryside Act 1968 prompted ADAS involvement, leading, for instance, to the Silsoe Conference in 1969 (Barber 1970), in which officers from the then Lands Arm of the Ministry played a major part. The obligation in the 1981 Act to 'advise on' sharpens the need for ADAS officers to have a greater awareness and understanding of conservation and natural amenity, and the response is seen in the recent instructions given to advisors, and the training courses on conservation (both wildlife and landscape) being run for them. Other, mainly administrative, initiatives at this time are outside the scope of this paper. The need is for more and better information about the ecology and management of the countryside that can be turned into practical advice for farmers and landowners. This information needs to be well founded to reinforce the rather generalized advice that is sometimes all that is available at the moment, so that an advisor can weigh up the problems of an individual site, and advise (for instance) not only to plant trees and which species to use, but also to know why they should be planted. Such information can only be gained from research, much of which will be ecological in nature, together with the socio-economic studies that are also required.

9 Conclusions

This paper has set out to describe the principal areas of MAFF's interest in ecological research required to help it to meet its obligations in relation to the wider countryside: that is, whilst accepting the Ministry's primary function in relation to agriculture, to allow it to discharge this function having regard to the needs of wildlife conservation, and of amenity, particularly in respect of the giving of advice. It has been emphasized that this advice should be based on sound ecological principles derived from research. It can be foreseen, if

it is not already happening, that the role of the ADAS advisor in relation to environmental research will be the same as his existing role in relation to agricultural research, ie interpretation, development, and promotion. ADAS officers have been very successful in this role for agriculture, and there is no reason why they should not be equally good at it for conservation.

The recipe for success in this greater emphasis on conservation is compounded of motivation, awareness, understanding and direction. So far as motivation is concerned, it is probably true to say that there are proportionally more officers in ADAS concerned about conservation, than there are members of the conservation movement concerned about agriculture, even though a prosperous agricultural industry is of fundamental importance to the nation's welfare now and in the future. So far as awareness and understanding are concerned, a significant proportion of the training budget is currently allocated to conservation training, both spent on in-house courses run by ADAS, and by sending participants to courses run by others. It is on these courses, and in other contacts with environmental ecologists, that opportunities occur for the results (and methods) of environmental research to be communicated to ADAS advisors. Clearly there will be a continuing and increasing need for this communication, and for positive relationships to be built up. The fourth component, direction, is being given, and, as the involvement of ADAS in conservation matters develops further, so direction may need to be modified, but patience is needed for the effects to be seen more widely on the ground.

MAFF sees research as part of the essential process of reconciling the needs of agriculture with those of wildlife conservation and amenity in the countryside, and is concerned with the use of the results of this research. Unless environmental research can be communicated in such a way that it can be understood by the advisor, however, and presented by him so that it arouses the farmer's interest and enthusiasm, there will be very little point, from MAFF's point of view, in doing it.

10 Summary

The statutory responsibilities of MAFF determine the Ministry's needs for research on environmental topics. These responsibilities include land use, restoration of mineral workings, river and coastal engineering, pesticide registration and control, and the obligations to advise on the conservation and enhancement of the natural beauty and amenity of the countryside in the Countryside Act 1968, and the Wildlife and Countryside Act 1981. The principal interests in soundly based information, derived from ecological research, are for use in advisory work connected with these functions, and for use in deciding upon payment of grants for grant-aidable work where there is a conflict with environmental interests. Similarly, it is important that the advice given to the Ministry by conservation organizations in respect of these matters, and in connection with the notification of statutory Sites of Special Scientific Interest, and the making of nature conservation orders, should be based on the most up-to-date information available, to obtain which there is a continuing need for research to be undertaken by these organizations.

ADAS has an essential role to play in interpreting the results of research to land managers. It is of crucial importance to make research results available in such a form that they can be used in stimulating the interest of farmers and landowners, and in advising them on the conservation of the countryside.

11 References

Agricultural Advisory Council. 1970. *Modern farming and the soil.* London: HMSO.

Barber, D. ed. 1970. *Farming and wildlife: a study in compromise.* Sandy: Royal Society for the Protection of Birds.

Bradshaw, A.D. & Chadwick, M.J. 1980. *The restoration of land.* Oxford: Blackwell Scientific.

Bunyan, P.J. & Stanley, P.I. 1983. The environmental cost of pesticide usage in the United Kingdom. *Agric. Ecosyst. Environ.,* **9,** 187-209.

Game Conservancy. 1982. *Annual review, 1981,* no. 13. Fordingbridge: The Game Conservancy.

Green, B.H. 1983. The management of herbaceous vegetation for wildlife conservation. In: *Management of vegetation,* edited by J.M. Way, 99-116. (Monograph no. 26). Croydon: British Crop Protection Council.

Her Majesty's Stationery Office. 1944. *Agriculture (Miscellaneous Provisions) Act.* London: HMSO.

Her Majesty's Stationery Office. 1968. *Countryside Act 1968.* London: HMSO.

Her Majesty's Stationery Office. 1970. *Agriculture Act 1970.* London: HMSO.

Her Majesty's Stationery Office. 1976a. *Development involving agricultural land. (DOE Circ. 75/76, WO Circ. 110/76).* London: HMSO.

Her Majesty's Stationery Office. 1976b. *Land Drainage Act 1976.* London: HMSO.

Her Majesty's Stationery Office. 1981. *Wildlife and Countryside Act 1981.* London: HMSO.

Ministry of Agriculture, Fisheries and Food. 1983. *Heather and grass burning.* (Press Notice no. 90, March 25, 1983). London: MAFF.

Ratcliffe, D.A. 1977. *A nature conservation review: the selection of biological sites of national importance to nature conservation in Britain.* Vol. 1. Cambridge: Cambridge University Press.

Royal Commission on Environmental Pollution. 1979. *7th Report: Agriculture and pollution.* London: HMSO.

Stanley, P.I. & Hardy, A.R. 1984. The environmental implications of current pesticide usage on cereals. In: *Agriculture and the environment,* edited by D. Jenkins, 66-72. (ITE symposium no. 13). Cambridge: Institute of Terrestrial Ecology.

Stewart, A.J.A. & Lance, A.N. 1983. Moor-draining: a review of impacts on land use. *J. environ. Manage.,* **17,** 81-99.

Wilson, A. 1969. *Further review of certain persistent organochlorine pesticides used in Great Britain.* London: HMSO.

DISCUSSIONS

The discussions were organized in syndicates, every participant being invited to join one of 3 groups. Each group discussed research needs on the impacts of agriculture on wildlife and natural and semi-natural habitats in (i) lowlands and (ii) uplands, and also (iii) on the effects of agrochemicals on wildlife (with wildlife defined broadly to include soil fauna, as well as terrestrial and aquatic plants and animals). Each syndicate group had a reporter: D F Ball for the lowland discussion, O W Heal for uplands and I Newton for agrochemicals. These 3 reporters each summarized the conclusions or recommendations of the 3 syndicates and their reports follow.

REPORT ON THE DISCUSSIONS OF THE SYNDICATE ON LOWLANDS
D F Ball, Reporter

1 Availability of advice

Before considering the need for further research on the ecological impacts of agriculture on lowland Britain, the syndicate placed a strong emphasis on improved communication of existing knowledge between ecologists and farmers. Farmers should be able to get practical, action-oriented summaries of current recommendations for habitat and wildlife integration with modern agriculture, through the extension and advisory services of MAFF and the Scottish Colleges of Agriculture, and through the newly co-ordinated Farming and Wildlife Advisory Groups (FWAG). Those organizations concerned with wildlife ecology and with ecology applied to agriculture were urged to respond co-operatively towards providing material for such practical summaries.

2 The background to agricultural impacts in the lowlands

A large majority held the view that efficient modern farming techniques would, and should, be sustained, and optimistically believed that it was not inevitable that current intensive farming, or its extension, need damage other environmental interests as severely as it is now seen to do. An approach that aims to maintain or increase agricultural production could be compatible with minimizing habitat loss and restoring habitat diversity.

Land use in Britain is increasingly influenced by EEC policies. Recently, the Community has decided to cease payment of capital grants related to dairying, with reduced support and quotas for milk production, while at the upland margin there has been an increase in land with 'less-favoured area' status. It is foreseeable that cereal production may be restricted, with or without support price changes. Some pasture and even arable land may be turned to the production of high value timber or energy crops. If economic pressures and options change, then more diversified farming could result, which in turn may assist the restitution or retention of habitat diversity.

3 Detection and monitoring of changes and their causes

The major impacts of agricultural change on the environment rapidly become obvious, but are we able to identify the early stages of potentially critical ecological impacts of less conspicuous land management modifications, whether these are stimulated by economic and social factors or by evolving agricultural techniques?

It was generally agreed that our ability to detect change, and our quantitative knowledge of past changes were defective. There was acceptance of the need for an effective, quantitative assessment of the current distribution of habitats, nationally and regionally, which should be resurveyed ('monitored') at frequent intervals. Monitoring should not be restricted to key conservation sites, such as those of SSSI status, but should include the broader countryside which, from the landscape and general public points of view, is of more conspicuous significance. However, not all species and site characteristics can be monitored. There must be an element of selectivity. As a result, 2 types of monitoring were envisaged: extensive, broad-brush, national and regional evaluations; and intensive, site-oriented monitoring, focusing on key species or assemblages of species. Irrespective of scale, extensive or intensive, the objectives of monitoring in relation to practical policies and methods need to be constantly borne in mind.

4 The areas and distribution of different habitats effective for wildlife conservation

On balance, it was thought that the present trend towards the consolidation of fields into larger units will continue in the lowlands. This further consolidation of fields will result in a continued fragmentation and loss of small areas of semi-natural habitats which survive in lowland Britain. While something is known of the minimum areas required to sustain some species of plants and animals, more information is needed to take account of the different requirements of mobile and non-mobile species. Biogeographical studies must include work on the effective and optimum size of habitat 'islands' for individual species and assemblages of species. The most appropriate patterns of 'island' distribution to ensure adequate population densities, diversity, and effective dispersal within an agricultural landscape must be studied. This research, allied to autecological and ecosystem studies, should encourage the evolution of management practices that

are acceptable in agricultural terms, but produce reduced ecological damage. At the same time, more needs to be known about the re-introduction of plants and animals in the intensive agricultural environment, and about the re-creation, in patterns compatible with modern farming, of habitats broadly comparable to those which have been reduced or eliminated by recent changes in land use. This approach warrants more attention than it has so far attracted.

5 Ecosystem studies

Autecology is concerned with the distribution of plants and animals. Studies in a range of environmental conditions should be focused on species with different growth requirements and strategies. Particular attention should be paid to soil water relations, a major problem for the maintenance of some habitats and species assemblages in the lowlands, where large areas have been directly and/or indirectly affected by improved land drainage. However, the management of ecosystems necessitates knowledge of the interactions between species, in addition to the responses of individual species. An integrated approach to plant species is required in site management, taking account of water relations and the requirements for, and availability of, nutrients. The effects of agrochemicals (both pesticides and fertilizers) on the occurrence and survival of ecologically valuable but agriculturally 'weed' species need study. These species are often important for their associated fauna, including seed eating birds. There is also a need for comparative studies of agricultural and semi-natural ecosystems in order to determine whether restoration of particular habitats remains a practical option. The role of wild plants and animals as carriers or reservoirs of pests and pathogens of crop plants and animals was also thought to warrant more investigation, for example 'Q-disease' in deer.

6 Major land management experiments

Management trials on a farm scale, as done at the Boxworth Experimental Husbandry Farm (Stanley & Hardy 1984), were discussed. While welcomed in principle, there were reservations about problems of statistical design and interpretation. For the future, would the very considerable resources required for this scale of experiment be better rewarded by a dispersed set of less extensive trials?

7 General issues

Three aspects should be stressed: (i) an over-riding concern that more research should be oriented to management objectives; (ii) ecologists should not be afraid to give advice on less than (unattainably) perfect information (it is not always necessary to do more research); (iii) in seeking a realistic balance between agriculture and the maintenance of the rural landscape, with its attendant assemblages of wildlife, the emphasis should, wherever possible, be on minor modifications of current agricultural practices, and on habitat restoration of acceptable scale and location. Such actions, eg leaving bands along field boundaries untreated by herbicides and pesticides, may have little impact on crop production, but major beneficial effects on landscape and wildlife.

8 Recommendations

8.1 More advice should be provided, as soon as possible, on minimizing the impacts of agriculture on wildlife. This advice should be drawn from existing ecological knowledge and disseminated through the FWAGs and the advisory/extension services of MAFF, and the Colleges of Agriculture, Scotland.

8.2 An integrated data base should be established, at national and regional scales, of existing land cover, land use and landscape; this data base should form the basis against which future changes can be monitored.

8.3 'Island' biogeographical studies need to be made of the sizes and patterns of distribution of wildlife habitats that could enable selected species and assemblages of species (plant and animal) to be sustained in areas dominated by different types of agriculture.

8.4 Autecological studies of key species (plant and animal, mobile and sedentary) are required, taking particular note of water relations (the impact of land drainage) and the flow of nutrients.

8.5 On the basis of present knowledge, and as improved by 8.3 and 8.4, experimental work should aim, so far as possible, to re-create habitats, and their associated plant and animal assemblages, which have been lost as a result of recent agricultural developments.

8.6 Consideration should be given to the establishment of a series of dispersed trials to test the effects of agricultural practices, changes in these practices, and the results of habitat loss and re-introduction, on the abundance and diversity of wildlife.

8.7 Accepting that the interests of productive agriculture and conservation need not always conflict, it is mutually desirable to know more about wildlife as a possible reservoir of pests and pathogens of domesticated plants and animals, and *vice versa*.

8.8 Desk studies should be made to predict possible regional impacts on landscape and wildlife of agricultural changes that could follow a modified CAP approach to agricultural production within the European Community.

8.9 If interests in agriculture, wildlife, and landscape are to be harmonized, it is essential that effective mechanisms are established by which environmental impacts can be predicted in advance of potential changes in land use and in management methods.

Reference

Stanley, P.I. & Hardy, A.R. 1984. The environmental implications of current pesticide usage on cereals. In: *Agriculture and the environment*, edited by D. Jenkins, 66-72. (ITE symposium no. 13). Cambridge: Institute of Terrestrial Ecology.

REPORT ON THE DISCUSSIONS OF THE SYNDICATE ON UPLANDS
O W Heal, Reporter

An initial basis for assessing research priorities is to identify those areas of the uplands in which agriculture is likely to change and where such changes will influence wildlife, either directly or through consequent changes in other land uses. This basis is provided by Eadie's (1984) scenarios, which also serve to emphasize the need to recognize the variability in the climate, soil, vegetation and land use within the uplands*. The most likely pattern of agricultural development is given below.

i. In the higher and remote Hill farms, agricultural production as a primary land use objective will continue to decline. Management for nature and landscape conservation and for recreation may depend on artificial maintenance of farming and manpower.

ii. On Upland farms, particularly those with relatively high proportions of sown pasture, agriculture will remain strong, intensification is likely to continue, and wildlife objectives will have to be incorporated within farm management.

iii. On the better Hill farms in the less remote areas, the options for change are greatest, and potentially most controversial. The extent of conversion of indigenous pasture to sown grassland will depend on economic incentives and social priorities, but with associated control of the indigenous vegetation through grazing management. Forestry is a major alternative in these areas, again with the potential to minimize conflict through collaboration in defining objectives and through sensitive management.

This generally accepted scenario identifies the broad variation in land use, related to land type, and shows the combinations of user interests which characterize the uplands. The background papers and discussions

*The general term 'uplands' is used for land on which farming is dominated by sheep or sheep and cattle rearing. In Eadie's scenario, the distinction is made between the higher Hill farms where sheep rearing is dominant, and the Upland farms, on lower or better land, with mixed sheep and cattle rearing. This distinction is applied to England and Wales as well as to Scotland.

identified a very wide variety of research topics, which are considered under 4 headings: (1) strategic planning problems, (2) specific aspects of management, (3) general problems, and (4) ecological principles. Additional comments about the research are grouped under (5) practicalities and implementation.

1 Strategic planning

Although agriculture is, historically, the major land use in the uplands, its extensive rather than intensive management practices, combined with the natural features of the environment, have allowed and encouraged a mixture of land uses. Nature and landscape conservation, recreation, game management, and water catchment often combine within an area, one or other sometimes being dominant. There is a gradual shift in land use interests, for economic, social or political reasons. For example, in recent years the demand for land for forestry has increased and is likely to continue to increase, and additional uses such as biofuel production may be considered, even if only on a local scale. In this way, the inter-relationships between agriculture and wildlife influence, and are influenced by, other land uses. Because of the intimate mixture of uses, even if not actually integrated on the same piece of land, interactions between agriculture and wildlife cannot be considered in isolation. Although most of the uplands are privately owned and there is no central rural planning responsibility, the various national Departments and Agencies have distinct objectives. These objectives are implemented through a complex combination of financial incentives, price controls, education, advice, etc, as well as by land ownership.

It was recognized that ecological research must be considered within this general framework. Research priorities are influenced by the land use interests, and ecological information is required in assessing possible changes in land use. Three linked aspects of strategic planning were considered to have priority in this area of research.

1.1 Assessment of the compatibility of the objectives of land use interests in the uplands

There is potential conflict (constructive tension) between user interests, particularly in the land identified in Eadie's (1984) scenario as the better Hill farms. Changing patterns of agriculture with related development of forestry are likely to produce greater changes in wildlife and landscape on this land than elsewhere in the uplands, and will affect the social and economic systems. This conflict was identified by the Countryside Commission in their publication *What future for the uplands?* and requires independent research to define the extent to which user objectives are compatible within this zone and to examine options which will provide maximum mutual benefit to user interests. Such research requires the development, and acceptance by users, of methods applicable at national, regional and local scales.

1.2 Interaction between land uses and wildlife

The uplands consist of a mosaic of uses and habitats. Changes in one land use affect adjacent uses, eg stock densities and distribution on indigenous pastures are influenced by afforestation, and many of the more mobile wildlife (insects, mammals and birds) respond to changes in the composition and arrangement of the habitat mosaic. Research has tended to concentrate on effects of specific land uses, and more information is needed on the interactions between land uses and on the wildlife response to the habitat mosaic.

1.3 Efficiency of mechanisms controlling land use

Although outside the direct field of ecological research, it was recognized that further research was necessary to quantify the relationship between change in the target land use to various incentives and disincentives, and to identify the consequent responses of non-target uses, including the application of compensatory controls.

2 Specific aspects of management

2.1 Grazing interactions with indigenous vegetation

From the frequency with which the subject was raised, the response of indigenous vegetation to variation in type and intensity of grazing pressure was regarded as a high priority for ecological research. Grazing is a dominant factor controlling the composition and pattern of upland vegetation. Although the general trends in vegetation change in response to grazing are understood, many of the details necessary to predict change and to define management policies are still obscure. The subject has been developed by Milner (1984) and is applicable (i) to Upland farms where intensification leads to stock changes on rough grazing, (ii) to the better Hill farms where stock density and distribution are modified by changes in the type and pattern of land use, and (iii) to areas with poorer Hill farms where management for nature and landscape conservation may have to be defined, given a decline in agriculture. Central to this research must be the recognition of the adaptive behaviour of mammals.

2.2 Management of indigenous vegetation

Again, although the general principles of vegetation management through burning and draining are understood, variations related to the range of upland climatic and soil conditions and their interactions with grazing still require research. The dynamics and control of dominant species such as bracken, heather, purple moor-grass and mat-grass are focal points in relation to nature and landscape conservation, in terms of both the control of unwanted species and the regeneration of desired communities. Associated with heather management, there is a need for continued research on grouse population dynamics, emphasized by uncertainty on the factors responsible for recent population decline and the role of ticks as disease vectors.

2.3 Effects of agricultural improvement on wildlife

Within the Upland farms, intensification is likely to continue, with changes in the patterns of sown pastures along the moorland fringe and in winter feeding regimes. These changes will affect grazing intensities and distribution on the rough grazings, and require research on the relationship of agricultural intensification to stocking characteristics. The selection of areas for improvement can also affect wildlife directly, for example feeding grounds for golden plover, and research is required to identify the type of area which is most sensitive for wildlife and which should be excluded from reclamation schemes on conservation grounds.

2.4 Recreation and wildlife

In the uplands, informal recreation is claimed to conflict with nature conservation and with field sports, eg deer stalking. There is much argument amongst different interest groups as to the correct balance of objectives for upland areas. Thus, there is need for more quantitative information on the nature of the impact of different types of recreation on various forms of wildlife, under the varying upland conditions.

2.5 Interaction of afforestation and wildlife

Afforestation, and subsequent forestry practices do not influence wildlife in isolation but in combination with agriculture and other land uses in the area. A recurrent research theme was for more quantitative information on the effects of varying types of forestry on wildlife, recognizing the diversity of the uplands. The aim is to define distribution and types of forestry which are most acceptable to nature and landscape conservation, as well as being commercially viable.

3 General problems

3.1 Acid deposition

Whilst it was accepted that there was already significant research on 'acid rain', it was emphasized that more factual information was required on the short- and long-term effects of increased acid deposition in the uplands on wildlife, and of particular concern was the extent to which interaction of deposition with forest cover results in soil and water acidification, and also the potential of management practices, eg liming, to ameliorate acidification.

3.2 Upland/lowland interactions

Changes in the wildlife populations of the uplands are influenced by lowland as well as upland agricultural practices, particularly birds and mammals which either migrate seasonally or which feed in the lowlands. Thus, research on upland wildlife must include analysis of the effects of lowland agriculture.

4 General principles

The need to develop basic ecological research and improve the theoretical basis of upland ecology was a recurrent theme in discussions. Specific management problems may be approached by *ad hoc* research, but solutions are likely to be more sound and of wider application if developed from a theoretical as well as a practical base. Although not discussed in detail, the areas of fundamental research most relevant to upland wildlife problems were identified.

4.1 Ecosystems

The essential concept is that the subject influences, and is influenced by, other components of the system. The relationships involve feedback effects which account for responses which are not predicted from more superficial analysis. The principle applies at each level of study, eg a particular species such as bracken, an element such as nitrogen, or a land use such as forestry. In each case, the subject must be considered as part of a wider ecosystem, the research requiring an understanding of processes in other disciplines.

4.2 Island biogeography

Analysis of the principles of wildlife response to the size and spatial arrangement of habitats is particularly important in relation to changes in land use and the resulting habitat mosaic.

4.3 Nutrient balance and soil fertility

Management practices modify the nutrient economy of upland ecosystems and the soil characteristics. Such modifications must be analysed in the context of natural trends in nutrient balance and soil development, and their reversibility.

4.4 Plant community dynamics

Abrupt or gradual increases or decreases in management intensity result in changes in vegetation composition which can be understood in the framework of succession theory. This theory includes understanding of the biological characteristics of species which determine their ability to colonize, establish and survive under varying degrees of competition and stress. In the uplands, 'stress' must be considered in terms of the pervasive influences of grazing, climatic severity, and low fertility soils.

4.5 Animal population dynamics

Conservation of individual species and control of pests and disease vectors are aided by research on population dynamics, recognizing that population regulation in the uplands is often density independent for species at or near the edge of their environmental range, but density dependent for typical upland species. Introduction of new crops and conditions results in population changes that can be related to concepts of succession which require further development.

5 Practical aspects of ecological research

In addition to the priority research topics identified in the symposium, certain emphases in the research and some practical requirements were highlighted.

5.1 National and regional data base

Although many data are available from different organizations and from different parts of the country, there is still a need for a comprehensive national data base which defines environmental and land characteristics, current (and past) land use, habitats and species distributions. A key feature is for these data to be compatible in resolution and spatial presentation. Such base-line data are not an end in themselves, but provide a basis for planning and for assessment of potential and actual change, and enable local and regional features to be placed in a national context.

5.2 Monitoring

Recurrent debate about the rate and direction of change in land use and associated wildlife and landscape could be more profitable, if the fragmented monitoring schemes were integrated and related to forecasts.

5.3 Prediction

Whilst information on the current state of land use and wildlife and on recent change is important, it is more important to assess the options for change and to predict probable change. Descriptive research tends to dominate, but an essential requirement in planning and decision-making is for ecological research to be more predictive, and to anticipate change rather than react to it.

5.4 Large-scale experiments

The need for large-scale experiments, including catchment studies, arises from the recognition of the interaction between land uses (2.2) and management practices (3.1-3.5) and the importance of an integrated ecosystem approach to research (5.1). Such experiments need not necessarily involve major management treatments, but require a multidisciplinary approach to the study of selected areas. The danger of non-replicated experiments was emphasized, as was the need to link main study sites to the wider range of upland variation through more extensive sites with a lower intensity of research input.

5.5 Communication, interpretation and implementation of research

Communication of research results from research scientists to managers and policy-makers needs to be improved. It requires a willingness on both sides and, in some cases, an intermediate stage of field demonstration through organizations such as ADAS. The efficiency of communication and interpretation may be a key research area in itself, with analysis of the variety of mechanisms involved. There was repeated comment that a wealth of information and experience on upland ecology already exists but that this capital is not being fully utilized, often because of the artificial barriers of technical expression of results by scientists, and resistance to sophisticated methods by planners and managers.

A final point, expressed by many, was that much of the research and its implementation does not usually fall simply within the responsibility of one organization. The research often requires experience from different backgrounds and disciplines and demands both in-

creased collaboration between organizations and more flexible funding arrangements, particularly in the funding of strategic research designed to clarify and solve the problems of tomorrow, rather than *ad hoc* research on today's problems.

References

Eadie J. 1984. Trends in agricultural land use: the hills and uplands. In: *Agriculture and the environment*, edited by D. Jenkins, 13-20. (ITE symposium no. 13). Cambridge, Institute of Terrestrial Ecology.

Milner C. 1984. Some ecological principles underlying hill sheep management. In: *Agriculture and the environment*, edited by D. Jenkins. (139-142). (ITE symposium no. 13). Cambridge: Institute of Terrestrial Ecology.

REPORT ON THE DISCUSSIONS OF THE SYNDICATE ON THE USE OF AGROCHEMICAL
I Newton, Reporter

The aim of this syndicate was to define the research needed for a better understanding of the long-term effects of chemicals on agricultural ecosystems. Discussion was limited to chemicals used in agriculture, and excluded those (such as sulphur) which reached farmland from other sources. As most pesticides and herbicides are not specific, they inevitably affect many non-target species, and thus alter the whole community of animals and plants. Despite the importance of the problem, large gaps in knowledge emerged, probably due to the research needs in this field falling between the traditional remits of existing research organizations (particularly AFRC and NERC), or at best being near the borders of their remits; hence, neither organization has funded substantial work in this field. Discussion centred on the following aspects.

1 Detection of problems caused by chemicals

Monitoring programmes are at present run by MAFF (incident scheme), Water Authorities (water quality and pollution incidents), BTO (bird censuses), ITE (organochlorine and metal residue analyses) and others, while beekeepers and other members of the public have often reported mortalities associated with chemicals. In these schemes, vertebrates are well covered, but, with a few exceptions, invertebrates and plants are not.

More monitoring of invertebrates and plant communities was thought desirable, along the lines of the Game Conservancy's North Farm project, and with the aim of following changes in the whole ecosystem which accompany changes in total chemical use. Such work is costly and time-consuming, and may be best done as a joint project, involving several organizations. One way to begin may be in conjunction with autecological studies of particular farmland species.

In any agricultural system, most of the changes resulting from chemical use may have already occurred, and the best that can be achieved is to follow the further changes as one group of chemicals is replaced in time by another. On the other hand, in commercial forest plantations, pesticide use is just beginning, thus providing opportunities to follow from the start the resulting changes in wildlife. Such monitoring programmes may detect changes in fauna and flora, but further research is needed to identify the cause of these changes, and to assess the importance of chemicals, as opposed to other factors.

2 Specific chemicals

The main stated need was for more information on the fate of fertilizers and persistent chemicals (including organochlorines) in the environment, and particularly on the persistence of different chemicals in different types of soil. This need was felt in relation to the growing nitrate problem, to eutrophication, and to the continuing persistence of DDE in soils and wildlife samples. The whole field of soil biology, including the effects of different chemicals on soil organisms, was seen as requiring more attention. In particular, little research has been done on the cumulative effects of repeated applications of chemicals over large areas of cereals grown year after year on the same land.

Work on the toxicology and environmental effects of specific insecticides was not regarded as a priority, though further monitoring of organochlorine levels and of mortality incidents should continue. For herbicides, further assessments were considered desirable on the effects of leaving field margins unsprayed, both on crop yields and on fauna and flora.

3 Pesticides in non-cultivated areas

In addition to the foregoing, more information was thought necessary on the extent of pesticide drift and transfer from treated to untreated areas. In districts of intensive agriculture, most wildlife survives on small islands of uncultivated habitat in the midst of large areas that are under chemical treatment. The drift of chemicals from farmland could easily endanger wildlife on these unsprayed havens. Further work is required on the persistence of different animals and plants on these islands, on the dispersal of different species between them, and on long-term trends in species abundance.

In addition, further work was considered desirable on the value of chemicals to control unwanted vegetation in nature reserves and other uncultivated habitat.

4 Studies of different pesticide regimes

In the MAFF project at Boxworth, the effects of different frequencies of pesticide application on crop yields, profits, and wildlife are being investigated. Further experimental work of this type was considered highly desirable, but difficult to initiate because of the need for control of experimental farms and the high costs involved. It should nonetheless be considered a priority, and be designed in a way which will satisfy statistical as well as biological considerations.

5 Mis-use of chemicals

More information is needed on the extent of mis-use of agricultural chemicals to kill vertebrate pests and birds of prey. Illegal use of strychnine, mevinphos and other chemicals, mainly for fox control, may incidentally be limiting the distribution and numbers of several bird of prey species in Britain. Work on specific poisons for killing mammals, such as moles and foxes, was considered desirable, but is probably too costly to attract commercial interest.

6 Alternatives to pesticide use

The need for substantial reduction in the current level of chemical use on farmland was considered paramount, on grounds of economy, human health, environmental effects and ignorance of long-term consequences. Priorities were to expand existing limited research effort in the following aspects.

6.1 Studies of predator/pest and predator/pest/ pesticide interactions, in the hope of maximizing the influence of the predators, as opposed to the pesticides, in controlling invertebrate pests.

6.2 Studies of correlations between pest populations and damage levels to assess 'threshold populations' of pests, beyond which significant damage is likely. Better knowledge of pest/damage relationships may help to reduce the 'insurance use' of pesticides, by defining those pest population levels below which pesticide use is unnecessary.

6.3 Studies of the development, spread and nature of resistance in pest populations, in the hope of slowing the development of resistance, so that particular chemicals will remain effective for longer.

6.4 Studies of biological and integrated pest control, including, besides pesticides, predators, parasites and diseases of the pest.

6.5 Studies of the application and fate of pesticides to ensure maximum uptake by target organisms from minimum use.

6.6 Further work on the breeding of resistant plant varieties, in order to make protective chemicals less necessary.

In all these fields, agricultural research interests have so far played the major role, and limited work is being undertaken now. There is great scope for further work, but, for such methods to be accepted by farmers, they have to be cheaper than existing methods of chemical control.

7 Communication of research findings

There is a need for better communication of the findings of research, in a form that is readily understandable by farmers. Greater understanding of the attitudes of farmers to chemicals might also help to bring farmers and environmentalists closer together.

Summary
The main research needs concerning agrochemicals are for:

i. more long-term, large-scale monitoring of wildlife communities in agricultural habitats in relation to total chemical use;

ii. more research on the effects of chemicals on soil organisms, and on the persistence of different chemicals in different types of soil; and

iii. more research on alternative methods of pest control.

The most immediate need, however, is to find some way in which research in these fields can be funded, in the face of a shrinking budget, when it is not central to the traditional concerns of any one organization.

Conclusions

This symposium on the relationship between agriculture and the environment has had several unexpected outcomes. I think that most of us taking part in the symposium were surprised to discover that this was the first opportunity that participants from so many diverse fields of activity had had to discuss this important topic. While there has, of course, been much discussion of the topic within each of the separate groups of interests represented at this symposium, there has been no discussion of the kind we have had over the past few days. From the vigour of our discussions, and the very large measure of agreement that has been reached, it is clear that something similar should have been attempted before, and that we should now try to widen the range of participants in further discussion of these issues.

From the start, it has been apparent that there is some polarization of views about the need for further research. As one might expect, the research scientists have been anxious to point out the need for more research, and have been at pains to identify the particular issues on which research is required. Understandably, they have emphasized the painful fact that ecological and environmental research has a long lead time, so that today's research scientists need to be working on the problems with which we will be faced in 5, 10 or 15 years' time. Those participants who are closer to the more practical tasks of agriculture, while accepting the need for research on tomorrow's problems, have been equally emphatic that today's problems still have to be solved, with or without the help of the research scientist. If research scientists have a practical contribution to make, then the transfer of information from our papers in scientific journals to formats which are capable of being understood and used by farmers, administrators, and the general public needs to be given as much, if not more, attention as the planning of new research.

The truth undoubtedly lies somewhere in between the 2 extremes. Certainly, we need to plan for more research, and this research needs to be both efficient and relevant to tomorrow's, rather than today's, problems. On the other hand, there are problems which have to be faced now, and there exists information which is not freely available, but which could make a substantial contribution to their solutions. We need to find ways to make this transfer of information effective.

Having embarked on this strategy of bringing together the providers of research information and those who might use this information, ITE will continue to do what it can to develop and extend the discussions, and to translate them into practical actions. The publication of the proceedings of this symposium will provide a basis for further collaboration between the various research interests and between research and agricultural practice. In order for this symposium to be a practical proposition, the numbers of participants were limited to those invited because they were known to have a strong interest in the topic. We now know from the expressions of interest and, indeed, often of disappointment by those we just could not squeeze in, that perhaps at least 3 times as many people would have liked to take part. We hope that they will continue to show the same interest in the further meetings on this and related topics that we intend to arrange.

Finally, I would like to thank all the participants for their encouragement and for the way in which they have debated the issues forcefully, but with good humour and tolerance. It would be very easy, in discussing so emotive a topic, for tempers to become frayed and for arguments to become heated rather than enlightening. That neither of these things happened is a credit to everyone who took part in the symposium and bodes well for future collaboration.

J N R Jeffers
August 1984

Appendix I

LIST OF CONTRIBUTORS AND PARTICIPANTS

Lord Adrian, Chairman, House of Lords Select Committee, House of Lords, *London,* SW1A 0PW.

Miss Anne Brenchley, Maidstone (formerly University of Aberdeen, Culterty Field Station, Newburgh, *Ellon,* Aberdeenshire, AB4 0AA).

Dr C J Cadbury, Royal Society for the Protection of Birds, The Lodge, *Sandy,* Bedfordshire, SG19 2DL.

Mr E S Carter, Farming and Wildlife Advisory Group, The Lodge, *Sandy,* Bedfordshire, SG19 2DL.

Dr T H Coaker, Department of Applied Biology, University of Cambridge, Pembroke Street, *Cambridge,* CB2 3DX.

Dr A S Cooke, Nature Conservancy Council, PO Box 6, Godwin House, George Street, *Huntingdon,* Cambridgeshire, PE18 6BU.

Mr E B Cowell, British Petroleum Company, Britannic House, Moor Lane, *London,* EC2Y 9BU.

Dr D B Davies, Agricultural Development and Advisory Service, Ministry of Agriculture, Fisheries and Food, Block C, Government Buildings, Brooklands Avenue, *Cambridge,* CB2 2DR.

Miss M De Groose, Clerk, House of Lords Sub-committees, House of Lords, *London,* SW1A 0PW.

Dr D C Drummond, Ministry of Agriculture, Fisheries and Food, Slough Laboratory, London Road, *Slough,* Buckinghamshire, SL3 7HJ.

Mr J Eadie, Hill Farming Research Organisation, Bush Estate, *Penicuik,* Midlothian, EH26 0PY.

Dr C A Edwards, Rothamsted Experimental Station, *Harpenden,* Hertfordshire, AL5 2JQ.

Dr F B Ellis, Ministry of Agriculture, Fisheries and Food, Great Westminster House, Horseferry Road, *London,* SW1P 2AE.

Mr W J Ferguson, Rothiebrisbane, *Fyvie,* Aberdeenshire, AB5 8LE.

Mr J A Forster, Nature Conservancy Council, Wynne-Edwards House, 17 Rubislaw Terrace, *Aberdeen,* AB1 1XE.

Professor J D Fryer, Weed Research Organization, Begbroke Hill, Yarnton, *Oxford,* OX5 1PF.

Dr A R Hardy, Environmental Chemistry Section, Ministry of Agriculture, Fisheries and Food, Tolworth Laboratory, Hook Rise South, Tolworth, *Surbiton,* Surrey, KT6 7NF.

Mr P D G Hayter, Committee Office, House of Lords, *London,* SW1A 0PW.

Mr B Huber, Commission of the European Communities, Division VI-F-2, Rue de la Loi 200, B-1049, *Brussels,* Belgium.

Dr P J Hudson, The Game Conservancy, North of England Grouse Research Project, Mews House, Askrigg, *Leyburn,* North Yorkshire, DL8 3HG.

Mr T Huxley, Countryside Commission for Scotland, Battleby, Redgorton, *Perth,* PH1 3EW.

Dr D Langslow, Nature Conservancy Council, PO Box 6, Godwin House, George Street, *Huntingdon,* Cambridgeshire, PE18 6BU.

Dr P B Leeds-Harrison, Silsoe College, Silsoe, *Bedford,* MK45 4DT.

Mr P Leonard, Countryside Commission, John Dower House, Crescent Place, *Cheltenham,* Gloucestershire, GL50 3RA.

Dr D W Macdonald, Department of Zoology, University of Oxford, South Parks Road, *Oxford,* OX1 3PS.

Mr C Mackay, Department of Agriculture and Fisheries for Scotland, Chesser House, 500 Gorgie Road, *Edinburgh,* EH11 3AW.

Mr M Mackie, AFRC Council, Westertown, *Rothienorman,* Aberdeenshire, AB5 8US.

Professor J S Marsh, Department of Agricultural Economics & Management, University of Reading, PO Box 237, 4 Earley Gate, Whiteknights Road, *Reading,* RG6 2AR.

Lord Peter Melchett, House of Lords, *London,* SW1A 0PW.

Professor N W Moore, The Farm House, Swavesey, *Cambridge,* CB4 5RA.

Dr J Morris, Silsoe College, Silsoe, *Bedford,* MK45 4DT.

Mr J M M Munro, Grassland Agronomy Department, Welsh Plant Breeding Station, Plas Gogerddan, *Aberystwyth,* Dyfed, SY23 3EB.

Dr W E S Mutch, Department of Forestry & Natural Resources, University of Edinburgh, Darwin Building, The King's Buildings, Mayfield Road, *Edinburgh,* EH9 3JU.

Dr R J O'Connor, British Trust for Ornithology, Beech Grove, *Tring,* Hertfordshire, HP23 5NR.

Mr J Oliver-Bellasis, Wootton House, Wootton St Lawrence, *Basingstoke,* Hampshire, RG23 8PE.

The Earl Peel, House of Lords, *London,* SW1A 0PW.

Mr J C Peters, Department of the Environment, Room 202, Tollgate House, Houlton Street, *Bristol,* BS2 9DJ.

Dr G R Potts, The Game Conservancy, *Fordingbridge,* Hampshire, SP6 1EF.

Mr I Prestt, Royal Society for the Protection of Birds, The Lodge, *Sandy,* Bedfordshire, SG19 2DL.

Professor W F Raymond, Christmas Common, *Watlington,* Oxon, OX9 5HR.

Dr D Riley, Imperial Chemical Industries PLC, Plant Protection Division, Jealott's Hill Research Station, *Bracknell,* Berkshire, RG12 6EY.

Mr K V Runcie, The East of Scotland College of Agriculture, West Mains Road, *Edinburgh,* EH9 3JG.

Mr M Shrubb, Royal Society for the Protection of Birds Council, Fairfields, Sidlesham, *Chichester,* West Sussex, PO20 7NX.

Dr P I Stanley, Ministry of Agriculture, Fisheries and Food, Slough Laboratory, London Road, *Slough,* Buckinghamshire, SL3 7HJ.

Mr H V Thompson, Cantab Group Ltd, Rose Cottage, Lower Farm Road, Effingham, *Leatherhead,* Surrey, KT24 5JL.

Dr J M Way, Ministry of Agriculture, Fisheries and Food, Room 389, Great Westminster House, Horseferry Road, *London,* SW1P 2AE.

Mr D A Wells, Nature Conservancy Council, PO Box 6, Godwin House, George Street, *Huntingdon,* Cambridgeshire, PE18 6BU.

Baroness White, House of Lords, *London,* SW1A 0PW.

The following staff of the Institute were present:

Drs D Jenkins, H Kruuk, J Miles, B W Staines, Institute of Terrestrial Ecology, Banchory Research Station, Hill of Brathens, Glassel, *Banchory,* Kincardineshire, AB3 4BY.

Drs D F Ball, M Hornung, B K Wyatt, Institute of Terrestrial Ecology, Bangor Research Station, Penrhos Road, *Bangor,* Gwynedd, LL57 2LQ.

Professor F T Last, Institute of Terrestrial Ecology, Bush Estate, *Penicuik,* Midlothian, EH26 0QB.

Dr P S Maitland, Institute of Terrestrial Ecology, 78 Craighall Road, *Edinburgh,* EH6 4RO.

Drs J D Goss-Custard, M G Morris, Institute of Terrestrial Ecology, Furzebrook Research Station, *Wareham,* Dorset, BH20 5AS.

Drs R G H Bunce, O W Heal (now The Science Division, NERC, Polaris House, North Star Avenue, *Swindon,* Wilts, SN2 1EU).

Mr J N R Jeffers, Institute of Terrestrial Ecology, Merlewood Research Station, *Grange-over-Sands,* Cumbria, LA11 6JU.

Drs J P Dempster, M D Hooper, I Newton, J Sheail, Mr T C E Wells, Institute of Terrestrial Ecology, Monks Wood Experimental Station, Abbots Ripton, *Huntingdon,* Cambridgeshire, PE17 2LS.

Appendix II

LIST OF PLANT AND ANIMAL SPECIES REFERRED TO IN THE TEXT WITH BOTH THEIR COMMON ENGLISH NAME AND THE LATIN BINOMIAL

1 Plants

1.1 Listed by common English name
(Dony, J.G., Perring, F. & Rob, C.M. 1974. *English names of wild flowers*. London: Butterworths for BSBI.)

Barren brome	*Bromus sterilis*
Bent	*Agrostis* spp.
Bilberry	*Vaccinium myrtillus*
Birch	*Betula* spp.
Bistort	*Polygonum* spp.
Black-bindweed	*Polygonum convolvulus*
Black-grass	*Alopecurus myosuroides*
Bracken	*Pteridium aquilinum*
Branched bur-reed	*Sparganium erectum*
Charlock	*Sinapis arvensis*
Cleavers	*Galium aparine*
Clover	*Trifolium* spp.
Cock's-foot	*Dactylis glomerata*
Common chickweed	*Stellaria media*
Common couch	*Agropyron repens*
Common hemp-nettle	*Galeopsis tetrahit*
Common reed	*Phragmites australis*
Corncockle	*Agrostemma githago*
Cornflower	*Centaurea cyanus*
Cottongrass	*Eriophorum* spp.
Cross-leaved heath	*Erica tetralix*
Darnel	*Lolium temulentum*
Deergrass	*Trichophorum cespitosum*
Dock	*Rumex* spp.
Eelgrass	*Zostera* spp.
Elm	*Ulmus* spp.
Eyespot fungus	*Pseudocercosporella herpotrichoides*
Fescue	*Festuca* spp.
Field pansy	*Viola arvensis*
Flowering rush	*Butomus umbellatus*
Fool's water-cress	*Apium nodiflorum*
Frogbit	*Hydrocharis morsus-ranae*
Fumitory	*Fumaria* spp.
Greater water-parsnip	*Sium latifolium*
Groundsel	*Senecio vulgaris*
Hare's-tail cottongrass	*Eriophorum vaginatum*
Hawthorn	*Crataegus* spp.
Heath rush	*Juncus squarrosus*
Heather	*Calluna vulgaris*
Hogweed	*Heracleum sphondylium*
Horseshoe vetch	*Hippocrepis comosa*
Italian rye-grass	*Lolium multiflorum*
Lesser water-parsnip	*Berula erecta*
Lodgepole pine	*Pinus contorta*
Marsh cudweed	*Gnaphalium uliginosum (Filaginella uliginosa)*
Mat-grass	*Nardus stricta*
Meadow-grass	*Poa* spp.
Osage-orange	*Maclura pomifera*
Perennial rye-grass	*Lolium perenne*
Pheasant's-eye	*Adonis annua*
Poppy	*Papaver* spp.
Purple moor-grass	*Molinia caerulea*
Red fescue	*Festuca rubra*
Rough meadow-grass	*Poa trivialis*
Rush	*Juncus* spp.
Scarlet pimpernel	*Anagallis arvensis*
Sharp-leaved fluellen	*Kickxia elatine*
Sitka spruce	*Picea sitchensis*
Sun spurge	*Euphorbia helioscopia*
Thistle	*Cirsium* spp.
Thorow-wax	*Bupleurum rotundifolium*
Timothy	*Phleum pratense*
Tubular water-dropwort	*Oenanthe fistulosa*
Tufted forget-me-not	*Myosotis laxa (caespitosa)*
White campion	*Silene alba*
White clover	*Trifolium repens*
Wild radish	*Raphanus raphanistrum*
Wild-oat	*Avena fatua*
Yellow iris	*Iris pseudacorus*
Yellow rattle	*Rhinanthus minor*
Yorkshire-fog	*Holcus lanatus*

1.2 Listed by Latin binomial
(Dony, J.G., Perring, F. & Rob, C.M. 1974. *English names of wild flowers*. London: Butterworths for BSBI.)

Adonis annua	Pheasant's-eye
Agropyron repens	Common couch
Agrostemma githago	Corncockle
Agrostis spp.	Bent
Alopecurus myosuroides	Black-grass
Anagallis arvensis	Scarlet pimpernel
Apium nodiflorum	Fool's water-cress
Avena fatua	Wild-oat
Berula erecta	Lesser water-parsnip
Betula spp.	Birch
Bromus sterilis	Barren brome
Bupleurum rotundifolium	Thorow-wax
Butomus umbellatus	Flowering rush
Calluna vulgaris	Heather
Centaurea cyanus	Cornflower
Cirsium spp.	Thistle
Crataegus spp.	Hawthorn
Dactylis glomerata	Cock's-foot
Erica tetralix	Cross-leaved heath
Eriophorum spp.	Cottongrass
Eriophorum vaginatum	Hare's-tail cottongrass
Euphorbia helioscopia	Sun spurge
Festuca rubra	Red fescue
Festuca spp.	Fescue
Filaginella uliginosa (Gnaphalium uliginosum)	Marsh cudweed
Fumaria spp.	Fumitory
Galeopsis tetrahit	Common hemp-nettle
Galium aparine	Cleavers
Gnaphalium uliginosum (Filaginella uliginosa)	Marsh cudweed
Heracleum sphondylium	Hogweed
Hippocrepis comosa	Horseshoe vetch
Holcus lanatus	Yorkshire-fog
Hydrocharis morsus-ranae	Frogbit
Iris pseudacorus	Yellow iris
Juncus spp.	Rush
Juncus squarrosus	Heath rush
Kickxia elatine	Sharp-leaved fluellen
Lolium multiflorum	Italian rye-grass
Lolium perenne	Perennial rye-grass
Lolium temulentum	Darnel
Maclura pomifera	Osage-orange
Molinia caerulea	Purple moor-grass
Myosotis laxa (caespitosa)	Tufted forget-me-not
Nardus stricta	Mat-grass
Oenanthe fistulosa	Tubular water-dropwort
Papaver spp.	Poppy

Phalaris paradoxa	
Phleum pratense	Timothy
Phragmites australis	Common reed
Picea sitchensis	Sitka spruce
Pinus contorta	Lodgepole pine
Poa spp.	Meadow-grass
Poa trivialis	Rough meadow-grass
Polygonum convolvulus	Black-bindweed
Polygonum spp.	Bistort
Pseudocercosporella	
herpotrichoides	Eyespot fungus
Pteridium aquilinum	Bracken
Raphanus raphanistrum	Wild radish
Rhinanthus minor	Yellow rattle
Rumex spp.	Dock
Senecio vulgaris	Groundsel
Silene alba	White campion
Sinapis arvensis	Charlock
Sium latifolium	Greater water-parsnip
Sparganium erectum	Branched bur-reed
Stellaria media	Common chickweed
Trichophorum cespitosum	Deergrass
Trifolium repens	White clover
Trifolium spp.	Clover
Ulmus spp.	Elm
Vaccinium myrtillus	Bilberry
Viola arvensis	Field pansy
Zostera spp.	Eelgrass

2 Animals

2.1 Vertebrates

2.1.1 Listed by common English name

Badger	*Meles meles*
Bank vole	*Clethrionomys glareolus*
Barn owl	*Tyto alba*
Bewick's swan	*Cygnus columbianus bewickii*
Bittern	*Botaurus stellaris*
Black-headed gull	*Larus ridibundus*
Black-tailed godwit	*Limosa limosa*
Blackbird	*Turdus merula*
Blackcap	*Sylvia atricapilla*
Blue tit	*Parus caeruleus*
Bobwhite quail	*Colinus virginianus*
Brent goose	*Branta bernicla*
Brown hare	*Lepus capensis*
Brown rat	*Rattus norvegicus*
Bullfinch	*Pyrrhula pyrrhula*
Canada goose	*Branta canadensis*
Carrion crow	*Corvus corone*
Chaffinch	*Fringilla coelebs*
Charr	*Salvelinus* spp.
Chiffchaff	*Phylloscopus collybita*
Collared dove	*Streptopelia decaocto*
Corn bunting	*Miliaria calandra*
Corncrake	*Crex crex*
Coypu	*Myocastor coypus*
Cuckoo	*Cuculus canorus*
Curlew	*Numenius arquata*
Dartford warbler	*Sylvia undata*
Dotterel	*Eudromias morinellus*
Dunlin	*Calidris alpina*
Dunnock	*Prunella modularis*
Feral goat	*Capra hircus*
Fieldfare	*Turdus pilaris*
Fox	*Vulpes vulpes*
Garden warbler	*Sylvia borin*
Garganey	*Anas querquedula*
Golden eagle	*Aquila chyrysaetos*
Golden plover	*Pluvialis apricaria*
Goldfinch	*Carduelis carduelis*
Great tit	*Parus major*

Greenfinch	*Carduelis chloris*
Greenshank	*Tringa nebularia*
Greylag goose	*Anser anser*
Grey squirrel	*Sciurus carolinensis*
Hedgehog	*Erinaceus europaeus*
Hen harrier	*Circus cyaneus*
Heron	*Ardea cinerea*
House mouse	*Mus domesticus*
House sparrow	*Passer domesticus*
Jackdaw	*Corvus monedula*
Kestrel	*Falco tinnunculus*
Lapwing	*Vanellus vanellus*
Lesser whitethroat	*Sylvia curruca*
Linnet	*Carduelis cannabina*
Little owl	*Athene noctua*
Long-eared owl	*Asio otis*
Long-tailed tit	*Aegithalos caudatus*
Magpie	*Pica pica*
Mallard	*Anas platyrhynchos*
Marsh tit	*Parus palustris*
Meadow pipit	*Anthus pratensis*
Merlin	*Falco columbarius*
Mink	*Mustela vison*
Mistle thrush	*Turdus viscivorus*
Moorhen	*Gallinula chloropus*
Mountain hare	*Lepus timidus*
Nightingale	*Luscinia megarhynchos*
Nightjar	*Caprimulgus europaeus*
Otter	*Lutra lutra*
Oystercatcher	*Haematopus ostralegus*
Partridge	*Perdix perdix*
Peregrine	*Falco peregrinus*
Pheasant	*Phasianus colchicus*
Pied wagtail	*Motacilla alba*
Pigeon	*Columba* spp.
Pink-footed goose	*Anser brachyrhynchus*
Pintail	*Anas acuta*
Ptarmigan	*Lagopus mutus*
Quail	*Coturnix coturnix*
Rabbit	*Oryctolagus cuniculus*
Raven	*Corvus corax*
Red deer	*Cervus elaphus*
Red grouse	*Lagopus lagopus scoticus*
Red kite	*Milvus milvus*
Red-legged partridge	*Alectoris rufa*
Red-throated diver	*Gavia stellata*
Redshank	*Tringa totanus*
Redstart	*Phoenicurus phoenicurus*
Redwing	*Turdus iliacus*
Reed bunting	*Emberiza schoeniclus*
Ring ousel	*Turdus torquatus*
Robin	*Erithacus rubecula*
Roe deer	*Capreolus capreolus*
Rook	*Corvus frugilegus*
Ruff	*Philomachus pugnax*
Sedge warbler	*Acrocephalus schoenobaenus*
Shelduck	*Tadorna tadorna*
Short-eared owl	*Asio flammeus*
Shoveler	*Anas clypeata*
Skylark	*Alauda arvensis*
Snipe	*Gallinago gallinago*
Song thrush	*Turdus philomelos*
Sparrowhawk	*Accipiter nisus*
Spotted flycatcher	*Muscicapa striata*
Starling	*Sturnus vulgaris*
Stoat	*Mustela erminea*
Stock dove	*Columba oenas*
Stonechat	*Saxicola torquata*
Swallow	*Hirundo rustica*
Titmice	*Parus* spp.
Treecreeper	*Certhia familiaris*
Tree sparrow	*Passer montanus*
Trout	*Salmo trutta*

Turtle dove	*Streptopelia turtur*
Twite	*Acanthus flavirostris*
Wheatear	*Oenanthe oenanthe*
Whimbrel	*Numenius phaeopus*
Whitefish	*Coregonus* spp.
White-fronted goose	*Anser albifrons*
Whitethroat	*Sylvia communis*
Whooper swan	*Cygnus cygnus*
Wigeon	*Anas penelope*
Willow warbler	*Phylloscopus trochilus*
Wireworm	*Agriotes* spp.
Wolf	*Canis lupus*
Wood mouse	*Apodemus sylvaticus*
Wood pigeon	*Columba palumbus*
Wren	*Troglodytes troglodytes*
Yellow wagtail	*Motacilla flava flavissima*
Yellowhammer	*Emberiza citrinella*

2.1.2 Listed by Latin binomial

Acanthus flavirostris	Twite
Accipiter nisus	Sparrowhawk
Acrocephalus schoenobaenus	Sedge warbler
Aegithalos caudatus	Long-tailed tit
Agriotes spp.	Wireworm
Alauda arvensis	Skylark
Alectoris rufa	Red-legged partridge
Anas acuta	Pintail
Anas clypeata	Shoveler
Anas penelope	Wigeon
Anas platyrhynchos	Mallard
Anas querquedula	Garganey
Anser albifrons	White-fronted goose
Anser anser	Greylag goose
Anser brachyrhynchus	Pink-footed goose
Anthus pratensis	Meadow pipit
Apodemus sylvaticus	Wood mouse
Aquila chyrysaetos	Golden eagle
Ardea cinerea	Heron
Asio flammeus	Short-eared owl
Asio otis	Long-eared owl
Athene noctua	Little owl
Botaurus stellaris	Bittern
Branta bernicla	Brent goose
Branta canadensis	Canada goose
Calidris alpina	Dunlin
Canis lupus	Wolf
Capra hircus	Feral goat
Caprimulgus europaeus	Nightjar
Capreolus capreolus	Roe deer
Carduelis cannabina	Linnet
Carduelis carduelis	Goldfinch
Carduelis chloris	Greenfinch
Certhia familiaris	Treecreeper
Cervus elaphus	Red deer
Circus cyaneus	Hen harrier
Clethrionomys glareolus	Bank vole
Colinus virginianus	Bobwhite quail
Columba spp.	Pigeon
Columba oenas	Stock dove
Columba palumbus	Wood pigeon
Coregonus spp.	Whitefish
Corvus corax	Raven
Corvus corone	Carrion crow
Corvus frugilegus	Rook
Corvus monedula	Jackdaw
Coturnix coturnix	Quail
Crex crex	Corncrake
Cuculus canorus	Cuckoo
Cygnus columbianus bewickii	Bewick's swan
Cygnus cygnus	Whooper swan
Emberiza citrinella	Yellowhammer
Emberiza schoeniclus	Reed bunting
Erinaceus europaeus	Hedgehog
Erithacus rubecula	Robin
Eudromias morinellus	Dotterel
Falco columbarius	Merlin
Falco peregrinus	Peregrine
Falco tinnunculus	Kestrel
Fringilla coelebs	Chaffinch
Gallinago gallinago	Snipe
Gallinula chloropus	Moorhen
Gavia stellata	Red-throated diver
Haematopus ostralegus	Oystercatcher
Hirundo rustica	Swallow
Lagopus lagopus scoticus	Red grouse
Lagopus mutus	Ptarmigan
Larus ridibundus	Black-headed gull
Lepus capensis	Brown hare
Lepus timidus	Mountain hare
Limosa limosa	Black-tailed godwit
Luscinia megarhynchos	Nightingale
Lutra lutra	Otter
Meles meles	Badger
Miliaria calandra	Corn bunting
Milvus milvus	Red kite
Motacilla alba	Pied wagtail
Motacilla flava flavissima	Yellow wagtail
Mus domesticus	House mouse
Muscicapa striata	Spotted flycatcher
Mustela erminea	Stoat
Mustela vison	Mink
Myocastor coypus	Coypu
Numenius arquata	Curlew
Numenius phaeopus	Whimbrel
Oenanthe oenanthe	Wheatear
Oryctolagus cuniculus	Rabbit
Parus caeruleus	Blue tit
Parus major	Great tit
Parus palustris	Marsh tit
Parus spp.	Titmice
Passer domesticus	House sparrow
Passer montanus	Tree sparrow
Perdix perdix	Partridge
Phasianus colchicus	Pheasant
Philomachus pugnax	Ruff
Phoenicurus phoenicurus	Redstart
Phylloscopus collybita	Chiffchaff
Phylloscopus trochilus	Willow warbler
Pica pica	Magpie
Pluvialis apricaria	Golden plover
Prunella modularis	Dunnock
Pyrrhula pyrrhula	Bullfinch
Rattus norvegicus	Brown rat
Salmo trutta	Trout
Salvelinus spp.	Charr
Saxicola torquata	Stonechat
Sciurus carolinensis	Grey squirrel
Streptopelia decaocto	Collared dove
Streptopelia turtur	Turtle dove
Sturnus vulgaris	Starling
Sylvia atricapilla	Blackcap
Sylvia borin	Garden warbler
Sylvia communis	Whitethroat
Sylvia curruca	Lesser whitethroat
Sylvia undata	Dartford warbler
Tadorna tadorna	Shelduck
Tringa nebularia	Greenshank
Tringa totanus	Redshank
Troglodytes troglodytes	Wren
Turdus iliacus	Redwing
Turdus merula	Blackbird
Turdus philomelos	Song thrush
Turdus pilaris	Fieldfare
Turdus torquatus	Ring ousel
Turdus viscivorus	Mistle thrush
Tyto alba	Barn owl

Vanellus vanellus	Lapwing
Vulpes vulpes	Fox

2.2 Invertebrates
2.2.1 Listed by common English name

Adonis blue butterfly	*Lysandra bellargus*
Brassica pod midge	*Dasineura brassicae*
Cabbage root fly	*Erioischia brassicae*
Cabbage seed weevil	*Ceutorhynchus assimilis*
Chalkhill blue butterfly	*Lysandra coridon*
Earthworm	*Allolobophora caliginosa*
	Allolobophora chlorotica
	Allolobophora longa
	Lumbricus terrestris
Fritfly	*Oscinella frit*
Grain aphid	*Sitobion avenae*
Pine beauty moth	*Panolis flammea*
Pygmy mangold beetle	*Atomaria lineatus*
Sheep tick	*Ixodes ricinus*
Wheat bulb fly	*Delia coarctata*
Yellow cereal fly	*Opomyza florum*

2.2.2 Listed by Latin binomial

Allolobophora caliginosa	Earthworm
Allolobophora chlorotica	Earthworm
Allolobophora longa	Earthworm
Atomaria lineatus	Pygmy mangold beetle
Ceutorhynchus assimilis	Cabbage seed weevil
Dasineura brassicae	Brassica pod midge
Delia coarctata	Wheat bulb fly
Erioischia brassicae	Cabbage root fly
Ixodes ricinus	Sheep tick
Lumbricus terrestris	Earthworm
Lysandra bellargus	Adonis blue butterfly
Lysandra coridon	Chalkhill blue butterfly
Opomyza florum	Yellow cereal fly
Oscinella frit	Fritfly
Panolis flammea	Pine beauty moth
Sitobion avenae	Grain aphid